Ghosts, Castles, and Victims:
Studies in Gothic Terror

Another Fawcett Book
edited by Jack C. Wolf:

PAST, PRESENT, AND FUTURE PERFECT
(with Gregory Fitz Gerald)

Ghosts, Castles, and Victims: Studies in Gothic Terror

Edited by

JACK C. WOLF and BARBARA H. WOLF

A FAWCETT CREST BOOK

Fawcett Publications, Inc., Greenwich, Conn.

GHOSTS, CASTLES, AND VICTIMS: Studies in Gothic Terror

A Fawcett Crest Original

Library of Congress Catalog Card Number: 74-76209

Printed in the United States of America,
August 1974

The editors and publisher are grateful for permission to reprint the following:

"From Beyond," by H. P. Lovecraft. Copyright © 1965 by Arkham House. Reprinted by permission of Arkham House.

"The Dead Planet," by Edmond Hamilton. Copyright © 1946 by Better Publications, Inc. for *Startling Stories*, Spring 1946. Reprinted by permission of the Author and his agents, Scott Meredith Literary Agency, Inc., 580 Fifth Avenue, New York, New York 10036.

From "Day of the Triffids," by John Wyndham, included in *The John Wyndham Omnibus*, Simon & Schuster, 1964. Reprinted by permission of the Author's Estate and the agents for the Estate, Scott Meredith Literary Agency, Inc., 580 Fifth Avenue, New York, New York 10036.

Contents

Ghosts, Castles, and Victims: Studies in Gothic Terror

Origins of Gothic in Literature

Since the eighteenth century, Gothic literature has come more and more to be that branch of Romantic literature whose primary goal is to evoke the emotion of fear. In looking back from the perspective of twentieth-century considerations, however, it is not always a simple matter to separate this coherent Gothic "mainstream" from various divagations which, over the centuries, have led into blind alleys. Much of the difficulty is due to the amorphous and multiple meanings ascribed to the adjective "Gothic," depending on the contexts in which this has been used; of course, as these contexts were viewed in retrospect by succeeding ages, the confusion was compounded. Thus, while the term "Gothic" has served to identify an important trend generally within the Romantic movement, and a trend which in itself did much to bring about the flowering of Romanticism in the eighteenth century, the accretions of meaning surrounding the term have made definition elusive and agreement precarious.

Very generally speaking, the term "Gothic" has three broad interpretations applicable to literary production. First, because the medieval period came to be known as the Gothic period, "Gothic" and "medieval" became synonymous as a historical label, and all works of the Middle Ages became thereby Gothic. This led to a diffusion of the meaning of the term, however, because it embraced not only heroic works such as *The Song of*

Roland and social commentary such as *The Book of the Courtier* (neither of which is Gothic in the sense in which the term was used originally or later), but also the chivalric romance such as *Amadis de Gaul* which, though not a terror tale, was to have great influence on the eighteenth-century Gothic movement.

Second, Gothic was utilized as a descriptive term for literature which concerned itself with architecture and other appurtenances of that later period of the Middle Ages, a time characterized by the style of architecture now looked upon as Gothic. When this tendency was conjoined with a kind of fantasy of free play of the imagination, it produced a literature such as Beckford's *Vathek* or the works of Lord Dunsany—a kind of Byzantine or Oriental tale which, for the most part, eschewed any concern with evoking fear and terror as its principal aim.

When use of Gothic architecture was combined with strange and foreboding settings, a third type of Gothic literature was created. This thread of development originally, as in Walpole's *The Castle of Otranto,* used Gothic architecture and other medieval settings and devices because such features were so in contrast to the prevailing spirit of neoclassicism. Thus, the very usage of these features instilled a feeling of strangeness and alienation essential to the "suspension of disbelief" which underlies Romantic and Gothic literature. This is the Gothic tradition which has eventually led to modern Gothic—be it literature of the past or literature of the future (as science fiction); and this is the tradition which has focused the meaning of the term on the evocation of fear. Many of the devices used to arouse fear are to be found in other literature, but it should be noted that occasional use of "Gothic elements" does not make a novel Gothic, any more than use of a love story necessarily makes a novel a chivalric romance.

But to understand the flexibility of the term "Gothic" and how it has developed into a descriptive term for the literature of fear, it is essential to examine the term from its racial, historical origins through its development over the centuries. Particularly, one must examine the term in contexts and disciplines other than literary, for "Gothic" was used as a descriptive term some thirteen centuries before it became adopted to literature, and roughly six centuries before it was used as an architectural designation. But it has always, either implicitly or explicitly, contained at least a germ of its original pejorative usage from the fifth century A.D., and it has, even in its many ramifications, reflected not so much a style or form as it has a mentality or attitude.

HISTORICAL CONSIDERATIONS

The adjective Gothic stems from the noun "Goth," a designation for a group of Teutonic tribes which moved southward in the fifth century A.D. and overthrew the classical Roman Empire. Three major kingdoms emerged: that of the Ostrogoths in the Italian peninsula and the Balkans, that of the Visigoths in Western France and the Iberian peninsula, and that of the Vandals in North Africa and the Mediterranean islands.

This destruction of classical Roman culture and society (though certainly other factors operated in addition to the advent of the Goths), earned for the Goths the same reputation as it did for the Vandals—a reputation for wanton destruction and barbarity. But whereas "vandalism" remained a pejorative term from then on, the term "Gothic" through the ages acquired new meanings, including that of praise, though it has never completely lost the connotations associated with barbarism. Thus, Sir Christopher Wren could remark in the eighteenth century that "the Goths were rather Destroyers than Builders" and write of "the Gothick rudeness of the old Design." It is this continuing association of Gothic and destruction which is historically important because of its implication that the term suggests opposition to established order.

Obviously those who destroyed the classical culture of the Mediterranean would be considered barbarians by those whom the destroyers had conquered, particularly when the *Weltanschauung,* or outlook on life, of the conquering Goths was so culturally primitive compared to the classical, from the standpoint of sophistication and complexity. The vaunted civilization of classical Rome with its stability, laws, and disciplined social structures was almost diametrically opposed to Gothic values. It is not surprising, therefore, that when the classical Roman age of Augustus was selected as the model for the neoclassical Augustan age in eighteen-century England, any cultural or artistic opposition to this society of balance, control, law, and order should be regarded as Gothic.

The destruction of the Roman Empire by the Goths had given rise to a new type of society, known as the feudal system, which was to be the dominant social structure throughout the Middle Ages and even into the Renaissance. Yet this society was based not on Gothic but on Roman principals. The early transitional phase of this medieval period was a heroic age based on a developing code of chivalry with ideals of loyalty, honor, and courage. Later this code was extended to include a doctrine of courtly love, based on a sensuous, illicit relationship, which, still later, under the influence of Christianity (especially the rise of the Cult of the Virgin Mary in the tenth century), developed into a chivalric code which exalted womanhood and insisted on strict ideas of licit love. Thus, around the middle of the medieval period, the earlier heroic code of chivalry, as reflected in *The Song of Roland,* was transformed into a sentimentalized chivalric code, reflected in such romances as *Amadis de Gaul.* Both types of literature, however, became designated as Gothic by later generations who, through indifference or ignorance, made no distinctions between early and late medieval periods. Still, this application of the term "Gothic" by later ages gave for the first time positive and praiseworthy connotations to the term.

By applying the term "Gothic" to the Middle Ages as a whole, the eighteenth century gave currency to the positive aspects of Gothic by the inclusion of idealized love, the code of chivalry, spiritual yearning, and religious fervor. But at the same time, such usage deepened the confusion because the Middle Ages, hence Gothic, also included the earlier illicit courtly love and violence of the heroic phase. It was therefore possible to speak of the Gothic movement and to have contradictory characteristics of the term in mind.

This ambiguity has decreased from the eighteenth century onward, however, at least in literature, as the term Gothic has become increasingly associated with its earliest connotations of threat or destruction—even though this threat is no longer necessarily directed against civilizations or cultures. Yet the increasing accent on terror and the increasing trend toward substitution of the preternatural for the supernatural has not obliterated all connotations of the mysterious and the awesome, the qualities so characteristic of the religiosity of the later medieval epoch. It is therefore fitting that the term "Gothic," born of adventure and imagination and disregard for rules and order, should develop as it has over the centuries into a term including diverse and contrasting concepts in numerous fields, and that it should be adopted into literature to designate the mysterious or nonrational, the dark, the fearful. For the Gothic mode is, above all other interpretations, a world view, a way of looking at the mysterious and contradictory potentialities of life.

ARCHITECTURAL CONSIDERATIONS

What eventually came to be referred to as the Gothic style of architecture is generally conceded to have originated in the twelfth century in France with the renovation of the Romanesque Abbey of St. Denis near Paris. At that time, neither the term "Gothic" nor "Romanesque" was used to characterize these two contrasting architectural types, known respectively only as the "new" and the "old." It was later ages, seeking in retrospect to distinguish two coexistent and distinct kinds, that labeled the old, round-arch style dating from classical Roman times as Romanesque, in recognition of its origins, and the new, pointed-arch, and innovative style as Gothic because, just as the Goths had broken the sway of the Roman Empire, this style successfully challenged the dominance of the Romanesque. But it is well to point out again that these labels, although in this case understood in a context of architectural styles and techniques, still refer as much to an attitude or a way of looking at the universe as to any specific architectural accomplishment.

How true this is becomes more evident if Sir Christopher Wren's remarks, made in eighteenth-century England when the classical and Gothic modes of life styles were again opposing each other, are considered. Wren, speaking of ways to beautify the Romanesque architectural style by addition of Gothic embellishments, suggests that Gothic might better be called Saracen because it reflects an Oriental influence rather that a northern, Gothic influence. Despite this view of Gothic as Saracen or Oriental (airy), Wren agrees with John Evelyn's dictum that the Gothic style is heavy and grotesque.

Either point of view, Saracen or Goth, reflects a consideration of Gothic style as one opposed to the classical tradition—a view, it will be recalled, similar to that held by the Romans after the collapse of the Roman Empire. Romanesque architecture represents a classical outlook on life; the Gothic represents a romantic outlook stressing the irrational.

The Romanesque style tends toward the horizontal or area-occupying form. As such, it evokes a feeling of control and limitation, a sense of mass or weight pressing downward. This feeling is further enhanced by the presence of thick walls supporting the heavy arches and vaultings of the roof. In turn, the height-thickness ratio of the walls imposes practical limitations on the height of the edifice. Further, the rectilinear forms of such horizontal building tend to create a sense of blocks, of units massed side by side, and this feeling is carried through into the interior where, because of need for support structures and divided wall members, space becomes separated into discrete areas. The result is a feeling of rationalization or intellectualization, an analyzing rather than a synthesizing, activity.

On the outside of the edifice, this feeling of a separation of elements is intensified by the absence of any ornamentation breaking the profile or silhouette. Despite the decorations of the tympani and elsewhere, nothing is permitted to break the edge lines and interfere with the sense of clean demarcation and propriety. Thus the classical proportions are not obscured, outside or inside, even by distortion of lighting. Sunlight, the classical light, enters the classical interior and emphasizes that analytical division of space which the outside of the building suggests. As for distortion from colored light, there is none, even though colored glass is utilized in Romanesque architecture. Its use is neither functional nor integrated with the overall feeling as it is in the Gothic.

It is here, in the realm of feeling or sensation, that the ultimately important distinctions between Romanesque and Gothic styles of architecture must be made. Whatever the architectural reasons for such elements as the pointed arch, the quadripartite vaulting, the flying buttress, and the pointed spire, it is knowledge of the emotional origins and results which is most important to an understanding of what the Gothic mind involves. This can only be reached through a comprehension of what Gothic architectural elements signify to, or arouse in, the minds and emotions of the viewer, and the first step toward this understanding is the recognition that there is no single, unique element, architecturally, mentally, or emotionally, which sufficiently describes the Gothic. And while Gothic is a whole which is indeed greater that the sum of its parts, an examination of some of these parts is useful in comprehending the whole.

First, whereas Romanesque or classical architectural is horizontal, Gothic is vertical. The Romanesque, with its evocation of mass, presses downward; the Gothic rises upward as though the stone has lost its material component, its corporeal nature, and almost seems to float. This effect of upward thrust, associated in the medieval and later minds with spirituality and aspiration, is furthered by the use of pointed spires, narrow pointed arches and sloping roofs, while the edge decorations break up the sharp line of demarcation between the edifice and its background, so tending to fuse the two. In addition, the use of the flying buttress permits much higher structures, so the Gothic edifice rises towering above the neighboring rooftops and seems to hang suspended over its immediate surroundings. The effect is not only one of spirituality and aspiration—it is distinctly one of awe. Whether the viewer perceives the Gothic structures from the outside or the inside, the mere act of lifting the eyes to encompass the height of the building is enough to evoke a feeling of soaring. Thus the Gothic, responding to the solidity and stability of the Romanesque, gives an impression of movement, of incorporeality, of change and fusion.

This contrast to the stolidity of the classical is further evident in the structure of the Gothic wall. Through use of the flying buttress for support, Gothic architecture is able to achieve astonishing heights without the necessity of increasing wall thickness and so having the wall broad and heavy at the base, for the flying buttress provides support at the necessary pressure points to counteract the outward thrust caused by the heavy vaulted ceilings and the roof. The outer walls can thus be limited to supporting pillars, allowing the intervening spaces to be made into stained glass windows. The overall external effect is one of delicacy, almost laciness (despite Wren's and Evelyn's castigation of Gothic as "heavy").

Internally, the effect is much the same, with the additional component of the play of colored light through stained glass. The same soaring effect of the external view carries through to the internal, and the quadripartite vaulting, like the pointed arches of the windows, tends to augment this effect. Furthermore, a fusion of pillar and vaulting creates an internal profile which blends and integrates space, producing an organic or synthetic effect of wholeness—contrary to the analytical effect of the classical.

To a large degree, the organic character of Gothic architecture is due to the manipulation of light, to a fusion of colored light and form, to the heavy contrast between bright light and deep shadow occasioned by the more three-dimensional character of Gothic decoration, both internally and externally, to the mysticism of white sunlight transformed into the variegated and symbolic colors of gems. Thus Gothic light serves to create a sense of the continuous rather than of the discrete, as classical light does, and the result is an emotional effect which is nonintellectual—at least in its initial impact. This is not to be taken as an indication that the Gothic approach is only emotional, lacking harmony, proportion, and control. Such is not the case, any more than Gothic architecture can be faulted merely because it does not adhere to the same rules of aesthetics and construction that classical architecture does. What the classical mind finds disproportionate and excessive in the Gothic is counterbalanced by the rigidity and sterility which the Gothic mind finds in the classical. Instead of presenting its material in an orderly, discursive manner, the Gothic mode in architecture presents the viewer with such a simultaneous wealth of visual material that he cannot begin to cope with it analytically until he has overcome the initial emotional response. And even then, as in Gothic literature, the intellectual reaction can never again be entirely separated from the primary emotional response.

SOCIAL CONSIDERATIONS

The aspects of medieval life which became important in the Gothic literature of the eighteenth century were largely those identified with the trappings of feudal nobility and with the chivalric code of conduct that included such later developments as the doctrine of courtly love. The feudal system itself was an authoritarian, agricultural society in which the king was the prime landowner who doled out holdings to various nobility under his sovereignty in exchange for military and financial support. Each noble in turn parceled out land to lesser nobles who in turn swore loyalty to him and provided him with military and financial support. These holdings formed a rather loose confederation of highly autonomous fiefs, each headed by one who owed fealty or loyalty to the next higher noble, on whose beneficence he depended. It is obvious from this that each noble had, in his own fief, a high degree of power, not infrequently absolute. This arbitrary power of the nobleman over his subjects is often the motivation of action in Gothic literature, because this power could provide an unscrupulous noble with the means for taking possession of lands and chattel not rightfully his, as in the case of illegitimate succession in Walpole's *The Castle of Otranto*. In fact, the theme of illicit appropriation of property by a usurper or by someone not in the legitimate line of succession is a favorite theme of authors who preceded the Gothic writers of the eighteenth century.

The actual physical conditions which accompanied the feudal system were a product of both accident and necessity. The wealth and luxuries enjoyed by the nobility were such as might be indulged in by the wealthy of any age, but the accouterments of the knights and the castles of the nobility were determined by the times. Knights wore armor when outside the castle walls, particularly during the early phase of the Middle Ages, because combat was a way of life and any man was a potential foe. Small wonder then that homes were self-sustaining castles, providing everything needed for survival, and that the walls were thick, high, and fortified, protected by moats and drawbridges. Even less can one wonder that these castle-cities contained secret tunnels and chambers suitable for hiding, dungeons for imprisoning enemies, torture chambers, and secret escape routes for the nobles and their families in case the occupants were forced to flee.

When eighteenth-century Gothic writers looked to the Middle Ages for material, they selected according to their Romantic needs. Consequently, they selected some materials from the early, heroic phase, and others, such as Christianized, courtly love, from the later phases. The result was a fused picture in which the chivalric knight exhibited a spirit of adventure, a sense of individual honor, a desire for valorous action and for succoring those in need, combined with a pride in redressing wrongs, an overall courtesy, a gallantry toward women, and, if not religious fervor, at least a religious character. He also became the savior of maiden-victims, a theme which continued in Gothic romances, with, of course, changes in the identity of the knight and victim to fit changes in public taste. For a long time, this last-minute rescue of an innocent maiden in distress remained the most successful way of arousing sympathy and creating terror.

LITERARY CONSIDERATIONS

It is a literary convenience to consider Walpole's *The Castle of Otranto* as the beginning of Gothic literature in eighteenth-century England for two reasons. First, Walpole referred to his work as a Gothic tale because it was set in a medieval castle, an indication of his interest in the past, especially in the Gothic era. As a result of this association, the term "Gothic" was subsequently applied to romances with a medieval setting. Second, the popular response to *The Castle of Otranto* made it an instant success, calling attention to this type of writing, while, as is usually the case with a pivotal work, obscuring its forerunners; it must not be forgotten that Walpole's novel did not spring full-blown out of nothing. There were many works prior to his publication, most notably Thomas Leland's *Longsword, Earl of Salisbury,* which dealt with Gothic themes and materials even though they may not have been brought into such limited, clear focus as in *The Castle of Otranto*. Nor is it at all improbable that Walpole, with his interest in everything Gothic, was acquainted with them. Still, it is Walpole's work that whetted public interest in the genre of Gothic literature and provided a label that critics could use as a convenient adjective to describe the movement. How loosely this label was used, how confusingly it operated, how broadly it had been applied in previous times and in other fields, has been indicated in the foregoing discussion.

The eighteenth century in English letters was ripe for a change in mood. While the predominant styles of the novel, as exemplified in the works of Fielding, Sterne, Smollett, and Richardson, constituted the mainstream of literary production—at least in perspective—there was a genuine yearning for a liberation of fancy, for a return to the imaginative literature generally associated with the medieval or Gothic ages. The insistence on prudence, judgment, and the social realism of character studies combined with the minutiae of daily life had become something of a straitjacket whose restraints produced a mental tedium. Writers and audiences both, particularly those not interested in classical themes or in social and intellectual probings, welcomed narratives which allowed freer rein to the imagination. This is not to say, however, that Gothic literature appealed only to those who wanted an escape from daily life and from current "acceptable" literature with its insistence on didacticism. For many Gothic writers also intended moral lessons in their work— among them Clara Reeve, who insisted on moral purpose in her novels, and Walpole, who maintained there was a moral behind *The Castle of Otranto*. But Gothic writers, convinced that unvarnished moralizing leads to poverty of imagination and feeling, adopted Bacon's precept that "truth is a naked and open daylight, that does not show the masques, and mummeries, and triumphs of the world, half so stately and daintily as candle-lights. . . . A mixture of a lie doth ever add pleasure." Walpole himself remarked, "I almost think there is no wisdom comparable to that of exchanging what is called the realities of life for dreams."

To break away both from the familiar setting of every day life (and its tendency to restrict the mind to practical considerations) and from the tradition of realism of classical thought, Gothic writers adopted the age-old device of setting their novels in other times and locations. Many, if not most, turned, like Walpole, to the medieval past with its heroism and romantic code of chivalry. To some extent this choice of the past may have been prompted, as in Walpole's case, by the sense of certainty that the past offers, that "one holds fast and surely what is past" because the events are recorded in history and can be trusted. But in a larger sense, the looking backward was dictated by the need to find settings foreign to the writer's own time and place if he expected to successfully involve his audience in such free play of imagination. Further, the elements of the medieval chivalric romance were precisely the elements desired by eighteenth-century Gothic writers. How the individual writers used this material, and how they conceived of the meaning of the adjective

"Gothic" as it related to their own work led first to an expansion in meaning of the term and then, ultimately, to a retrenchment or return to a meaning closer to its original connotation—destruction and terror.

Much of the diversity surrounding use of the term rose from that very wealth of association which the word Gothic had acquired through the ages from its widespread use in so many fields. Thus, a writer interested in the supernatural could, because the use of Gothic as equivalent to medieval implied an age of interest in the supernatural, consider his work Gothic. Another, interested in strange architecture as lending an aura of mystery to his work, could easily provide settings of castles and walled cities and call his work Gothic also, even if the supernatural were left out. Novels dealing with romance and set in the distant past could, because of the association of courtly love and the Gothic epoch, be considered Gothic, and anti-clerical works dedicated to quite the opposite of the Christian supernaturalism of the Middle Ages could likewise be termed Gothic. Due to the proliferation of concepts which could, at one point or another, relate to some aspect of medieval life—and at times the connection was rather remote—the term "Gothic" eventually became hardly more descriptive than the term Romantic. As time passed and more Gothic literature made its appearance, it became increasingly apparent that what was buidling up as a tradition in Gothic literature was no longer necessarily related to the Middle Ages at all. The worn stereotype of medieval setting became in itself a limiting tradition which was in turn rejected by the Gothic mind, always in search of the strange. Eventually it was recognized that only the evocation of fear was essential to Gothic, and in perspective such fantasy writings as Lord Dunsany's tales and Beckford's *Vathek* were seen to be outside the limits of what mainstream Gothic was revealing itself to be.

One of the common devices for creating an atmosphere

of terror was the introduction of the supernatural, as in Walpole's *The Castle of Otranto*. Here, however, the supernatural was used not only for this reason but also to provide an explanation of that which would have been otherwise incredible and to provide an agent of retribution. Walpole, like subsequent Gothic authors, needed a degree of freedom from the intellectual spirit, freedom from that hard light of reason.

But the disagreement as to the legitimacy of usage of the supernatural was great, with authors such as Ann Radcliffe insisting on presentation of logical or natural explanations of all supernatural phenomena before the end of the story. Walpole, of course, allowed the use of crass supernaturalism, and Clara Reeve prefigured those who made use of the unexplained supernatural but limited it to a level which would not grate on the reader's sensibility.

Coupled to the supernatural was a visionary or bizarre world which had a complex appeal. Part of this appeal was to man's curiosity, his desire to delve into the mysteries of the past and of alien worlds. This bizarre world contained ruined abbeys, mysterious castles, and brooding landscapes, all of which has led ultimately to contemporary worlds of science fiction.

A further strength in the Gothic lay in the awareness that beauty is enhanced by terror, and terror in turn is sharpened by the presence of the beautiful. Clara Reeve was one of the earliest Gothic practitioners to recognize that sensationalism whets the interest of the reader and is most easily achieved by presenting a beautiful, innocent young woman threatened with disaster. The terror is accentuated by being unjustly directed against this sympathetic victim, and the victim's beauty and virtue is accentuated by being threatened. The accompanying settings of ruined abbeys and dour woodlands, having an atmosphere of past grandeur and dark melancholy or foreboding, contribute heavily to the overall effect.

Eventually, with changing patterns of society, the stereotyping of technique based on the supernatural and the Middle Ages became too trite to arouse sympathy in any but the most naïve of readers, and substitute devices had to be found. The hoary tradition of ruined castles, secret chambers, moldy manuscripts, lost and illegible letters, mistaken identity and so forth became outmoded limitations which no longer appealed to audiences. The horrors of the Spanish Inquisition were no longer terrible for those who had little or no idea of what the Inquisition had been, and medieval torture chambers held little terror for those in daily contact with the horrors of nineteenth-and twentieth-century warfare. As man's inhumanity to man marched inexorably onward, outmoded Gothic devices were updated to keep pace with man's hardening emotional arteries.

Thus, contemporary concepts do not demand that Gothic literature involve the medieval era or any other particular age or place. It need not have reference to courtly love, feudalism, or damsels in distress, and if there is a woman in distress, she can as readily be a twenty-first-century woman as an eleventh-century one. A villain can as easily be a nineteenth-century Mr. Hyde or an unidentifiable Something-from-Outer-Space as he can be a monk or priest of the Inquisition. In perspective, all that is now considered Gothic depends on terror, and the distinctions to be made are not among any "types" of Gothic (for it is all one type), but only among the devices used to create the effect of terror.

These devices fall into seven general categories—setting, human threat, supernatural threat, human monsters, monsters of unknown origin, psychological threat, and unknown threat—each of which is discussed more fully in the introductory material immediately preceding the selections used to exemplify that particular device.

Part One

Setting

The use of physical setting in the Gothic tale is two-fold. First, it keys the reader's mood to a receptivity of horror or terror, and, second, it helps suppress the tendency of the reader to insist on a rational explanation of events. By touching the primordial depths of the reader's emotions, the author arouses the dark, unfathomed fears in man and reminds him of those possibilities of demonism which eternally lurk just beneath the veneer of rationalization. Most Gothic writers make no great effort to explain the story in rational terms, content with leaving it on the plane of Hamlet's statement, "There are more things in heaven and earth, Horatio, than are dreamt of in your philosophy." And the reader, touched in that adytum of his being that no amount of technology will eradicate, accepts this. He responds with a kind of tacit agreement, though not a conscious one, that under these circumstances, in these surroundings, in this atmosphere, such a thing is not only possible but probable. In fact, by the clever accumulation of hints and staging, the successful Gothic writer will produce an atmosphere in which the reader *expects* something unusual, something sinister, to occur. More than that, the reader collaborates by *insisting* that it occur, in order to justify the expectation which has been aroused in him; if this requires a rejection of the empirically rational in order to bring it about, so be it.

This purely emotional component of the Gothic also makes it possible for setting alone to function as protagonist. Given a story such as "The Willows," in which the characters are isolated in a strange and weird landscape in the marshes of Hungary, trapped on an island and seemingly without hope for escape, the reader knows that something terrifying and unusual *must* happen. It is imperative. And when it happens, that in itself is the resolution of the story, the culmination of the expectation aroused by the descriptions of the setting, and it matters not how inexplicable the rest may be. It is enough that the story (like a Gothic cathedral) is complete and logical within itself, within its own terms. A parallel situation is found in Edmond Hamilton's fairly recent story, "The Dead Planet," and demonstrates clearly that Gothic is still with us on its own terms, despite changes in style. The Gothic castle may now be an abandoned planet, but the methods and effects of modern Gothic are still the same as in its predecessors. This will hold true so long as man has a spirit greater than the measurable and finite rationalizations of his daylight thinking.

The medieval castle itself was, in eighteenth-century Gothic literature, sufficient to suggest to the reader of the time the dark, mysterious, evil horrors which lay just beyond man's rational comprehension. Underground passages, secret rooms, trapdoors, gloomy chambers, and other paraphernalia reminiscent of the Middle Ages were weighty contributions to the early Gothic reader's feeling of terror, and for this reason it is possible to maintain that in a real sense the "main character" of *The Castle of Otranto* is the castle itself. Walpole was a master at placing his victims in castle settings calculated to frighten the most hardened eighteenth-century reader:

> An awful silence reigned throughout those subterraneous regions, except now and then some blasts of winds that shook the doors she had passed, and which, grating on the rusty hinges, were re-echoed through that long labyrinth of darkness. Every murmur struck her with new terror.

His removal of the action from the familiar settings of the eighteenth century, in order to induce the reader to accept a situation which rationally could not be acceptable, is similar to the technique of the *Arabian Nights* which, by presenting events in another culture, another time, induces even the contemporary reader to accept the rationally improbable because it eliminates the possibility of comparison. Use of setting to make such Gothic devices as the supernatural acceptable to the reader indicates the extent to which setting is essential in *The Castle of Otranto* and why it is here included in the section of setting, even though it could justifiably have been placed in the "curse" or "supernatural" category. Historically Walpole's story is the progenitor of Gothic stories which stress the medieval and the castle settings (and other strange, uncommon settings).

Clara Reeve, following Walpole, uses the castle setting to stimulate her reader's interest, but her intention is to use it just enough to create an ambiance of mystery, of the past, of the sinister. *The Old English Baron* really contains little Gothic setting, but what historical claim the book has to being a Gothic novel (despite the author's own subtitle "A Gothic Story") rests on that small portion of the book. It is just enough to trigger anticipation of the mysterious, or, as one might also say, of the "evil." Subsequent writers, in tune with the times and aware that the castle with its lugubrious, medieval trappings could no longer sufficiently trigger the reader's irrational faculties and arouse terror, replace the castle setting with that of the haunted or mysterious house. Hawthorne makes ample use of this in *The House of The Seven Gables,* as does Bulwer-Lytton in "The Haunted and the Haunters," and as do many modern Gothic writers. Others have begun to replace the house with the even more modern setting of the rocket or spaceship.

But whether or not the writer uses a castle, house, or rocket, the setting is such that the intended victim is isolated and initially helpless, part of the plan intended to heighten the reader's empathy with the victim. Emily Brontë introduces her Gothic tale *Wuthering Heights* with such a description of isolation:

In all England, I do not believe that I could have fixed on a situation so completely removed from the stir of society. A perfect misanthropist's heaven—and Mr. Heathcliff and I are such a suitable pair to divide the desolation between us.

Robert Louis Stevenson, in an equally effective passage, isolates his main character in *Dr. Jekyll and Mr. Hyde* in a shuttered London house, Hawthorne isolates his characters inside the family enclave of the Pyncheon household, and Maturin uses a London madhouse as one of his alienating settings. The use of isolation continues into contemporary stories in the form of psychological isolation, as that of Charlotte Perkins Gilman's "The Yellow Wall Paper" and Saki's (H. H. Munro) delightfully chilling "Sredni Vashtar," and it reaches a kind of futuristic climax in Edmond Hamilton's "The Dead Planet."

Frequently coupled with the isolation is Nature in her wild or demonic aspect. The time is night, either physical night or the night of the mind; the mood is heavy, gloomy, and the elements stormy. Emily Brontë writes:

Wuthering Heights is the name of Mr. Heathcliff's dwelling. "Wuthering" being a significant provincial adjective, descriptive of the atmospheric tumult to which its station is exposed in stormy weather. Pure, bracing ventilation they must have up there, at all times, indeed: one may guess the power of the north wind, blowing over the edge, by the excessive slant of a few stunted firs at the end of the house; and by a range of gaunt thorns all stretching their limbs one way, as if craving alms of the sun.

Without the night, the storm, the wind whistling around the house and the snow whipping into Lockwood's bed chamber, the appearance of Catherine's ghost would be more ludicrous than terrifying, for ghosts and the supernatural are traditionally, though not necessarily, of the night.

Furthermore, Emily Brontë and others have identified their characters with isolation and the violent, dark side of nature. Heathcliff, himself a foundling, a "child of Nature," is passionate, violent, attuned to the desolate moorlands surrounding Wuthering Heights. Whatever one thinks of Brontë's technique as a sort of literary "naturalism" or even the threshold of the "pathetic fallacy," it is in any case Gothic and highly successful in rousing apprehension and fear in the reader.

In contrast to Emily Brontë's fusion of the moods of man and Nature, Edmond Hamilton in "The Dead Planet" avoids the personal approach almost entirely. He deliberately builds on a description of a planet and its long-dead civilization, stimulating the reader's curiosity in such a way that there is an impending though vague sense of doom. But, unlike the early Gothic, "The Dead Planet" has no use of the supernatural, no explicit victim, no sense of evil. It is a slowly cumulative effect, and the impact of doom and horror is brought home with force only when the denouement is reached and the reader realizes the full significance of the descriptive passages. "The Dead Planet" stimulates one of the most basic fears of man and one of the sources of Gothic speculation: the concern with isolation and death.

It is perhaps unnecessary to point out the impossibility of separating all of the Gothic devices completely. No story exists without setting, for example, but the setting may not be the major source of terror. In Blackwood's "The Willows," for example, the setting is a major element, yet it attains its quality of terror only because it reveals the presence of a malignant "unknown." It is ultimately, therefore, more a question of degree than of kind which dictates the category into which any particular selection is placed.

from

The Castle of Otranto
A Gothic Story

by Horace Walpole

CHAPTER I.

Manfred, Prince of Otranto, had one son and one daughter: the latter, a most beautiful virgin, aged eighteen, was called Matilda. Conrad, the son, was three years younger, a homely youth, sickly, and of no promising disposition; yet he was the darling of his father, who never showed any symptoms of affection to Matilda. Manfred had contracted a marriage for his son with the Marquis of Vicenza's daughter, Isabella; and she had already been delivered by her guardians into the hands of Manfred, that he might celebrate the wedding as soon as Conrad's infirm state of health would permit. Manfred's impatience for this ceremonial was remarked by his family and neighbours. The former, indeed, apprehending the severity of their prince's disposition, did not dare to utter their surmises on this precipitation. Hippolita, his wife, an amiable lady, did sometimes venture to represent the danger of marrying their only son so early, considering his great youth, and greater infirmities; but she never received any other answer than reflections on her own

sterility, who had given him but one heir. His tenants
and subjects were less cautious in their discourses: they
attributed this hasty wedding to the prince's dread of
seeing accomplished an ancient prophecy, which was said
to have pronounced that *the Castle and Lordship of
Otranto should pass from the present family whenever
the real owner should be grown too large to inhabit it*.
It was difficult to make any sense of this prophecy, and
still less easy to conceive what it had to do with the
marriage in question. Yet these mysteries, or contradictions, did not make the populace adhere the less to their
opinion.

Young Conrad's birthday was fixed for his espousals.
The company was assembled in the chapel of the castle,
and everything ready for beginning the divine office,
when Conrad himself was missing. Manfred, impatient of
the least delay, and who had not observed his son retire,
despatched one of his attendants to summon the young
prince. The servant, who had not stayed long enough
to have crossed the court to Conrad's apartment, came
running back breathless, in a frantic manner, his eyes
staring, and foaming at the mouth. He said nothing, but
pointed to the court. The company were struck with
terror and amazement. The Princess Hippolita, without
knowing what was the matter, but anxious for her son,
swooned away. Manfred, less apprehensive than enraged
at the procrastination of the nuptials, and at the folly of
his domestic, asked imperiously what was the matter? The
fellow made no answer, but continued pointing towards
the court-yard; and, at last, after repeated questions put
to him, cried out,—

"Oh! the helmet! the helmet!"

In the meantime, some of the company had run into
the court, from whence was heard a confused noise of
shrieks, horror, and surprise. Manfred, who began to be
alarmed at not seeing his son, went himself to get information of what occasioned this strange confusion. Matilda

remained endeavouring to assist her mother, and Isabella stayed for the same purpose, and to avoid showing any impatience for the bridegroom, for whom, in truth, she had conceived little affection.

The first thing that struck Manfred's eyes was a group of his servants endeavouring to raise something that appeared to him a mountain of sable plumes. He gazed without believing his sight. "What are ye doing?" cried Manfred, wrathfully. "Where is my son?"

A volley of voices replied, "Oh! my lord! the prince! the prince! the helmet! the helmet!"

Shocked with these lamentable sounds, and dreading he knew not what, he advanced hastily—but, what a sight for a father's eyes!—he beheld his child dashed to pieces, and almost buried under an enormous helmet, a hundred times more large than any casque ever made for human being, and shaded with a proportionable quantity of black feathers.

The horror of the spectacle, the ignorance of all around how this misfortune had happened, and, above all, the tremendous phenomenon before him, took away the prince's speech. Yet his silence lasted longer than even grief could occasion. He fixed his eyes on what he wished in vain to believe a vision; and seemed less attentive to his loss than buried in meditation on the stupendous object that had occasioned it. He touched, he examined, the fatal casque; nor could even the bleeding mangled remains of the young prince divert the eyes of Manfred from the portent before him. All who had known his partial fondness for young Conrad were as much surprised at their prince's insensibility as thunderstruck themselves at the miracle of the helmet. They conveyed the disfigured corpse into the hall, without receiving the least direction from Manfred. As little was he attentive to the ladies who remained in the chapel; on the contrary, without mentioning the unhappy princesses, his wife and daughter, the first sounds that dropped from Manfred's lips were, "Take care of the Lady Isabella."

The domestics, without observing the singularity of this direction, were guided by their affection to their mistress, to consider it as peculiarly addressed to her situation, and flew to her assistance. They conveyed her to her chamber more dead than alive, and indifferent to all the strange circumstances she heard, except the death of her son. Matilda, who doted on her mother, smothered her own grief and amazement, and thought of nothing but assisting and comforting her afflicted parent. Isabella, who had been treated by Hippolita like a daughter, and who returned that tenderness with equal duty and affection, was scarce less assiduous about the princess; at the same time endeavouring to partake and lessen the weight of sorrow which she saw Matilda strove to suppress, for whom she had conceived the warmest sympathy of friendship. Yet her own situation could not help finding its place in her thoughts. She felt no concern for the death of young Conrad, except commiseration; and she was not sorry to be delivered from a marriage which had promised her little felicity, either from her destined bridegroom, or from the severe temper of Manfred, who, though he had distinguished her by great indulgence, had impressed her mind with terror, from his causeless rigour to such amiable princesses as Hippolita and Matilda.

While the ladies were conveying the wretched mother to her bed, Manfred remained in the court, gazing on the ominous casque, and regardless of the crowd which the strangeness of the event had now assembled around him. The few words he articulated tended solely to enquiries whether any man knew from whence it could have come? Nobody could give him the least information. However, as it seemed to be the sole object of his curiosity, it soon became so to the rest of the spectators, whose conjectures were as absurd and improbable as the catastrophe itself was unprecedented. In the midst of their senseless guesses, a young peasant, whom rumor had drawn thither from a neighboring village, observed that the miraculous helmet was exactly like that on the figure in black marble of Alfonso the Good, one of their former princes, in the church of St. Nicholas.

"Villain! what sayest thou?" cried Manfred, starting from his trance in a tempest of rage, and seizing the young man by the collar. "How darest thou utter such treason? Thy life shall pay for it."

The spectators, who as little comprehended the cause of the prince's fury as all the rest they had seen, were at a loss to unravel this new circumstance. The young peasant himself was still more astonished, not conceiving how he had offended the prince; yet recollecting himself, with a mixture of grace and humility, he disengaged himself from Manfred's gripe, and then, with an obeisance which discovered more jealousy of innocence than dismay, he asked with respect of what he was guilty? Manfred, more enraged at the vigour, however decently exerted, with which the young man had shaken off his hold, than appeased by his submission, ordered his attendants to seize him, and if he had not been withheld by his friends, whom he had invited to the nuptials, would have poniarded the peasant in their arms.

During this altercation, some of the vulgar spectators had run to the great church, which stood near the castle, and came back open-mouthed, declaring that the helmet was missing from Alfonso's statue. Manfred, at this news, grew perfectly frantic; and, as if he sought a subject on which to vent the tempest within him, he rushed again on the young peasant, crying, "Villain! monster! sorcerer! 'tis thou hast done this! 'tis thou hast slain my son!"

The mob, who wanted some object within the scope of their capacities on whom they might discharge their bewildered reasonings, caught the words from the mouth of their lord, and re-echoed, "Ay, ay; 'tis he, 'tis he!

He has stolen the helmet from good Alfonso's tomb, and dashed out the brains of our young prince with it," never reflecting how enormous the disproportion was between the marble helmet that had been in the church, and that of steel before their eyes; nor how impossible it was for a youth, seemingly not twenty, to wield a piece of armour of so prodigious a weight.

The folly of these ejaculations brought Manfred to himself: yet, whether provoked at the peasant having observed the resemblance between the two helmets, and thereby led to the farther discovery of the absence of that in the church, or wishing to bury any fresh rumour under so impertinent a supposition, he gravely pronounced that the young man was certainly a necromancer, and that till the church could take cognisance of the affair, he would have the magician whom they had thus detected, kept prisoner under the helmet itself, which he ordered his attendants to raise, and place the young man under it; declaring he should be kept there without food, with which his own infernal art might furnish him.

It was in vain for the youth to represent against this preposterous sentence; in vain did Manfred's friends endeavour to divert him from this savage and ill-grounded resolution. The generality were charmed with their lord's decision, which to their apprehensions carried great appearance of justice, as the magician was to be punished by the very instrument with which he had offended; nor were they struck with the least compunction at the probability of the youth being starved, for they firmly believed that by his diabolical skill he could easily supply himself with nutriment.

Manfred thus saw his commands even cheerfully obeyed, and appointing a guard, with strict orders to prevent any food being conveyed to the prisoner, he dismissed his friends and attendants and retired to his own chamber, after locking the gates of the castle, in which he suffered none but his domestics to remain.

In the mean time, the care and zeal of the young ladies had brought the Princess Hippolita to herself, who, amidst the transports of her own sorrow, frequently demanded news of her lord, would have dismissed her attendants to watch over him, and at last enjoined Matilda to leave her, and visit and comfort her father. Matilda, who wanted not affectionate duty to Manfred, though she trembled at his austerity, obeyed the orders of Hippolita, whom she tenderly recommended to Isabella; and enquiring of the domestics of her father, was informed that he was retired to his chamber, and had commanded that nobody should have admittance to him. Concluding that he was immersed in sorrow for the death of her brother, and fearing to renew his tears by the sight of his sole remaining child, she hesitated whether she should break in upon his affliction: yet solicitude for him, backed by the commands of her mother, encouraged her to venture disobeying the orders he had given; a fault she had never been guilty of before. The gentle timidity of her nature made her pause for some minutes at his door. She heard him traverse his chamber backwards and forwards with disordered steps; a mood which increased her apprehensions. She was however just going to beg admittance, when Manfred suddenly opened the door; and as it was now twilight, concurring with the disorder of his mind, he did not distinguish the person, but asked angrily who it was. Matilda replied, trembling, "My dearest father, it is I, your daughter."

Manfred, stepping back hastily, cried, "Begone, I do not want a daughter;" and, flinging back abruptly, clapped the door against the terrified Matilda.

She was too well acquainted with her father's impetuosity to venture a second intrusion. When she had a little recovered the shock of so bitter a reception, she wiped away her tears, to prevent the additional stab that the knowledge of it would give Hippolita, who questioned her in the most anxious terms on the health of

Manfred, and how he bore his loss. Matilda assured her he was well, and supported his misfortune with manly fortitude.

"But will he not let me see him?" said Hippolita, mournfully; "will he not permit me to blend my tears with his, and shed a mother's sorrows in the bosom of her lord? Or do you deceive me, Matilda? I know how Manfred doted on his son; is not the stroke too heavy for him? has he not sunk under it? You do not answer me:—alas! I dread the worst!—raise me, my maidens; I will, I will see my lord. Bear me to him instantly. He is dearer to me even than my children."

Matilda made signs to Isabella to prevent Hippolita's rising; and both those lovely young women were using their gentle violence to stop and calm the princess, when a servant, on the part of Manfred, arrived and told Isabella that his lord demanded to speak with her.

"With me!" cried Isabella.

"Go," said Hippolita, relieved by a message from her lord: "Manfred cannot support the sight of his own family. He thinks you less disordered than we are, and dreads the shock of my grief. Console him, dear Isabella, and tell him I will smother my own anguish rather than add to his."

As it was now evening, the servant who conducted Isabella bore a torch before her. When they came to Manfred, who was walking impatiently about the gallery, he started and said hastily,—

"Take away that light, and begone." Then shutting the door impetuously, he flung himself upon a bench against the wall and bade Isabella sit by him. She obeyed trembling.

"I sent for you, lady," said he, and then stopped, under great appearance of confusion.

"My lord!"

"Yes, I sent for you on a matter of great moment," resumed he. "Dry your tears, young lady:—you have lost your bridegroom. Yes, cruel fate! and I have lost the hopes of my race! but Conrad was not worthy of your beauty."

"How! my lord," said Isabella; "sure you do not suspect me of not feeling the concern I ought! my duty and affection would have always——"

"Think no more of him," interrupted Manfred: "he was a sickly, puny child; and Heaven has perhaps taken him away that I might not trust the honours of my house on so frail a foundation. The line of Manfred calls for numerous supports. My foolish fondness for that boy blinded the eyes of my prudence—but it is better as it is. I hope in a few years to have reason to rejoice at the death of Conrad."

Words cannot paint the astonishment of Isabella. At first she apprehended that grief had disordered Manfred's understanding. Her next thought suggested that this strange discourse was designed to ensnare her: she feared that Manfred had perceived her indifference for his son, and in consequence of that idea she replied,—

"Good my lord, do not doubt my tenderness: my heart would have accompanied my hand. Conrad would have engrossed all my care; and wherever fate shall dispose of me, I shall always cherish his memory, and regard your highness and the virtuous Hippolita as my parents."

"Curse on Hippolita!" cried Manfred: "forget her from this moment, as I do. In short, lady, you have missed a husband undeserving of your charms: they shall now be better disposed of. Instead of a sickly boy, you shall have a husband in the prime of his age, who will know how to value your beauties, and who may expect a numerous offspring."

"Alas! my lord," said Isabella, "my mind is too sadly engrossed by the recent catastrophe in your family to think of another marriage. If ever my father returns, and it shall be his pleasure, I shall obey, as I did when I consented to give my hand to your son; but until his return permit me to remain under your hospitable roof, and employ the melancholy hours in assuaging yours, Hippolita's and the fair Matilda's affliction."

"I desired you once before," said Manfred, angrily, "not to name that woman. From this hour she must be a stranger to you, as she must be to me:—in short, Isabella, since I cannot give you my son, I offer you myself."

"Heavens!" cried Isabella, waking from her delusion, "what do I hear? You, my lord! You! my father-in-law, the father of Conrad! the husband of the virtuous and tender Hippolita!"

"I tell you," said Manfred imperiously, "Hippolita is no longer my wife; I divorce her from this hour. Too long has she cursed me by her unfruitfulness. My fate depends on having sons, and this night I trust will give a new date to my hopes."

At those words he seized the cold hand of Isabella, who was half dead with fright and horror. She shrieked and started from him. Manfred rose to pursue her, when the moon, which was now up and gleamed in at the opposite casement, presented to his sight the plumes of the fatal helmet, which rose to the height of the windows, waving backwards and forwards in a tempestuous manner and accompanied with a hollow and rustling sound. Isabella, who gathered courage from her situation, and who dreaded nothing so much as Manfred's pursuit of his declaration, cried,—

"Look, my lord! see, Heaven itself declares against your impious intentions!"

"Heaven nor hell shall impede my designs," said Manfred, advancing again to seize the princess. At that instant the portrait of his grandfather, which hung over the bench where they had been sitting, uttered a deep sigh and heaved its breast. Isabella, whose back was turned to the picture, saw not the motion, nor whence the sound came, but started and said,—"Hark, my lord!

what sound was that?" and at the same time made towards the door. Manfred, distracted between the flight of Isabella, who had now reached the stairs, and yet unable to keep his eyes from the picture, which began to move, had, however, advanced some steps after her, still looking backwards on the portrait, when he saw it quit its panel, and descend on the floor with a grave and melancholy air.

"Do I dream?" cried Manfred, returning; "or are the devils themselves in league against me? Speak, infernal spectre! or, if thou art my grandsire, why dost thou too conspire against thy wretched descendant, who too dearly pays for——" Ere he could finish the sentence, the vision sighed again, and made a sign to Manfred to follow him.

"Lead on!" cried Manfred: "I will follow thee to the gulf of perdition." The spectre marched sedately, but dejected, to the end of the gallery, and turned into a chamber on the right hand. Manfred accompanied him at a little distance, full of anxiety and horror, but resolved. As he would have entered the chamber, the door was clapped to with violence by an invisible hand. The prince, collecting courage from this delay, would have forcibly burst open the door with his foot, but found that it resisted his utmost efforts.

"Since hell will not satisfy my curiosity," said Manfred, "I will use the human means in my power for preserving my race; Isabella shall not escape me."

That lady, whose resolution had given way to terror the moment she had quitted Manfred, continued her flight to the bottom of the principal staircase There she stopped, not knowing whither to direct her steps, nor how to escape from the impetuosity of the prince. The gates of the castle she knew were locked, and guards placed in the court. Should she, as her heart prompted her, go and prepare Hippolita for the cruel destiny that awaited her, she did not doubt but Manfred would seek her there, and that his violence would incite him to double the injury he meditated, without leaving room for them to avoid the impetuosity of his passions. Delay might give him time to reflect on the horrid measures he had conceived, or produce some circumstance in her favour, if she could for that night at least avoid his odious purpose. Yet where conceal herself? how avoid the pursuit he would infallibily make throughout the castle? As these thoughts passed rapidly through her mind, she recollected a subterraneous passage which led from the vaults of the castle to the church of St. Nicholas. Could she reach the altar before she was overtaken, she knew even Manfred's violence would not dare to profane the sacredness of the place; and she determined, if no other means of deliverance offered, to shut herself up for ever among the holy virgins, whose convent was contiguous to the cathedral. In this resolution she seized a lamp that burned at the foot of the staircase, and hurried towards the secret passage.

The lower part of the castle was hollowed into several intricate cloisters; and it was not easy for one under so much anxiety to find the door that opened into the cavern. An awful silence reigned throughout those subterraneous regions, except now and then some blasts of wind that shook the doors she had passed, and which, grating on the rusty hinges, were re-echoed through that long labyrinth of darkness. Every murmur struck her with new terror;—yet more she dreaded to hear the wrathful voice of Manfred urging his domestics to pursue her. She trod as softly as impatience would give her leave,—yet frequently stopped and listened to hear if she was followed. In one of those moments she thought she heard a sigh. She shuddered and recoiled a few paces. In a moment she thought she heard the step of some person. Her blood curdled: she concluded it was Manfred. Every suggestion that horror could inspire rushed into her mind. She condemned her rash flight, which had thus exposed her to his rage in a place where her cries were not likely to draw anybody to her assistance. Yet the sound seemed not to come from behind: if Manfred knew where she was, he must have followed her: she was still in one of the cloisters, and the steps she had heard were too distinct to proceed from the way she had come. Cheered with this reflection, and hoping to find a friend in whoever was not the prince, she was going to advance, when a door that stood ajar at some distance to the left was opened gently; but ere her lamp, which she held up, could discover who opened it, the person retreated precipitately on seeing the light.

Isabella, whom every incident was sufficient to dismay, hesitated whether she should proceed. Her dread of Manfred soon outweighed every other terror. The very circumstance of the person avoiding her, gave her a sort of courage. It could only be, she thought, some domestic belonging to the castle. Her gentleness had never raised her an enemy, and conscious innocence made her hope that, unless sent by the prince's order to seek her, his servants would rather assist than prevent her flight. Fortifying herself with these reflections, and believing, by what she could observe, that she was near the mouth of the subterraneous cavern, she approached the door that had been opened; but a sudden gust of wind that met her at the door extinguished her lamp, and left her in total darkness.

Words cannot paint the horror of the princess's situation. Alone, in so dismal a place, her mind impressed with all the terrible events of the day, hopeless of escaping, expecting every moment the arrival of Manfred and far from tranquil on knowing she was within reach of somebody, she knew not whom, who for some cause seemed concealed thereabouts; all these thoughts crowded on her distracted mind, and she was ready to sink under her apprehensions. She addressed herself to every saint in heaven, and inwardly implored their assistance. For a considerable time she remained in an agony of despair. At last, as softly as was possible, she felt for the door, and having found it, entered trembling into the vault whence she had heard the sigh and steps. It gave her a kind of momentary joy to perceive an imperfect ray of clouded moonshine gleam from the roof of the vault, which seemed to be fallen in, and from whence hung a fragment of earth or building, she could not distinguish which, that appeared to have been crushed inwards. She advanced eagerly towards this chasm, when she discerned a human form standing close against the wall.

She shrieked, believing it the ghost of her betrothed Conrad. The figure, advancing, said in a submissive voice, "Be not alarmed, lady; I will not injure you."

Isabella, a little encouraged by the words and tone of voice of the stranger, and recollecting that this must be the person who had opened the door, recovered her spirits enough to reply, "Sir, whoever you are, take pity on a wretched princess standing on the brink of destruction; assist me to escape from this fatal castle, or, in a few moments I may be made miserable for ever."

"Alas!" said the stranger, "what can I do to assist you? I will die in your defence, but I am unacquainted with the castle, and want——"

"Oh!" said Isabella, hastily interrupting him, "help me but to find a trap-door that must be hereabout, and it is the greatest service you can do me, for I have not a minute to lose." Saying these words, she felt about on the pavement, and directed the stranger to search likewise, for a smooth piece of brass enclosed in one of the stones. "That," said she, "is the lock, which opens with a spring of which I know the secret. If we can find that, I may escape; if not, alas courteous stranger, I fear I shall have involved you in my misfortunes. Manfred will suspect you for the accomplice of my flight, and you will fall a victim to his resentment."

"I value not my life," said the stranger; "and it will be some comfort to lose it in trying to deliver you from his tyranny."

"Generous youth!" said Isabella, "how shall I ever requite——"

As she uttered these words, a ray of moonshine, streaming through a cranny of the ruin above, shone directly on the lock they sought.—"Oh! transport!" said Isabella, "here is the trap-door;" and, taking out the key, she touched the spring, which, starting aside, discovered an iron ring. "Lift up the door," said the princess. The stranger obeyed, and beneath appeared some stone steps descending into a vault totally dark. "We must go down here," said Isabella; "follow me; dark and dismal as it is, we cannot miss our way. It leads directly to the church of St. Nicholas—but, perhaps," added the princess, modestly, "you have no reason to leave the castle, nor have I further occasion for your service; in a few minutes I shall be safe from Manfred's rage—only let me know to whom I am so much obliged."

"I will never quit you," said the stranger eagerly, "until I have placed you in safety—nor think me, princess, more generous than I am; though you are my principal care——"

The stranger was interrupted by a sudden noise of voices that seemed approaching, and they soon distinguished these words:—"Talk not to me of necromancers; I tell you she must be in the castle; I will find her in spite of enchantment."

"Oh, heavens!" cried Isabella, "it is the voice of Manfred; make haste, or we are ruined! and shut the trap-door after you." Saying this, she descended the steps precipitately; and, as the stranger hastened to follow her, he let the door slip out of his hands: it fell, and the spring closed over it. He tried in vain to open it, not having observed Isabella's method of touching the spring; nor had he many moments to make an essay. The noise of the falling door had been heard by Manfred, who, directed by the sound, hastened thither, attended by his servants with torches.

"It must be Isabella," cried Manfred, before he entered the vault: "she is escaping by the subterraneous passage, but she cannot have got far." What was the astonishment of the prince, when, instead of Isabella, the light of the torches discovered to him the young peasant, whom he thought confined under the fatal helmet. "Traitor!" said Manfred, "how camest thou here? I thought thee in durance above in the court."

"I am no traitor," replied the young man boldly, "nor am I answerable for your thoughts."

"Presumptuous villain!" cried Manfred, "dost thou provoke my wrath? Tell me; how hast thou escaped from above? Thou hast corrupted thy guards, and their lives shall answer it."

"My poverty," said the peasant calmly, "will disculpate them: though the ministers of a tyrant's wrath, to thee they are faithful, and but too willing to execute the orders which you unjustly imposed upon them."

"Art thou so hardy as to dare my vengeance?" said the prince; "but tortures shall force the truth from thee. Tell me; I will know thy accomplices."

"There was my accomplice!" said the youth, smiling and pointing to the roof.

Manfred ordered the torches to be held up, and perceived that one of the cheeks of the enchanted casque had forced its way through the pavement of the court, as his servants had let it fall over the peasant, and had broken through into the vault, leaving a gap through which the peasant had pressed himself some minutes before he was found by Isabella. "Was that the way by which thou didst descend?" said Manfred.

"It was," said the youth.

from

The Old English Baron
A Gothic Story

by Clara Reeve

[*Edmund Twyfold, a young man of poor circumstances but of excellent qualities, is befriended by the wealthy Lord Fitz-Owen. The situation would be ideal for Edmund except that he does not enjoy the same cordial relationship with Fitz-Owen's jealous eldest son and nephews. A friar, Father Oswald, advises Edmund to bear with patience and fortitude the injustices inflicted upon him because of envy and jealousy and he will be rewarded in the future.*]

One day, as they were walking in a wood near the castle, Edmund asked the Father what meant those preparations for building, the cutting down trees and burning of bricks?—What, said Oswald, have not you heard that my Lord is going to build a new apartment on the west side of the castle?—And why, said Edmund, should my Lord be at that expence when there is one on the east side that is never occupied?—That apartment, said the friar, you must have observed is always shut up. I have observed it often, said Edmund; but I never presumed to ask any questions about it.—You had then, said Oswald, less curiosity and more discretion than is common at your age.—You have raised my curiosity, said Edmund; and, if it be not improper, I beg of you to gratify it.—We are alone, said Oswald, and I am so well assured of your prudence, that I will explain this mystery in some degree to you.

You must know, that apartment was occupied by the last Lord Lovel when he was a batchelor. He married in his father's life-time, who gave up his own apartment to him, and offered to retire to this himself; but the son would not permit him, he chose to sleep here, rather than in any other. He had been married about three months when his father, the old Lord, died of a fever. About twelve months after his marriage, he was called upon to attend the King, Henry the Fourth, on an expedition into Wales, whither he was attended by many of his dependants. He left his lady big with child, and full of care and anxiety for his safety and return.

After the King had chastised the Rebels, and obtained the victory, the Lord Lovel was expected home every day; various reports were sent home before him; one messenger brought an account of his health and safety— soon after another came with bad news, that he was slain in battle. His kinsman, Sir Walter Lovel, came here on a visit to comfort the Lady; and he waited to receive his kinsman at his return. It was he that brought the news of the sad event of the battle to the Lady Lovel.

She fainted away at the relation; but, when she revived, exerted the utmost resolution; saying, it was her duty to bear this dreadful stroke with Christian fortitude and patience, especially in regard to the child she went with, the last remains of her beloved husband, and the undoubted heir of a noble house. For several days she seemed an example of patience and resignation; but then, all at once, she renounced them, and broke out into passionate and frantic exclamations; she said, that her dear Lord was basely murdered; that his ghost had appeared to her, and revealed his fate: She called upon Heaven and earth to revenge her wrongs; saying, she would never cease complaining to God, and the King, for vengeance and justice.

Upon this, Sir Walter told the servants that Lady Lovel was distracted, from grief for the death of her Lord: that his regard for her was strong as ever; and that, if she recovered, he would himself be her comforter, and marry her. In the mean time she was confined in this very apartment, and in less than a month the poor Lady died.—She lies buried in the family vault in St. Austin's church in the village. Sir Walter took possession of the Castle, and all the other estates, and assumed the title of Lord Lovel.

Soon after, it was reported that the Castle was haunted, and that the ghosts of Lord and Lady Lovel had been seen by several of the servants. Whoever went into this apartment were terrified by uncommon noises and strange appearances; at length this apartment was wholly shut up, and the servants were forbid to enter it, or to talk of any thing relating to it: However, the story did not stop here; it was whispered about, that the new Lord Lovel was so disturbed every night that he could not sleep in quiet; and, being at last tired of the place, he sold the Castle and estate of his ancestors, to his brother-in-law the Lord Fitz-Owen, who now enjoys it, and left this country.

All this is news to me, said Edmund; but, Father, tell me what grounds there were for the Lady's suspicion that her Lord died unfairly.—Alas! said Oswald, that is only known to God. There were strange thoughts in the minds of many at that time; I had mine; but I will not disclose them, not even to you. I will not injure those who may be innocent; and I leave it to Providence, who will doubtless, in its own best time and manner, punish the guilty. But let what I have told you be as if you had never heard it.

I thank you for these marks of your esteem and confidence, said Edmund; be assured that I will not abuse them; nor do I desire to pry into secrets not proper to be revealed: I entirely approve your discretion, and acquiesce in your conclusion, that Providence will in its own time vindicate its ways to man: If it were not for that trust, my situation would be insupportable. I strive earnestly to deserve the esteem and favour of good men; I endeavour to regulate my conduct so as to avoid giving offence to any man; but I see, with infinite pain, that it is impossible for me to gain these points.—I see it too, with great concern, said Oswald; and every thing that I can say and do in your favour is misconstrued; and, by seeking to do you service, I lose my own influence: But I will never give my sanction to acts of injustice, nor join to oppress innocence. My dear child, put your trust in God: He who brought light out of darkness, can bring good out of evil.—I hope and trust so, said Edmund; but, Father, if my enemies should prevail, if my Lord should believe their stories against me, and I should be put out of the house with disgrace, what will become of me? I have nothing but my character to depend upon; if I lose that, I lose every thing; and I see they seek no less than my ruin.—Trust in my Lord's honour and justice, replied Oswald; he knows your virtue, and he is not ignorant of their ill-will towards you.—I know my Lord's justice too well to doubt it, said Edmund; but would it not be better to rid him of this trouble, and his family of an incumbrance? I would gladly do something for myself, but cannot without my Lord's recommendation; and such is my situation, that I fear the asking for a dismission would be accounted base ingratitude: Beside, when I think of leaving this house, my heart saddens at the thought, and tells me I cannot be happy out of it: Yet I think I could return to a peasant's life with cheerfulness, rather than live in a place under disdain and contempt.—Have patience a little longer, my son, said Oswald; I will think of some way to serve you, and to represent your grievances to my Lord, without offence to either: Perhaps the causes may be removed. Continue to observe the same irreproachable conduct; and be assured that Heaven will defend your innocence, and defeat the unjust designs of your enemies. Let us now return home.

About a week after this conference, Edmund walked out in the fields ruminating on the disagreeable circumstances of his situation. Insensible of the time, he had been out several hours without perceiving how the day wore away, when he heard himself called by name several times; looking backward he saw his friend Mr. William, and hallowed to him. He came running towards him; and, leaping over the style, stood still a while to recover his breath. What is the matter, Sir, said Edmund? your looks bespeak some tidings of importance. With a look of tender concern and affection, the youth pressed his hand and spoke. My dear Edmund, you must come home with me directly; your old enemies have united to ruin you with my father; my brother Robert has declared that he thinks there will be no peace in our family till you are dismissed from it, and told my father, he hoped he would not break with his kinsmen rather than give up Edmund.—But what do they lay to my charge? said Edmund.—I cannot rightly understand, answered William, for they make a great mystery of it; something of great consequence they say; but they will not tell me what: However, my father has told them that they must bring their accusation before your face, and he will have you answer them publicly. I have been seeking you this hour, to inform you of this, that you might be prepared to defend yourself against your accusers.—God reward you, Sir, said Edmund, for all your goodness to me! I see they are determined to ruin me if possible: I shall be compelled to leave the

Castle; but, whatever becomes of me, be assured you shall have no cause to blush for your kindness and partiality to your Edmund.—I know it, I am sure of it, said William; and here I swear to you, as Jonathan did to David, I beseech Heaven to bless me, as my friendship to you shall be steady and inviolable!—Only so long as I shall deserve so great a blessing, interrupted Edmund.—I know your worth and honour, continued William; and such is my confidence in your merit, that I firmly believe Heaven designs you for something extraordinary; and I expect that some great and unforseen event will raise you to the rank and station to which you appear to belong: Promise me, therefore, that whatever may be your fate you will preserve the same friendship for me that I bear to you.—Edmund was so much affected that he could not answer but in broken sentences. Oh my friend, my master! I vow, I promise, my heart promises!—He kneeled down with clasped hands, and uplifted eyes: William kneeled by him, and they invoked the Supreme to witness to their friendship, and implored his blessing upon it: They then rose up and embraced each other, while tears of cordial affection bedewed their cheeks.

As soon as they were able to speak, Edmund conjured his friend not to expose himself to the displeasure of his family out of kindness to him. I submit to the will of Heaven, said he, I wait with patience its disposal of me; if I leave the Castle I will find means to inform you of my fate and fortunes.—I hope, said William, that things may yet be accommodated; but do not take any resolution, let us act as occasions arise.

In this manner these amiable youths conferred, till they arrived at the Castle. The Baron was sitting in the great hall on a high chair with a footstep before, with the state and dignity of a judge; before him stood Father Oswald, as pleading the case for himself and Edmund. Round the Baron's chair stood his eldest son and his kinsmen, with their principal domestics. The old servant,

Joseph, at some distance with his head leaning forward, as listening with the utmost attention to what passed. Mr. William approached the chair.—My Lord, I have found Edmund, and brought him to answer for himself.— You have done well, said the Baron. Edmund, come hither; you are charged with some indiscretions, for I cannot properly call them crimes: I am resolved to do justice between you and your accusers; I shall therefore hear you as well as them; for no man ought to be condemned unheard.—My Lord, said Edmund, with equal modesty and intrepidity, I demand my trial; if I shall be found guilty of any crimes against my Benefactor, let me be punished with the utmost rigor: But if, as I trust, no charge can be proved against me, I know your goodness too well to doubt that you will do justice to me, as well as to others; and if it should so happen that by the misrepresentations of my enemies (who have long sought my ruin privately, and now avow it publicly), if by their artifices your Lordship should be induced to think me guilty, I would submit to your sentence in silence, and appeal to another tribunal.—See, said Mr. Wenlock, the confidence of the fellow! he already supposes that my Lord must be in the wrong if he condemns him; and then this meek creature will appeal to another tribunal: To whose will he appeal? I desire he may be made to explain himself.—That I will immediately, said Edmund, without being compelled; I only meant to appeal to Heaven that best knows my innocence.—'Tis true, said the Baron, and no offence to any one; man can only judge by appearances, but Heaven knows the heart: Let every one of you bear this in mind, that you may not bring a false accusation, nor justify yourself by concealing the truth. Edmund, I am informed that Oswald and you have made very free with me and my family in some of your conversations; you were heard to censure me for the absurdity of building a new apartment on the west side of the Castle when there was one on the east side uninhabited:

Oswald said, that apartment was shut up because it was haunted; that some shocking murther had been committed there; adding many particulars concerning Lord Lovel's family, such as he could not know the truth of, and if he had known, was imprudent to reveal. But further, you complained of ill treatment here; and mentioned an intention to leave the Castle, and seek your fortune elsewhere. I shall examine into all these particulars in turn. At present I desire you, Edmund, to relate all that you can remember of the conversation that passed between you and Oswald in the wood last Monday.——Good God! said Edmund, is it possible that any person could put such a construction upon so innocent a conversation?

Tell me then, said the Baron, the particulars of it.——I will, my Lord, as nearly as my memory will allow me. Accordingly he related most of the conversation that passed in the wood; but, in the part that concerned the family of Lovel, he abbreviated as much as possible. Oswald's countenance cleared up, for he had done the same before Edmund came. The Baron called to his eldest son,——You hear, Sir Robert, what both parties say: I have questioned them separately; neither of them knew what the other would answer, yet their accounts agree almost to a word.——I confess they do so, answered Sir Robert; but, Sir, it is very bold and presuming for them to speak of our family affairs in such a manner; if my uncle, Lord Lovel, should come to know it, he would punish them severely; and, if his honour is reflected upon, it becomes us to resent and to punish it. Here Mr. Wenlock broke out into passion, and offered to swear to the truth of his accusation. Be silent, Dick, said the Baron; I shall judge for myself. I protest, said he to Sir Robert, I never heard so much as Oswald has now told me concerning the deaths of Lord and Lady Lovel; I think it is best to let stories alone till they die away of themselves. I had, indeed, heard of an idle story of the east apartments being haunted when first I came hither, and my brother advised me to shut it up till it should be forgotten; but what has now been said, has suggested a thought that may make that apartment useful in future. I have thought of a punishment for Edmund that will stop the mouth of his accusers for the present; and, as I hope, will establish his credit with every body. Edmund will you undertake this adventure for me?—What adventure, my Lord, said Edmund? There is nothing I would not undertake to show my gratitude and fidelity to you. As to my courage, I would shew that at the expense of my malicious accusers, if respect to my Lord's blood did not tie up my hands; as I am situated I beg it may be put to the proof in whatever way is most for my master's service.—That is well said, cried the Baron: As to your enemies, I am thinking how to separate you from them effectually; of that I shall speak hereafter. I am going to try Edmund's courage; he shall sleep three nights in the east apartment, that he may testify to all whether it be haunted or not; afterwards I will have that apartment set in order, and my eldest son shall take it for his own; it will spare me some expence, and answer my purpose as well, or better: Will you consent Edmund? —With all my heart, my Lord, said Edmund. I have not wilfully offended God or man; I have, therefore, nothing to fear.—Brave boy! said my Lord; I am not deceived in you, nor shall you be deceived in your reliance on me. You shall sleep in that apartment to-night, and to-morrow I will have some private talk with you. Do you, Oswald, go with me; I want to have some conversation with you. The rest of you, retire to your studies and business; I will meet you at dinner.

Edmund retired to his own chamber, and Oswald was shut up with the Baron; he defended Edmund's cause and his own, and laid open as much as he knew of the malice and designs of his enemies. The Baron expressed much concern at the untimely deaths of Lord and Lady Lovel, and desired Oswald to be circumspect in regard to what he had to say of the circumstances attending them; adding, that he was both innocent and ignorant of any treachery towards either of them. Oswald excused himself for his communications to Edmund, saying, they fell undesignedly into the subject, and that he mentioned it in confidence to him only.

The Baron sent orders to the young men to come to dinner; but they refused to meet Edmund at table; accordingly he ate in the steward's apartment. After dinner the Baron tried to reconcile his kinsmen to Edmund; but found it impossible. They saw their designs were laid open; and judging of him by themselves, thought it impossible to forgive or be forgiven. The Baron ordered them to keep in separate apartments; he took his eldest son for his own companion, as being the most reasonable of the malecontents, and ordered his kinsmen to keep their own apartment, with a servant to watch their motions. Mr. William had Oswald for his companion. Old Joseph was bid to attend on Edmund; to serve him at supper; and, at the hour of nine, to conduct him to the haunted apartment. Edmund desired that he might have a light and his sword, lest his enemies should endeavour to surprise him. The Baron thought his request reasonable, and complied with it.

There was a great search to find the key of the apartment; at last it was discovered by Edmund himself among a parcel of old rusty keys in a lumber room. The Baron sent the young men their suppers to their respective apartments. Edmund declined eating, and desired to be conducted to his apartment. He was accompanied by most of the servants to the door of it; they wished him success, and prayed for him as if he had been going to execution.

The door was with great difficulty unlocked, and Joseph gave Edmund a lighted lamp, and wished him a good night; he returned his good wishes to them all with the utmost chearfulness, took the key on the inside of the door, and dismissed them.

He then took a survey of his chamber; the furniture, by long neglect, was decayed and dropping to pieces; the bed was devoured by the moths, and occupied by the rats, who had built their nests there with impunity for many generations. The bedding was very damp, for the rain had forced its way through the ceiling; he determined, therefore, to lie down in his clothes. There were two doors on the further side of the room with keys in them; being not at all sleepy, he resolved to examine them; he attempted one lock, and opened it with ease; he went into a large dining-room, the furniture of which was in the same tattered condition; out of this was a large closet with some books in it, and hung round with coats of arms, with genealogies and alliances of the house of Lovel; he amused himself here some minutes, and then returned into the bedchamber.

He recollected the other door, and resolved to see where it led to; the key was rusted into the lock, and resisted his attempts; he set the lamp on the ground, and exerting all his strength opened the door, and at the same instant the wind of it blew out the lamp, and left him in utter darkness. At the same moment he heard a hollow rustling noise like that of a person coming through a narrow passage. Till this moment not one idea of fear had approached the mind of Edmund; but just then, all the concurrent circumstances of his situation struck upon his heart, and gave him a new and disagreeable sensation. He paused a while; and, recollecting himself, cried out aloud—What should I fear? I have not wilfully offended God, or man; why, then, should I doubt protection? But I have not yet implored the divine assistance; how then can I expect it! Upon this, he kneeled down and prayed earnestly, resigning himself wholly to the will of Heaven; while he was yet speaking, his courage returned, and he resumed his usual confidence; again he approached the door from whence the noise proceeded; he thought he saw a glimmering light upon a staircase before him. If, said he, this apartment is haunted, I will use my endeavours to discover the cause of it; and if the spirit appears visibly, I will speak to it.

He was preparing to descend the staircase, when he heard several knocks at the door by which he first entered the room; and, stepping backward, the door was clapped to with great violence. Again fear attacked him, but he resisted it, and boldly cried out—Who is there?—A voice at the outer door answered,—It's I—Joseph, your friend! —What do you want, said Edmund?—I have brought you some wood to make a fire, said Joseph.—I thank you kindly, said Edmund; but my lamp is gone out; I will try to find the door, however. After some trouble he found, and opened it; and was not sorry to see his friend Joseph with a light in one hand, a flaggon of beer in the other, and a faggot upon his shoulder. I come, said the good old man, to bring you something to keep up your spirits; the evening is cold; I know this room wants airing; and beside that, my Master, I think your present undertaking requires a little assistance.

My good friend, said Edmund, I never shall be able to deserve or requite your kindness to me.—My dear Sir, you always deserved more than I could do for you; and I think I shall yet live to see you defeat the designs of your enemies, and acknowledge the services of your friends.—Alas, said Edmund, I see little prospect of that! —I see, said Joseph, something that persuades me you are designed for great things; and I perceive that things are working about to some great end: Have courage, my Master, my heart beats strangely high upon your account! —You make me smile, said Edmund.—I am glad to see it, Sir; may you smile all the rest of your life.—I thank your honest affection, returned Edmund, though it is too partial to me. You had better go to bed, however; if it is known that you visit me here, it will be bad for us both. —So I will presently; but, please God, I will come here again to-morrow night when all the family are a-bed; and

I will tell you some things that you never yet heard.—
But pray tell me, said Edmund, where does that door
lead to?—Upon a passage that ends in a staircase that
leads to the lower rooms; and there is likewise a door
out of that passage into the diningroom.—And what
rooms are there below stairs, said Edmund?—The same
as above, replied he.—Very well; then I wish you a
good night, we will talk further to-morrow.—Aye, to-
morrow night; and in this place, my dear Master.—Why
do you call me your Master? I never was, nor ever can
be, your Master. God only knows that, said the good old
man; good night, and Heaven bless you!—good night, my
worthy friend!

Joseph withdrew, and Edmund returned to the other
door, and attempted several times to open it in vain; his
hands were benumbed and tired; at length he gave over.
He made a fire in the chimney, placed the lamp on a
table, and opened one of the window-shutters to admit
the day-light; he then recommended himself to the divine
protection, and threw himself upon the bed; he presently
fell asleep, and continued in that state, till the sun saluted
him with his orient beams through the window he had
opened.

As soon as he was perfectly awake he strove to recollect
his dreams. He thought that he heard people coming up
the staircase that he had a glimpse of; that the door
opened, and there entered a Warrior, leading a Lady by
the hand, who was young and beautiful, but pale and
wan: The Man was dressed in complete armour, and
his helmet down. They approached the bed; they undrew
the curtains. He thought the Man said,—Is this our child?
The woman replied,—It is; and the hour approaches that
he shall be known for such. They then separated, and one
stood on each side of the bed; their hands met over his
head, and they gave him a solemn benediction. He strove
to rise and pay them his respects, but they forbad him;
and the Lady said,—Sleep in peace, oh my Edmund!

for those who are the true possessors of this apartment are employed in thy preservation: Sleep on, sweet hope of a house that is thought past hope!—Upon this they withdrew, and went out at the same door by which they entered, and he heard them descend the stairs.—After this, he followed a funeral as chief mourner; he saw the whole procession, and heard the ceremonies performed. He was snatched away from this mournful scene to one of a contrary kind, a stately feast, at which he presided; and he heard himself congratulated as a husband and a father: His friend William sat by his side; and his happiness was complete. Every succeeding idea was happiness without allay; and his mind was not idle a moment till the morning sun awakened him. He perfectly remembered his dreams, and meditated on what all these things should portend. Am I then, said he, not Edmund Twyford, but somebody of consequence in whose fate so many people are interested? Vain thought, that must have arisen from the partial suggestion of my two friends, Mr. William and old Joseph!

He lay thus reflecting, when a servant knocked at his door, and told him it was past six o'clock, and that the Baron expected him to breakfast in an hour. He rose immediately; paid his tribute of thanks to Heaven for its protection, and went from his chamber in high health and spirits.

*   *   *   *   *   *   *   *   *   *   *   *   *   *   *   *

About the same hour as the preceding evening, Joseph came to conduct Edmund to his apartment. You will find better accommodations than you had last night, said he, and all by my Lord's own order.—I every hour receive some new proof of his goodness, said Edmund. When they arrived, he found a good fire in the chamber, and a table covered with cold meats, and a flaggon of strong beer. Sit down and get your supper, my dear Master, said Joseph:

I must attend my Lord; but as soon as the family are gone to bed I will visit you again.—Do so, said Edmund; but first, see Father Oswald; he has something to say to you; You may trust him, for I have no reserves to him.—Well, Sir, I will see him if you desire it, and I will come to you as soon as possible. So saying, he went his way; and Edmund sat down to supper.

After a moderate refreshment he kneeled down, and prayed with the greatest fervency; he resigned himself to the disposal of Heaven: I am nothing, said he, I desire to be nothing but what thou, O Lord, pleasest to make me: If it is thy will that I should return to my former obscurity, be it obeyed with chearfulness! and, if thou art pleased to exalt me, I will look up to thee as the only fountain of honour and dignity. While he prayed, he felt an enlargement of heart beyond what he had ever experienced before; all idle fears were dispersed, and his heart glowed with divine love and affiance: He seemed raised above the world and all its pursuits. He continued wrapt up in mental devotion, till a knocking at the door obliged him to rise, and let in his two friends, who came without shoes, and on tiptoe, to visit him.

Save you, my son! said the friar; you look chearful and happy.—I am so, Father, said Edmund; I have resigned myself to the disposal of Heaven, and I find my heart strengthened above what I can express.—Heaven be praised! said Oswald: I believe you are designed for great things, my son.—What! do you too encourage my ambition? says Edmund; strange concurrence of circumstances! Sit down, my friends; and do you, my good Joseph tell me the particulars you promised last night. They drew their chairs round the fire, and Joseph began as follows.

You have heard of the untimely death of the late Lord Lovel, my noble and worthy Master; perhaps you may have also heard that, from that time, this apartment was haunted. What passed the other day, when my Lord questioned you both on this head, brought all the circumstances fresh into my mind. You then said, there were suspicions that he came not fairly to his end. I trust you both, and will speak what I know of it. There was a person suspected of this murder; and whom do you think it was?—You must speak out, said Oswald.—Why then, said Joseph, it was the present Lord Lovel.—You speak my thoughts, said Oswald; but proceed to the proofs.—I will, said Joseph. From the time that my Lord's death was reported, there were strange whisperings and consultations between the new Lord and some of the servants; there was a deal of private business carried on in this apartment: Soon after, they gave out that my poor Lady was distracted; but she threw out strong expressions that favoured nothing of madness: She said, that the ghost of her departed Lord had appeared to her, and revealed the circumstances of this murder. None of the servants, but one, were permitted to see her. At this very time Sir Walter, the new Lord, had the cruelty to offer love to her; he urged her to marry him; and one of her women overheard her say, she would sooner die than give her hand to the man who caused the death of her Lord: Soon after this, we were told my Lady was dead. The Lord Lovel made a publick and sumptuous funeral for her.—That is true, said Oswald; for I was a novice, and assisted at it.

Well, says Joseph, now comes my part of the story. As I was coming home from the burial, I overtook Roger our plowman. Said he, What think you of this burying? What should I think, said I, but that we have lost the best Master and Lady that we shall ever know? God he knows, quoth Roger, whether they be living or dead; but if ever I saw my Lady in my life, I saw her alive the night they say she died. I tried to convince him that he was mistaken; but he offered to take his oath, that the very night they said she died, he saw her come out at the garden gate into the fields; that she often stopped, like a person in pain, and then went forward again until he lost sight of her. Now it is certain that her time was out, and she expected to lay down every day: and they did not pretend that she died in childbed. I thought upon what I heard, but nothing I said. Roger told the same story to another servant; so he was called to an account, the story was hushed up, and the foolish fellow said, he was verily persuaded it was her ghost that he saw. Now you must take notice that from this time, they began to talk about that this apartment was troubled: and not only this, but at last the new Lord could not sleep in quiet in his own room; and this induced him to sell the castle to his brother-in-law, and get out of this country as fast as possible. He took most of the servants away with him, Roger among the rest. As for me, they thought I knew nothing, and so they left me behind; but I was neither blind nor deaf, though I could hear, and see, and say nothing.

This is a dark story, said Oswald.—It is so, said Edmund; but why should Joseph seem to think it concerns me in particular?—Ah, dear Sir! said Joseph, I must tell you, though I never uttered it to a mortal man before; the striking resemblance this young man bears to my dear Lord, the strange dislike his reputed father took to him, his gentle manners, his generous heart, his noble qualities so uncommon in those of his birth and breeding, the sound of his voice—You may smile at the strength of my fancy, but I cannot put it out of my mind but that he is my own Master's son.

At these words Edmund changed colour and trembled; he clapped his hand upon his breast; and looked up to Heaven in silence; his dream recurred to his memory, and struck upon his heart. He related it to his attentive auditors. The ways of providence are wonderful, said Oswald! If this be so, Heaven in its own time will make it appear.

Here a silence of several minutes ensued; when, suddenly, they were awakened from their reverie by a violent noise in the rooms underneath them. It seemed like the clashing of arms, and something seemed to fall down with violence.

They started, and Edmund rose up with a look full of resolution and intrepidity.—I am called! said he; I obey the call! He took up a lamp, and went to the door that he had opened the night before. Oswald followed with his rosary in his hand, and Joseph last with trembling steps. The door opened with ease, and they descended the stairs in profound silence.

The lower rooms answered exactly to those above; there were two parlours and a large closet. They saw nothing remarkable in these rooms, except two pictures that were turned with their faces to the wall. Joseph took the courage to turn them: These, said he, are the portraits of my late Lord and Lady. Father, look at this face, do you know who is like it?—I should think, said Oswald, it was done for Edmund!—I am, said Edmund, struck with the resemblance myself: But let us go on, I feel myself inspired with unusual courage.—Let us open the closet door.—Oswald stopped him short; Take heed, said he, lest the wind of the door put out the lamp. I will open this door. He attempted it without success; Joseph did the same, but to no purpose: Edmund gave the lamp to Joseph, he approached the door, tried the key, and it gave way to his hand in a moment. This adventure belongs, said he, to me only, that is plain; bring the lamp forward. Oswald repeated the paternoster, in which they all joined, and then entered the closet.

The first thing that presented itself to their view was a compleat suit of armour that seemed to have fallen down on an heap. Behold! said Edmund; this made the noise we heard above. They took it up, and examined it piece by piece; the inside of the breast-plate was stained with blood. See here! said Edmund; what think you of this?—'Tis my Lord's armour, said Joseph; I know it well: Here has been bloody work in this closet!—Going forward he stumbled over something; it was a ring with the arms of Lovel engraved upon it. This is my Lord's ring, said Joseph; I have seen him wear it: I give it to you, Sir, as the right owner; and most religiously do I believe you his son. Heaven only knows that, said Edmund; and, if it permits, I will know who was my father before I am a day older. While he was speaking he shifted his ground, and perceived that the boards rose up on the other side of the closet; upon farther examination they found that the whole floor was loose, and a table that stood over them concealed the circumstance from a casual observer. I perceive, said Oswald, that some great discovery is at hand.—God defend us! said Edmund, but I verily believe that the person that owned this armour lies buried under us. Upon this, a dismal hollow groan was heard as if from underneath. A solemn silence ensued, and marks of fear were visible upon all three; the groan was thrice heard: Oswald made signs for them to kneel, and he prayed audibly, that Heaven would direct them how to act; he also prayed for the soul of the departed, that it might rest in peace. After this he arose; but Edmund continued kneeling: He vowed solemnly to devote himself to the discovery of this secret, and the avenging the death of the person there buried. He then rose up. It would be to no purpose, said he, for us to examine further now, when I am properly authorized I will have this place opened: I trust that time is not far off.—I believe it, said Oswald; you are designed by Heaven to be its instrument in bringing this deed of darkness to light. We are your creatures, only tell us what you would have us do, and we are ready to obey your commands.—I only demand your silence, said Edmund, till I call for your evidence; and then, you must speak all you know, and all you suspect.—Oh, said Joseph, that I may but live to see that day, and I shall have lived long enough!—Come, said Edmund, let us return up stairs, and we will consult further how I shall proceed: So saying, he went out of the closet, and they followed him. He locked the door, and took the key out: I will keep this, said he, till I have power to use it to purpose, lest any one should presume to pry into the secret of this closet: I will always carry it about me, to remind me of what I have undertaken.

Upon this, they returned up stairs into the bed-chamber; all was still, and they heard nothing more to disturb them.

from

Wuthering Heights

by Emily Brontë

CHAPTER I.

1801——I have just returned from a visit to my landlord —the solitary neighbour that I shall be troubled with. This is certainly a beautiful country! In all England, I do not believe that I could have fixed on a situation so completely removed from the stir of society. A perfect misanthropist's heaven—and Mr. Heathcliff and I are such a suitable pair to divide the desolation between us. A capital fellow! He little imagined how my heart warmed towards him when I beheld his black eyes withdraw so suspiciously under their brows, as I rode up, and when his fingers sheltered themselves, with a jealous resolution, still further in his waistcoat, as I announced my name.

"Mr. Heathcliff?" I said.

A nod was the answer.

"Mr. Lockwood, your new tenant, sir. I do myself the honour of calling as soon as possible after my arrival, to express the hope that I have not inconvenienced you by my perserverance in soliciting occupation of Thrushcross

Grange: I heard, yesterday, you had had some thoughts—"

"Thrushcross Grange is my own, sir," he interrupted, wincing, "I should not allow any one to inconvenience me, if I could hinder it—walk in!"

The "walk in," was uttered with closed teeth and expressed the sentiment, "Go to the Deuce!". Even the gate over which he leant manifested no sympathizing movement to the words, and I think that circumstance determined me to accept the invitation: I felt interested in a man who seemed more exaggeratedly reserved than myself.

When he saw my horse's breast fairly pushing the barrier, he did pull out his hand to unchain it, and then sullenly preceded me up the causeway, calling, as we entered the court—

"Joseph, take Mr. Lockwood's horse; and bring up some wine."

"Here we have the whole establishment of domestics, I suppose," was the reflection, suggested by this compound order. "No wonder the grass grows up between the flags, and cattle are the only hedgecutters."

Joseph was an elderly, nay, an old man, very old, perhaps, though hale and sinewy.

"The Lord help us!" he soliloquized in an undertone of peevish displeasure, while relieving me of my horse: looking, meantime, in my face so sourly that I charitably conjectured he must have need of divine aid to digest his dinner, and his pious ejaculation had no reference to my unexpected advent.

Wuthering Heights is the name of Mr. Heathcliff's dwelling. "Wuthering" being a significant provincial adjective, descriptive of the atmospheric tumult to which its station is exposed in stormy weather. Pure, bracing ventilation they must have up there, at all times, indeed: one may guess the power of the north wind, blowing over the edge, by the excessive slant of a few stunted

firs at the end of the house; and by a range of gaunt
thorns all stretching their limbs one way, as if craving
alms of the sun. Happily, the architect had foresight to
build it strong: the narrow windows are deeply set in
the wall, and the corners defended with large jutting
stones.

Before passing the threshold, I paused to admire a
quantity of grotesque carving lavished over the front, and
especially about the principal door, above which, among
a wilderness of crumbling griffins and shameless little boys,
I detected the date "1500," and the name "Hareton Earnshaw." I would have made a few comments, and requested
a short history of the place from the surly owner, but his
attitude at the door appeared to demand my speedy entrance, or complete departure, and I had no desire to
aggravate his impatience, previous to inspecting the pene-
tralium.

One step brought us into the family sitting-room, without any introductory lobby or passage: they call it here
"the house" preeminently. It includes kitchen and parlour,
generally, but I believe at Wuthering Heights the kitchen
is forced to retreat altogether into another quarter; at
least I distinguished a chatter of tongues, and a clatter
of culinary utensils deep within; and I observed no
signs of roasting, boiling, or baking about the huge fire-
place; nor any glitter of copper saucepans and tin cul-
lenders on the walls. One end, indeed, reflected splendidly
both light and heat from ranks of immense pewter
dishes, interspersed with silver jugs and tankards, towering
row after row, in a vast oak dresser, to the very roof. The
latter had never been underdrawn: its entire anatomy lay
bare to an inquiring eye, except where a frame of wood
laden with oatcakes, and clusters of legs of beef, mutton,
and ham, concealed it. Above the chimney were sundry
villanous old guns, and a couple of horse-pistols, and, by
way of ornament, three gaudily-painted canisters disposed
along its ledge. The floor was of smooth, white stone;

the chairs, high-backed, primitive structures, painted green, one or two heavy black ones lurking in the shade. In an arch under the dresser, reposed a huge, liver-coloured bitch pointer surrounded by a swarm of squealing puppies, and other dogs haunted other recesses.

The apartment and furniture would have been nothing extraordinary as belonging to a homely, northern farmer, with a stubborn countenance, and stalwart limbs set out to advantage in knee-breeches and gaiters. Such an individual, seated in his arm-chair, his mug of ale frothing on the round table before him, is to be seen in any circuit of five or six miles among these hills, if you go at the right time, after dinner. But Mr. Heathcliff forms a singular contrast to his abode and style of living. He is a dark-skinned gypsy in aspect, in dress and manners a gentleman, that is, as much a gentleman as many a country squire: rather slovenly, perhaps, yet not looking amiss with his negligence, because he has an erect and handsome figure—and rather morose. Possibly, some people might suspect him of a degree of under-bred pride; I have a sympathetic chord within that tells me it is nothing of the sort: I know, by instinct, his reserve springs from an aversion to showy displays of feeling—to manifestations of mutual kindliness. He'll love and hate, equally under cover, and esteem it a species of impertinence to be loved or hated again—No, I'm running on too fast—I bestow my own attributes over-liberally on him. Mr. Heathcliff may have entirely dissimilar reasons for keeping his hand out of the way when he meets a would-be acquaintance, to those which actuate me. Let me hope my constitution is almost peculiar: my dear mother used to say I should never have a comfortable home, and only last summer I proved myself perfectly unworthy of one.

While enjoying a month of fine weather at the sea-coast, I was thrown into the company of a most fascinating creature, a real goddess in my eyes, as long as she took no notice of me. I "never told my love" vocally; still, if looks have language, the merest idiot might have guessed I was over head and ears: she understood me at last, and looked a return—the sweetest of all imaginable looks. And what did I do? I confess it with shame —shrunk icily into myself, like a snail; at every glance retired colder and farther; till, finally, the poor innocent was led to doubt her own senses, and, overwhelmed with confusion at her supposed mistake, persuaded her mamma to decamp.

By this curious turn of disposition I have gained the reputation of deliberate heartlessness, how undeserved, I alone can appreciate.

I took a seat at the end of the hearthstone opposite that towards which my landlord advanced, and filled up an interval of silence by attempting to caress the canine mother, who left her nursery and was sneaking wolfishly to the back of my legs, her lip curled up, and her white teeth watering for a snatch.

My caress provoked a long, guttural gnarl.

"You'd better let the dog alone," growled Mr. Heathcliff in unison, checking fiercer demonstrations with a punch of his foot. "She's not accustomed to be spoiled—not kept for a pet."

Then, striding to a side-door, he shouted again—"Joseph!"

Joseph mumbled indistinctly in the depths of the cellar, but gave no intimation of ascending; so his master dived down to him, leaving me *vis-à-vis* the ruffianly bitch and a pair of grim, shaggy sheep dogs, who shared with her a jealous guardianship over all my movements.

Not anxious to come in contact with their fangs, I sat still; but imagining they would scarcely understand tacit insults, I unfortunately indulged in winking and making faces at the trio, and some turn of my physiognomy so irritated madam, that she suddenly broke into a fury and leapt on my knees. I flung her back, and hastened to interpose the table between us. This proceeding roused the whole hive. Half-a-dozen four-footed fiends, of various sizes and ages, issued from hidden dens to the common centre. I felt my heels and coat-laps peculiar subjects of assault; and, parrying off the larger combatants as effectually as I could with the poker, I was constrained to demand, aloud, assistance from some of the household in re-establishing peace.

Mr. Heathcliff and his man climbed the cellar steps with vexatious phlegm. I don't think they moved one step faster than usual, though the hearth was an absolute tempest of worrying and yelping.

Happily, an inhabitant of the kitchen made more dispatch; a lusty dame, with tucked-up gown, bare arms, and fire-flushed cheeks, rushed into the midst of us flourishing a frying-pan; and used that weapon, and her tongue, to such purpose, that the storm subsided magically, and she only remained, heaving like a sea after a high wind, when her master entered on the scene.

"What the devil is the matter?" he asked, eyeing me in a manner that I could ill endure after this inhospitable treatment.

"What the devil, indeed!" I muttered. "The herd of possessed swine could have had no worse spirits in them than those animals of yours, sir. You might as well leave a stranger with a brood of tigers!"

"They won't meddle with persons who touch nothing," he remarked, putting the bottle before me, and restoring the displaced table. "The dogs do right to be vigilant. Take a glass of wine?"

"No, thank you."

"Not bitten, are you?"

"If I had been, I would have set my signet on the biter."

Heathcliff's countenance relaxed into a grin.

"Come, come," he said, "you are flurried, Mr. Lockwood. Here, take a little wine. Guests are so exceedingly rare in this house that I and my dogs, I am willing to own, hardly know how to receive them. Your health, sir!"

I bowed and returned the pledge, beginning to perceive that it would be foolish to sit sulking for the misbehaviour of a pack of curs: besides, I felt loath to yield the fellow further amusement, at my expense, since his humour took that turn.

He—probably swayed by prudential considerations of the folly of offending a good tenant—relaxed a little, in the laconic style of chipping off his pronouns and auxiliary verbs, and introduced what he supposed would be a subject of interest to me, a discourse on the advantages and disadvantages of my present place of retirement.

I found him very intelligent on the topics we touched; and, before I went home, I was encouraged so far as to volunteer another visit to-morrow.

He evidently wished no repetition of my intrusion. I shall go, notwithstanding. It is astonishing how sociable I feel myself compared with him.

CHAPTER II.

Yesterday afternoon set in misty and cold. I had half a mind to spend it by my study fire, instead of wading through heath and mud to Wuthering Heights.

On coming up from dinner, however (N. B. I dine between twelve and one o'clock; the housekeeper, a matronly lady taken as a fixture along with the house, could not, or would not comprehend my request that I might be served at five.)—on mounting the stairs with this lazy intention, and stepping into the room, I saw a servant-girl on her knees, surrounded by brushes and coal-scuttles, and raising an infernal dust as she extinguished the flames with heaps of cinders. This spectacle drove me back immediately; I took my hat, and, after a four miles' walk, arrived at Heathcliff's garden gate just in time to escape the first feathery flakes of a snow shower.

On that bleak hill-top the earth was hard with a black frost, and the air made me shiver through every limb. Being unable to remove the chain, I jumped over, and, running up the flagged causeway bordered with straggling gooseberry bushes, knocked vainly for admittance, till my knuckles tingled and the dogs howled.

"Wretched inmates!" I ejaculated, mentally, "you deserve perpetual isolation from your species for your churlish inhospitality. At least, I would not keep my doors barred in the day time. I don't care—I will get in!"

So resolved, I grasped the latch and shook it vehemently. Vinegarfaced Joseph projected his head from a round window of the barn.

"Whet are ye for?" he shouted. "T' maister's dahn i' t' fowld. Goa rahnd by th' end ut' laith, if yah went tuh spake tull him."

"Is there nobody inside to open the door?" I hallooed, responsively.

"They's nobbut t' missis; and shoo'll nut oppen't an ye mak yer flaysome dins till neeght."

"Why? cannot you tell her who I am, eh, Joseph?"

"Nor-ne me! Aw'll hae noa hend wi't," muttered the head, vanishing.

The snow began to drive thickly. I seized the handle to essay another trial, when a young man, without coat, and shouldering a pitchfork, appeared in the yard behind. He hailed me to follow him, and, after marching through a washhouse and a paved area containing a coal-shed, pump, and pigeon cote, we at length arrived in the large, warm, cheerful apartment where I was formerly received.

It glowed delightfully in the radiance of an immense fire, compounded of coal, peat, and wood; and near the table, laid for a plentiful evening meal, I was pleased to observe the "missis," an individual whose existence I had never previously suspected.

I bowed and waited, thinking she would bid me take a seat. She looked at me, leaning back in her chair, and remained motionless and mute.

"Rough weather!" I remarked. "I'm afraid, Mrs. Heathcliff, the door must bear the consequence of your servants' leisure attendance: I had hard work to make them hear me!"

She never opened her mouth. I stared—she stared also. At any rate, she kept her eyes on me, in a cool, regardless manner, exceedingly embarrassing and disagreeable.

"Sit down," said the young man, gruffly. "He'll be in soon."

I obeyed; and hemmed, and called the villain Juno, who deigned, at this second interview, to move the extreme tip of her tail, in token of owning my acquaintance.

"A beautiful animal!" I commenced again. "Do you intend parting with the little ones, madam?"

"They are not mine," said the amiable hostess more repellingly than Heathcliff himself could have replied.

"Ah, your favorites are among these!" I continued, turning to an obscure cushion full of something like cats.

"A strange choice of favourites," she observed scornfully.

Unluckily, it was a heap of dead rabbits. I hemmed once more, and drew closer to the hearth, repeating my comment on the wildness of the evening.

"You should not have come out," she said, rising and reaching from the chimney-piece two of the painted canisters.

Her position before was sheltered from the light; now, I had a distinct view of her whole figure and countenance. She was slender, and apparently scarcely past girlhood: an admirable form, and the most exquisite little face that I have ever had the pleasure of beholding: small features, very fair; flaxen ringlets, or rather golden, hanging loose on her delicate neck; and eyes—had they been agreeable in expression, they would have been irresistible. Fortunately for my susceptible heart, the only sentiment they evinced hovered between scorn and a kind of desperation singularly unnatural to be detected there.

The canisters were almost out of her reach; I made a motion to aid her; she turned upon me as a miser might turn if any one attempted to assist him in counting his gold.

"I don't want your help," she snapped, "I can get them for myself."

"I beg your pardon," I hastened to reply.

"Were you asked to tea?" she demanded, tying an apron over her neat black frock, and standing with a spoonful of the leaf poised over the pot.

"I shall be glad to have a cup," I answered.

"Were you asked?" she repeated.

"No," I said, half smiling. "You are the proper person to ask me."

She flung the tea back, spoon and all, and resumed her chair in a pet, her forehead corrugated, and her red under-lip pushed out, like a child's, ready to cry.

Meanwhile, the young man had slung onto his person a decidedly shabby upper garment, and, erecting himself before the blaze, looked down on me from the corner of his eyes, for all the world as if there were some mortal feud unavenged between us. I began to doubt whether he were a servant or not; his dress and speech were both rude, entirely devoid of the superiority observable in Mr. and Mrs. Heathcliff; his thick, brown curls were rough and uncultivated, his whiskers encroached bearishly over his cheeks, and his hands were embrowned like those of a common labourer. Still his bearing was free, almost haughty, and he showed none of a domestic's assiduity in attending on the lady of the house.

In the absence of clear proofs of his condition, I deemed it best to abstain from noticing his curious conduct, and, five minutes afterwards, the entrance of Heathcliff relieved me, in some measure, from my uncomfortable state.

"You see, sir, I am come according to promise!" I exclaimed, assuming the cheerful; "and I fear I shall be weather-bound for half an hour, if you can afford me shelter during that space."

"Half an hour?" he said, shaking the white flakes from his clothes; "I wonder you should select the thick of a snow-storm to ramble about in. Do you know that you run a risk of being lost in the marshes? People familiar with these moors often miss their road on such evenings, and, I can tell you, there is no chance of a change at present."

"Perhaps I can get a guide among your lads, and he might stay at the Grange till morning—could you spare me one?"

"No, I could not."

"Oh, indeed! Well, then, I must trust to my own sagacity."

"Umph."

"Are you going to mak th' tea?" demanded he of the shabby coat, shifting his ferocious gaze from me to the young lady.

"Is *he* to have any?" she asked, appealing to Heathcliff.

"Get it ready, will you?" was the answer, uttered so savagely that I started. The tone in which the words were said revealed a genuine bad nature. I no longer felt inclined to call Heathcliff a capital fellow.

When the preparations were finished, he invited me with—

"Now, sir, bring forward your chair." And we all, including the rustic youth, drew round the table, an austere silence prevailing while we discussed our meal.

I thought, if I had caused the cloud, it was my duty to make an effort to dispel it. They could not every day sit so grim and taciturn, and it was impossible, however ill-tempered they might be, that the universal scowl they wore was their every day countenance.

"It is strange," I began in the interval of swallowing one cup of tea and receiving another, "it is strange how custom can mould our tastes and ideas; many could not imagine the existence of happiness in a life of such complete exile from the world as you spend, Mr. Heathcliff; yet, I'll venture to say, that, surrounded by your family, and with your amiable lady as the presiding genius over your home and heart—"

"My amiable lady!" he interrupted, with an almost diabolical sneer on his face. "Where is she—my amiable lady?"

"Mrs. Heathcliff, your wife, I mean."

"Well, yes—Oh! you would intimate that her spirit has taken the post of ministering angel, and guards the fortunes of Wuthering Heights, even when her body is gone. It that it?"

Perceiving myself in a blunder, I attempted to correct it. I might have seen there was too great a disparity between the ages of the parties to make it likely that they were man and wife. One was about forty, a period of mental vigour at which men seldom cherish the delusion of being married for love, by girls: that dream is reserved for the solace of our declining years. The other did not look seventeen.

Then it flashed upon me—"The clown at my elbow, who is drinking his tea out of a basin and eating his bread with unwashed hands, may be her husband. Heathcliff, junior, of course. Here is the consequence of being buried alive: she has thrown herself away upon that boor, from sheer ignorance that better individuals existed! A sad pity—I must beware how I cause her to regret her choice."

The last reflection may seem conceited; it was not. My neighbor struck me as bordering on repulsive. I knew, through experience, that I was tolerably attractive.

"Mrs. Heathcliff is my daughter-in-law," said Heathcliff, corroborating my surmise. He turned, as he spoke, a peculiar look in her direction, a look of hatred, unless he has a most perverse set of facial muscles that will not, like those of other people, interpret the language of his soul.

"Ah, certainly—I see now; you are the favoured possessor of the beneficent fairy," I remarked, turning to my neighbour.

This was worse than before: the youth grew crimson, and clenched his fist with every appearance of a meditated assault. But he seemed to recollect himself, presently, and smothered the storm in a brutal curse, muttered on my behalf, which, however, I took care not to notice.

"Unhappy in your conjectures, sir!" observed my host; "we neither of us have the privilege of owning your good fairy; her mate is dead. I said she was my daughter-in-law, therefore, she must have married my son."

"And this young man is—"

"Not my son, assuredly!"

Heathcliff smiled again, as if it were rather too bold a jest to attribute the paternity of that bear to him.

"My name is Hareton Earnshaw," growled the other; "and I'd counsel you to respect it!"

"I have shown no disrespect," was my reply, laughing internally at the dignity with which he announced himself.

He fixed his eye on me longer than I cared to return the stare, for fear I might be tempted either to box his ears, or render my hilarity audible. I began to feel unmistakably out of place in that pleasant family circle. The dismal spiritual atmosphere overcame, and more than neutralized the glowing physical comforts round me; and I resolved to be cautious how I ventured under those rafters a third time.

The business of eating being concluded, and no one uttering a word of sociable conversation, I approached a window to examine the weather.

A sorrowful sight I saw: dark night coming down prematurely, and sky and hills mingled in one bitter whirl of wind and suffocating snow.

"I don't think it possible for me to get home now, without a guide," I could not help exclaiming. "The roads will be buried already; and, if they were bare, I could scarcely distinguish a foot in advance."

"Hareton, drive those sheep into the barn porch. They'll be covered if left in the fold all night; and put a plank before them," said Heathcliff.

"How must I do?" I continued, with rising irritation.

There was no reply to my question; and, on looking round, I saw only Joseph bringing in a pail of porridge for the dogs, and Mrs. Heathcliff, leaning over the fire, diverting herself with burning a bundle of matches which had fallen from the chimney-piece as she restored the tea-canister to its place.

The former, when he had deposited his burden, took a critical survey of the room, and, in cracked tones, grated out—

"Aw woonder hagh yah can faishion tuh stand thear i' idleness un war, when all on 'em's goan aght! Bud yah're a nowt, and it's noa use talking—yah'll niver mend uh yer ill ways; bud goa raight tuh t' divil, like yer mother afore ye!"

I imagined, for a moment, that this piece of eloquence was addressed to me; and, sufficiently enraged, stepped towards the aged rascal with an intention of kicking him out of the door.

Mrs. Heathcliff, however, checked me by her answer.

"You scandalous old hypocrite!" she replied. "Are you not afraid of being carried away bodily, whenever you mention the devil's name? I warn you to refrain from provoking me, or I'll ask your abduction as a special favour. Stop, look here, Joseph," she continued, taking a long, dark book from a shelf. "I'll show you how far I've progressed in the Black Art—I shall soon be competent to make a clear house of it. The red cow didn't die by chance; and your rheumatism can hardly be reckoned among providential visitations!"

"Oh, wicked, wicked!" gasped the elder, "may the Lord deliver us from evil!"

"No, reprobate! you are a castaway—be off, or I'll hurt you seriously! I'll have you all modelled in wax and clay; and the first who passes the limits I fix, shall— I'll not say what he shall be done to—but, you'll see! Go, I'm looking at you!"

The little witch put a mock malignity into her beautiful eyes, and Joseph, trembling with sincere horror, hurried out praying and ejaculating "wicked" as he went.

I thought her conduct must be prompted by a species of dreary fun; and, now that we were alone, I endeavoured to interest her in my distress.

"Mrs. Heathcliff," I said, earnestly, "you must excuse me for troubling you—I presume, because, with that face, I'm sure you cannot help being good-hearted. Do point out some landmarks by which I may know my way home. I have no more idea how to get there than you would have how to get to London!"

"Take the road you came," she answered, ensconcing herself in a chair, with a candle, and the long book open before her. "It is brief advice, but as sound as I can give."

"Then, if you hear of me being discovered dead in a bog, or a pit full of snow, your conscience won't whisper that it is partly your fault?"

"How so? I cannot escort you. They wouldn't let me go to the end of the garden-wall."

"*You!* I should be sorry to ask you to cross the threshold, for my convenience, on such a night," I cried. "I want you to *tell* me my way, not to *show* it; or else to persuade Mr. Heathcliff to give me a guide."

"Who? There is himself, Earnshaw, Zillah, Joseph, and I. Which would you have?"

"Are there no boys at the farm?"

"No, those are all."

"Then it follows that I am compelled to stay."

"That you must settle with your host. I have nothing to do with it."

"I hope it will be a lesson to you, to make no more rash journeys on these hills," cried Heathcliff's stern voice from the kitchen entrance. "As to staying here, I don't keep accommodations for visitors; you must share a bed with Hareton, or Joseph, if you do."

"I can sleep on a chair in this room," I replied.

"No, no! A stranger is a stranger, be he rich or poor— it will not suit me to permit any one the range of the place while I am off guard!" said the unmannerly wretch.

With this insult my patience was at an end. I uttered an expression of disgust, and pushed past him into the yard, running against Earnshaw in my haste. It was so dark that I could not see the means of exit, and, as I wandered round, I heard another specimen of their civil behaviour amongst each other.

At first, the young man appeared about to befriend me.

"I'll go with him as far as the park," he said.

"You'll go with him to hell!" exclaimed his master, or whatever relation he bore. "And who is to look after the horses, eh?"

"A man's life is of more consequence than one evening's neglect of the horses; somebody must go," murmured Mrs. Heathcliff, more kindly than I expected.

"Not at your command!" retorted Hareton. "If you set store on him, you'd better be quiet."

"Then I hope his ghost will haunt you; and I hope Mr. Heathcliff will never get another tenant, till the Grange is a ruin!" she answered sharply.

"Hearken, hearken, shoo's cursing on em!" muttered Joseph, towards whom I had been steering.

He sat within earshot, milking the cows by the aid of a lantern which I seized unceremoniously, and, calling out that I would send it back on the morrow, rushed to the nearest postern.

"Maister, maister, he's staling t' lantern!" shouted the ancient, pursuing my retreat. "Hey, Gnasher! Hey, dog! Hey, Wolf, holld him, holld him!"

On opening the little door, two hairy monsters flew at my throat, bearing me down and extinguishing the light, while a mingled guffaw, from Heathcliff and Hareton, put the copestone on my rage and humiliation.

Fortunately, the beasts seemed more bent on stretching their paws, and yawning and flourishing their tails, than devouring me alive; but they would suffer no resurrection, and I was forced to lie till their malignant masters pleased to deliver me: then hatless, and trembling with wrath, I ordered the miscreants to let me out—on their peril to keep me one minute longer—with several incoherent threats of retaliation that, in their indefinite depth of virulency, smacked of King Lear.

The vehemence of my agitation brought on a copious bleeding at the nose, and still Heathcliff laughed, and still I scolded. I don't know what would have concluded the scene had there not been one person at hand rather more rational than myself, and more benevolent than my entertainer. This was Zillah, the stout housewife, who at length issued forth to inquire into the nature of the uproar. She thought that some of them had been laying hands on me, and, not daring to attack her master, she turned her vocal artillery against the younger scoundrel.

"Well, Mr. Earnshaw," she cried, "I wonder what you'll have agait next! Are we going to murder folk on our very door-stones? I see this house will never do for me—look at t' poor lad, he's fair choking! Wisht, wisht! you mun'n't go on so—come in, and I'll cure that. There now, hold ye still."

With these words she suddenly splashed a pint of icy water down my neck, and pulled me into the kitchen. Mr.

Heathcliff followed, his accidental merriment expiring quickly in his habitual moroseness.

I was sick exceedingly, and dizzy and faint; and thus compelled, perforce, to accept lodgings under his roof. He told Zillah to give me a glass of brandy, and then passed on to the inner room, while she condoled with me on my sorry predicament, and having obeyed his orders, whereby I was somewhat revived, ushered me to bed.

CHAPTER III.

While leading the way upstairs, she recommended that I should hide the candle, and not make a noise, for her master had an odd notion about the chamber she would put me in, and never let anybody lodge there willingly.

I asked the reason.

She did not know, she answered; she had only lived there a year or two; and they had so many queer goings on, she could not begin to be curious.

Too stupified to be curious myself, I fastened my door and glanced round for the bed. The whole furniture consisted of a chair, a clothes-press, and a large oak case, with squares cut out near the top, resembling coach windows.

Having approached this structure, I looked inside, and perceived it to be a singular sort of old-fashioned couch, very conveniently designed to obviate the necessity for every member of the family having a room to himself. In fact, it formed a little closet, and the ledge of a window, which it enclosed, served as a table.

I slid back the panelled sides, got in with my light, pulled them together again, and felt secure against the vigilance of Heathcliff, and every one else.

The ledge, where I placed my candle, had a few mildewed books piled up in one corner; and it was covered with writing scratched on the paint. This writing, however, was nothing but a name repeated in all kinds of characters, large and small—*Catherine Earnshaw,* here and there varied to *Catherine Heathcliff,* and then again to *Catherine Linton.*

In vapid listlessness I leant my head against the window, and continued spelling over Catherine Earnshaw—Heathcliff—Linton, till my eyes closed; but they had not rested five minutes when a glare of white letters started from the dark, as vivid as spectres—the air swarmed with Catherines; and rousing myself to dispel the obtrusive name, I discovered my candle wick reclining on one of the antique volumes, and perfuming the place with an odour of roasted calf-skin.

I snuffed it off, and, very ill at ease under the influence of cold and lingering nausea, sat up, and spread open the injured tome on my knee. It was a Testament, in lean type, and smelling dreadfully musty: a fly-leaf bore the inscription—"Catherine Earnshaw, her book," and a date some quarter of a century back.

I shut it, and took up another, and another, till I had examined all. Catherine's library was select, and its state of dilapidation proved it to have been well used, though not altogether for a legitimate purpose; scarcely one chapter had escaped a pen and ink commentary—at least, the appearance of one—covering every morsel of blank that the printer had left.

Some were detached sentences; other parts took the form of a regular diary, scrawled in an unformed, childish hand. At the top of an extra page, quite a treasure probably when first lighted on, I was greatly amused to behold an excellent caricature of my friend Joseph, rudely yet powerfully sketched.

An immediate interest kindled within me for the unknown Catherine, and I began, forthwith, to decypher her faded hieroglyphics.

"An awful Sunday!" commenced the paragraph beneath. "I wish my father were back again. Hindley is a detestable substitute—his conduct to Heathcliff is atrocious—H. and I are going to rebel—we took our initiatory step this evening.

"All day had been flooding with rain; we could not go to church, so Joseph must needs get up a congregation in the garret; and, while Hindley and his wife basked downstairs before a comfortable fire—doing anything but reading their Bibles, I'll answer for it—Heathcliff, myself, and the unhappy plough-boy were commanded to take our Prayer-books, and mount. We were ranged in a row, on a sack of corn, groaning and shivering, and hoping that Joseph would shiver too, so that he might give us a short homily for his own sake. A vain idea! The service lasted precisely three hours; and yet my brother had the face to exclaim, when he saw us descending—

" 'What, done already?'

"On Sunday evenings we used to be permitted to play, if we did not make much noise; now a mere titter is sufficient to send us into corners!

" 'You forget you have a master here,' says the tyrant. 'I'll demolish the first who puts me out of temper! I insist on perfect sobriety and silence. Oh, boy! was that you? Frances, darling, pull his hair as you go by; I heard him snap his fingers.'

"Frances pulled his hair heartily; and then went and seated herself on her husband's knee, and there they were, like two babies, kissing and talking nonsense by the hour—foolish palaver that we should be ashamed of.

"We made ourselves as snug as our means allowed in the arch of the dresser. I had just fastened our pinafores together, and hung them up for a curtain, when in comes Joseph, on an errand from the stables. He tears down my handywork, boxes my ears, and croaks—

" 'T' maister nobbut just buried, and Sabbath nut oe'red, und t'sahnd uh't gospel still i' yer lugs, and yah darr be laiking! shame on ye! sit ye dahn, ill childer! they's good books eneugh if ye'll read 'em; sit ye dahn, and think uh yer sowls!'

"Saying this, he compelled us so to square our positions that we might receive, from the far-off fire, a dull ray to show us the text of the lumber he thrust upon us.

"I could not bear the employment. I took my dingy volume by the scroop, and hurled it into the dog-kennel, vowing I hated a good book.

"Heathcliff kicked his to the same place.

"Then there was a hubbub!

"'Maister Hindley!' shouted our chaplain. 'Maister, coom hither! Miss Cathy's riven th' back off "Th' Helmet uh Salvation," un' Heathcliff's pawsed his fit intuh t' first part uh "T' Brooad Way to Destruction!" It's fair flaysome ut yah let 'em goa on this gait. Ech! th' owd man ud uh laced 'em properly—bud he's goan!'

"Hindley hurried up from his paradise on the hearth, and seizing one of us by the collar, and the other by the arm, hurled both into the back-kitchen, where, Joseph asseverated, 'owd Nick' would fetch us as sure as we were living; and, so comforted, we each sought a separate nook to await his advent.

"I reached this book, and a pot of ink from a shelf, and pushed the house-door ajar to give me light, and I have got the time on with writing for twenty minutes; but my companion is impatient and proposes that we should appropriate the dairy woman's cloak, and have a scamper on the moors, under its shelter. A pleasant suggestion—and then, if the surly old man come in, he may believe his prophesy verified—we cannot be damper, or colder, in the rain than we are here."

I suppose Catherine fulfilled her project, for the next sentence took up another subject; she waxed lachrymose.

"How little did I dream that Hindley would ever make me cry so!" she wrote. "'My head aches, till I cannot keep it on the pillow; and still I can't give over. Poor Heathcliff! Hindley calls him a vagabond, and won't let him sit with us, nor eat with us any more; and, he says, he and I must not play together, and threatens to turn him out of the house if we break his orders.

"He has been blaming our father (how dared he?) for treating H. too liberally; and swears he will reduce him to his right place—"

I began to nod drowsily over the dim page; my eye wandered from manuscript to print. I saw a red ornamented title—"Seventy Times Seven, and the First of the Seventy-First. A Pious Discourse delivered by the Reverend Jabes Branderham, in the Chapel of Gimmerden Sough." And while I was, half consciously, worrying my brain to guess what Jabes Branderham would make of his subject, I sank back in bed, and fell asleep.

Alas, for the effects of bad tea and bad temper! what else could it be that made me pass such a terrible night? I don't remember another that I can at all compare with it since I was capable of suffering.

I began to dream, almost before I ceased to be sensible of my locality. I thought it was morning, and I had set out on my way home, with Joseph for a guide. The snow lay yards deep in our road; and, as we floundered on, my companion wearied me with constant reproaches that I had not brought a pilgrim's staff, telling me I could never get into the house without one, and boastfully flourishing a heavy-headed cudgel, which I understood to be so denominated.

For a moment I considered it absurd that I should need such a weapon to gain admittance into my own residence. Then, a new idea flashed across me. I was not going there; we were journeying to hear the famous Jabes Branderham preach from the text—"Seventy Times Seven"; and either Joseph, the preacher, or I had com-

mitted the "First of the Seventy-First," and were to be
publicly exposed and excommunicated.

* * * * * * * * * * * * * * *

And what was it that had suggested the tremendous
tumult, what had played Jabes's part in the row? Merely
the branch of a fir tree that touched my lattice, as the
blast wailed by, and rattled its dry cones against the panes!

I listened doubtingly an instant; detected the disturber,
then turned and dozed, and dreamt again; 'if possible,
still more disagreeably than before.

This time, I remembered I was lying in the oak closet,
and I heard distinctly the gusty wind, and the driving
of the snow; I heard, also, the fir-bough repeat its
teasing sound, and ascribed it to the right cause; but it
annoyed me so much, that I resolved to silence it, if
possible; and, I thought, I rose and endeavoured to un-
hasp the casement. The hook was soldered into the
staple, a circumstance observed by me when awake, but
forgotten.

"I must stop it, nevertheless!" I muttered, knocking
my knuckles through the glass, and stretching an arm out
to seize the importunate branch: instead of which, my
fingers closed on the fingers of a little, ice-cold hand!

The intense horror of nightmare came over me; I tried
to draw back my arm, but the hand clung to it, and a
most melancholy voice sobbed—

"Let me in—let me in!"

"Who are you?" I asked, struggling, meanwhile, to
disengage myself.

"Catherine Linton," it replied, shiveringly (why did I
think of *Linton*? I had read *Earnshaw* twenty times for
Linton). "I'm come home, I'd lost my way on the moor!"

As it spoke, I discerned, obscurely, a child's face looking through the window. Terror made me cruel; and,
finding it useless to attempt shaking the creature off, I

pulled its wrist on to the broken pane, and rubbed it to and fro till the blood ran down and soaked the bed-clothes: still it wailed, "Let me in!" and maintained its tenacious gripe, almost maddening me with fear.

"How can I?" I said at length. "Let *me* go, if you want me to let you in!"

The fingers relaxed, I snatched mine through the hole, hurriedly piled the books up in a pyramid against it, and stopped my ears to exclude the lamentable prayer.

I seemed to keep them closed above a quarter of an hour, yet, the instant I listened again, there was the doleful cry moaning on!

"Begone!" I shouted, "I'll never let you in, not if you beg for twenty years!"

"It's twenty years," mourned the voice, "twenty years, I've been a waif for twenty years!"

Thereat began a feeble scratching outside, and the pile of books moved as if thrust forward.

I tried to jump up, but could not stir a limb; and so yelled aloud, in a frenzy of fright.

To my confusion, I discovered the yell was not ideal. Hasty footsteps approached my chamber door; somebody pushed it open, with a vigorous hand, and a light glimmered through the squares at the top of the bed. I sat shuddering yet, and wiping the perspiration from my forehead: the intruder appeared to hesitate, and muttered to himself.

At last, he said in a half-whisper, plainly not expecting an answer—

"Is any one here?"

I considered it best to confess my presence, for I knew Heathcliff's accents, and feared he might search further, if I kept quiet.

With this intention, I turned and opened the panels. I shall not soon forget the effect my action produced.

Heathcliff stood near the entrance, in his shirt and trousers, with a candle dripping over his fingers, and his face as white as the wall behind him. The first creak of the oak startled him like an electric shock: the light leaped from his hold to a distance of some feet, and his agitation was so extreme that he could hardly pick it up.

"It is only your guest, sir," I called out, desirous to spare him the humiliation of exposing his cowardice further. "I had the misfortune to scream in my sleep, owing to a frightful nightmare. I'm sorry I disturbed you."

"Oh, God confound you, Mr. Lockwood! I wish you were at the——" commenced my host, setting the candle on a chair, because he found it impossible to hold it steady.

"And who showed you up to this room?" he continued, crushing his nails into his palms, and grinding his teeth to subdue the maxillary convulsions. "Who was it? I've a good mind to turn them out of the house this moment!"

"It was your servant, Zillah," I replied, flinging myself on to the floor, and rapidly resuming my garments. "I should not care if you did, Mr. Heathcliff; she richly deserves it. I suppose that she wanted to get another proof that the place was haunted, at my expense. Well, it is —swarming with ghosts and goblins! You have reason in shutting it up, I assure you. No one will thank you for a doze in such a den!"

"What do you mean?" asked Heathcliff, "and what are you doing? Lie down and finish out the night, since you *are* here; but, for heaven's sake! don't repeat that horrid noise. Nothing could excuse it, unless you were having your throat cut!"

"If the little fiend had gone in at the window, she probably would have strangled me!" I returned. "I'm not going to endure the persecutions of your hospitable ancestors again. Was not the Reverend Jabes Branderham akin to you on the mother's side? And that minx, Catherine Linton, or Earnshaw, or however she was called—she must have been a changeling—wicked little soul! She told me she had been walking the earth these twenty years: a just punishment for her mortal transgressions, I've no doubt!"

Scarcely were these words uttered, when I recollected the association of Heathcliff's with Catherine's name in the book, which had completely slipped from my memory till thus awakened. I blushed at my inconsideration; but, without showing further consciousness of the offence, I hastened to add—

"The truth is, sir, I passed the first part of the night in —" here, I stopped afresh—I was about to say "perusing those old volumes;" then it would have revealed my knowledge of their written, as well as their printed contents; so, correcting myself, I went on—"in spelling over the name scratched on that window-ledge. A monotonous occupation, calculated to set me asleep, like counting, or—"

"What *can* you mean by talking in this way to *me!*" thundered Heathcliff with savage vehemence. "How— how *dare* you, under my roof—God! he's mad to speak so!" And he struck his forehead with rage.

I did not know whether to resent this language, or pursue my explanation; but he seemed so powerfully affected that I took pity and proceeded with my dreams, affirming I had never heard the appellation of "Catherine Linton" before, but reading it often over produced an impression which personified itself when I had no longer my imagination under control.

Heathcliff gradually fell back into the shelter of the bed as I spoke, finally sitting down almost concealed behind it. I guessed, however, by his irregular and intercepted breathing, that he struggled to vanquish an access of violent emotion.

Not liking to show him that I heard the conflict, I continued my toilette rather noisily, looked at my watch, and soliloquized on the length of the night—

"Not three o'clock yet! I could have taken oath it had

been six. Time stagnates here—we must surely have retired to rest at eight!"

"Always at nine in winter, and always rise at four," said my host, suppressing a groan, and, as I fancied, by the motion of his shadow's arm, dashing a tear from his eyes.

"Mr. Lockwood," he added, "you may go into my room; you'll only be in the way, coming downstairs so early; and your childish outcry has sent sleep to the devil for me."

"And for me, too," I replied. "I'll walk in the yard till daylight, and then I'll be off; and you need not dread a repetition of my intrusion. I am now quite cured of seeking pleasure in society, be it country or town. A sensible man ought to find sufficient company in himself."

"Delightful company!" muttered Heathcliff. "Take the candle, and go where you please. I shall join you directly. Keep out of the yard, though; the dogs are unchained, and the house—Juno mounts sentinel there, and—nay, you can only ramble about the steps and passages. But, away with you! I'll come in two minutes."

I obeyed, so far as to quit the chamber; when, ignorant where the narrow lobbies led, I stood still, and was witness, involuntarily, to a piece of superstition on the part of my landlord, which belied, oddly, his apparent sense.

He got on to the bed and wrenched open the lattice, bursting, as he pulled at it, into an uncontrollable passion of tears.

"Come in! come in!" he sobbed. "Cathy, do come. Oh, do—*once* more! Oh! my heart's darling, hear me *this* time—Catherine, at last!"

The spectre showed a spectre's ordinary caprice; it gave no sign of being; but the snow and wind whirled wildly through, even reaching my station, and blowing out the light.

There was such anguish in the gush of grief that

accompanied this raving, that my compassion made me overlook its folly, and I drew off, half angry to have listened at all, and vexed at having related my ridiculous nightmare, since it produced that agony, though *why,* was beyond my comprehension.

I descended cautiously to the lower regions and landed in the back-kitchen, where a gleam of fire, raked compactly together, enabled me to rekindle my candle.

The Dead Planet

by Edmond Hamilton

It didn't look like such a forbidding little world at
first: It looked dark, icy, and lifeless, but there was no
hint of what brooded there. The only question in our
minds then was whether we would die when our crippled
ship crashed on it.

Tharn was at the controls. All three of us had put
on our pressure suits in the hope that they might save us
if the crash was bad. In the massive metal suits we
looked like three queer, fat robots, like three metal
globes with jointed mechanical arms and legs.

"If it hadn't happened here!" came Dril's hopeless voice
through the intercom. "Here in the most desolate and
unknown part of the whole galaxy!"

"We're lucky we were within reaching distance of a star
system when the generators let go," I murmured.

"Lucky, Oroc?" repeated Dril bitterly. "Lucky, to post-
pone our end by a few days of agony? It's all we can look
forward to on *that*."

The system ahead did look discouraging for wrecked

star explorers. Here in a thin region at the very edge of the galaxy, it centered around a sun that was somber dark red, ancient, dying.

Six worlds circled that smoldering star. We were dropping toward the innermost of the six planets, as the most possibly habitable. But now, we could clearly see that life could not exist on it. It was an airless sphere, sheathed in eternal snow and ice.

The other five planets were even more hopeless. And we could not change course now, anyway. It was a question of whether the two strained generators that still functioned would be able to furnish enough power to slow down our landing speed and save us from total destruction.

Death was close, and we knew it, yet we remained unshaken. Not that we were heroes. But we belonged to the Star Service, and while the Star Service yields glory, its members always have the shadow of death over them and so grow accustomed to it.

Many in the Star Service had died in the vast, endless task of mapping the galaxy. Of the little exploring ships that went out like ours to chart the farther reaches of stars, only two-thirds or less ever came back. Accidents accounted for the rest—accidents like the blowing of our generators from overload in attempting to claw our way quickly out of a mass of interstellar debris.

Tharn's voice came to us calmly.

"We'll soon hit it. I'll try to crabtail in, but the chances are poor. Better strap in."

Using the metal arms of our suits clumsily, we hooked into the resilient harnesses that might give us a chance of survival.

Dril peered at the largening white globe below.

"There look to be deep snows at places. It would be a little softer there."

"Yes," Tharn replied quietly. "But our ship would remain buried in the snow. On the ice, even if wrecked it could be seen. When another ship comes, they'll find us, and our charts won't be lost."

Well, for a moment that made me so proud of the Star Service that I was almost contemptuous of the danger rushing upon us.

It is that wonderful spirit that has made the Service what it is, that has enabled our race to push out from our little world to the farthest parts of the galaxy. Individual explorers might die, but the Service's conquest of the universe would go on.

"Here we go," muttered Dril, still peering downward.

The icy white face of the desolate world was rushing up at us with nightmare speed. I waited tensely for Tharn to act.

He delayed until the last moment. Then he moved the power bar, and the two remaining generators came on with a roar of power.

They could not stand that overload for more than a few moments before they blew out. But it was enough for Tharn to swing the falling ship around and use the blast of propulsive vibrations as a brake.

Making a crabtail landing is more a matter of luck than skill. The mind isn't capable of estimating the infinitesimal differences that mean disaster or survival. Use a shade too much power, and you're bounced away from your goal. A shade too little, and you smash to bits.

Tharn was lucky. Or maybe it wasn't luck as much as pilot's instinct. Anyway, it was all over in a moment. The ship fell, the generators screamed, there was a bumping crash, then silence.

The ship lay on its side on the ice. Its stern had crumpled and split open at one place, and its air had puffed out, though in our suits we didn't mind that. Also the last two generators had blown out, as expected, from the overload in cushioning our fall.

"We made it!" Dril bounded from despair to hope. "I

never thought we had a real chance. Tharn, you're the ace of all pilots."

But Tharn himself seemed to suffer reaction from tension. He unstrapped like ourselves and stood, a bulky figure in his globular suit, looking out through the quartz portholes.

"We saved our necks for the time being," he muttered. "But we're in a bad fix."

The truth of that sank in as we looked out with him. This little planet out on the edge of the galaxy was one of the most desolate I had ever seen. There was nothing but ice and darkness and cold.

The ice stretched in all directions, a rolling white plain. There was no air—the deep snows we had seen were frozen air, no doubt. Over the gelid plain brooded a dark sky, two-thirds of which was black emptiness. Across the lower third glittered the great drift of the galaxy stars, of which this system was a borderland outpost.

"Our generators are shot, and we haven't enough powerloy to wind new coils for *all* of them," Tharn pointed out. "We can't call a tenth the distance home with our little communicator. And our air will eventually run out."

"Our only chance," he continued decisively, "is to find on this planet enough tantalum and terbium and the other metals we need, to make powerloy and wind new coils. Dril, get out the radio sonde."

The radio sonde was the instrument used in our star mapping to explore the metallic resources of unknown planets. It works by projecting broad beams of vibrations that could be tuned to reflect from any desired elements, the ingenious device detecting and computing position thus.

Dril got out the compact instrument and tuned its frequencies to the half dozen rare metals we needed. Then we waited while he swung the projector tubes along their quadrants, closely watching the indicators.

"This is incredible luck!" he exclaimed finally. "The

sonde shows terbium, tantalum, and the other metals we need all together in appreciable quantities. They're just under the ice and not far from here!"

"It's almost too good to be true," I said wonderingly. "Those metals are never found all together."

Tharn planned quickly.

"We'll fit a rough sledge and on it we can haul an auxiliary power unit and the big dis-beam, to cut through the ice. We'll also have to take cables and tackle for a hoist."

We soon had everything ready and started across the ice, hauling our improvised sledge and its heavy load of equipment.

The frozen world, brooding beneath the sky that looked out into the emptiness of extra-galactic space, was oppressive. We had hit queer worlds before, but this was the most gloomy we had ever encountered.

The drift of stars that was our galaxy sank behind the horizon as we went on, and it grew even darker. Our krypton lamps cut a white path through the somber gloom as we stumbled on, the metal feet of our heavy suits slipping frequently on the ice.

Dril stopped frequently to make further checks with the radio sonde. Finally, after several hours of toilsome progress, he looked up from the instrument and made a quick signal.

"This is the position," he declared. "There should be deposits of the metals we need only a hundred feet or so beneath us."

It didn't look encouraging. We were standing on the crest of a low hill of ice, and it was not the sort of topography where you would expect to find a deposit of those metals.

But we did not argue with Dril's findings. We hauled the auxiliary power unit off the sledge, got its little ato-turbine going, and hooked its leads to the big dis-beam projector which we had dismounted from the bows of our ship.

Tharn played the dis-beam on the ice with expert skill.

Rapidly it cut a ten-foot shaft down through the solid ice. It went down for a hundred feet like a knife through cheese and then there was a sudden backlash of sparks and flame. He quickly cut the power.

"That must be the metal-bearing rock we just hit," he said.

Dril's voice was puzzled.

"It should be seventy or eighty feet lower to the metal deposits, by the sonde readings."

"We'll go down and see," Tharn declared. "Help me set up the winch."

We had brought the heavy girders and soon had them forming a massive tripod over the shaft. Strong cables ran through pulleys suspended from that tripod and were fastened to a big metal bucket in which we could descend by paying out cable through the tackle.

Only two of us should have gone down, really. But somehow, none of us wanted to wait alone up on the dark ice, nor did any of us want to go down alone into the shaft. So we all three crowded into the big bucket.

"Acting like children instead of veteran star explorers," grunted Tharn. "I shall make a note for our psychos on the upsetting effect of conditions on these worlds at the galaxy edge."

"Did you bring your beam guns?" Dril asked suddenly.

We had, all of us. Yet we didn't know quite why. Some obscure apprehension had made us arm ourselves when there was no conceivable need of it.

"Let's go," said Tharn. "Hang on to the cable and help me pay it out, Oroc."

I did as he bade, and we started dropping smoothly down into the shaft in the ice. The only light was the krypton whose rays Dril directed downward.

We went down a hundred feet, and then we all cried out. For we saw now the nature of the resistance which the dis-beam had met. Here under the ice there was a thick stratum of transparent metal, and the dis-beam had had to burn its way through that.

Underneath the burned-out hole in that metal stratum there was—nothing. Just empty space, a great hollow of some kind here beneath the ice.

Tharn's voice throbbed with excitement.

"I'd already begun to suspect it. Look down there!"

The krypton beam, angling downward into the emptiness below us, revealed a spectacle which stunned us.

Here, beneath the ice, was a city. It was a great metropolis of white cement structures, dimly revealed by our little light. And this whole city was shielded by an immense dome of transparent metal which withstood the weight of the ice that ages had piled upon it.

"Our dis-beam cut down through the ice and then through the dome itself," Tharn was saying excitedly. "This dead city may have been lying hidden here for ages."

Dead city? Yes, it was dead. We could see no trace of movement in the dim streets as we dropped toward it.

The white avenues, the vague façades and galleries and spires of the metropolis, were silent and empty. There was no air here. There could be no inhabitants.

Our bucket bumped down onto the street. We fastened the cables and climbed out, stood staring numbly about us. Then we uttered simultaneous cries of astonishment.

An incredible thing was happening. Light was beginning to grow around us. Like the first rosy flush of dawn it came at first, burgeoning into a soft glow that bathed all the far-flung city.

"This place can't be dead!" exclaimed Dril. "That light—"

"Automatic trips could start the light going," said Tharn. "These people had a great science, great enough for that."

"I don't like it," Dril murmured. "I feel that the place is haunted."

I had that feeling, too. I am not ordinarily sensitive to alien influences. If you are, you don't get accepted by the Star Service.

But a dark, oppressive premonition such as I had never felt before now weighed upon my spirits. Deep in my consciousness stirred vague awareness of horror brooding in this silent city beneath the ice.

"We came here for a metal, and we're going to get it," Tharn said determinedly. "The light won't hurt us, it will help us."

Drill set up the radio and took bearings again. They showed strongest indications of the presence of the metals we needed at a point some halfway across the city from us.

There was a towering building there, an enormous pile whose spire almost touched the dome. We took it as our goal and started.

The metal soles of our pressure suits clanked on the smooth cement paving as we walked. We must have made a strange picture—we three in our grotesque metal armor tramping through the eerily illuminated metropolis of silence and death.

"This city is old indeed," Tharn said in a low voice. "You notice that the buildings have roofs? That means they're older than—"

"Tharn! Oroc!" yelled Dril suddenly, swerving around and grabbing for his beam pistol.

We saw it at the same moment. It was rushing toward us from a side street we had just passed.

I can't describe it. It was like no normal form of life. It was a gibbering monstrosity of black flesh that changed from one hideous shape to another with protean rapidity as it *flowed* toward us.

The horror and hatred that assaulted our minds were not needed to tell us that this thing was inimical. We fired our beams at it simultaneously.

The creature sucked back with unbelievable rapidity

and disappeared in a flashing movement between two buildings. We ran forward. But it was gone.

"By all the devils of space!" swore Dril, his voice badly shaken. "What was *that?*"

Tharn seemed as stunned as we.

"I don't know. It was living, you saw that. And its swift retreat when we fired argues intelligence and volition."

"Ordinary flesh couldn't exist in this cold vacuum—" I began.

"There are perhaps more forms of life and flesh than we know," muttered Tharn. "Yet such things wouldn't build a city like this—"

"There's another!" I interrupted, pointing wildly.

The second of the black horrors advanced like a huge, unreared worm. But even as we raised our pistols, it darted away.

"We've got to go on," Tharn declared, though his own voice was a little unsteady. "The metals we need are in or near that big tower, and unless we get them we'll simply perish on the ice above."

"There may be worse deaths than freezing to death up there on the ice," said Dril huskily. But he came on with us.

Our progress through the shining streets of that magically beautiful white city was one of increasing horror.

The black monstrosities seemed to be swarming in the dead metropolis. We glimpsed and fired at dozens of them. Then we stopped beaming them, for we didn't seem able to hit them.

They didn't come to close quarters to attack us. They seemed rather to follow us and *watch* us, and their numbers and menacing appearance became more pronounced with every step we took toward the tower.

More daunting than the inexplicable creatures were the waves of horror and foreboding that were now crushing our spirits. I have spoken of the oppression we had felt since entering the city. It was becoming worse by the minute.

"We are definitely being subjected to psychological attack from some hostile source," muttered Tharn. "All this seems to be because we are approaching that tower."

"This system is on the edge of the galaxy," I reminded. "Some undreamed-of creature or creatures from the black outside could have come from there and laired up on this dead world."

I believe we would at that point have turned and retreated had not Tharn steadied us with a reminder.

"Whatever is here that is going to such lengths to force us to retreat is doing so because it's afraid of us! That argues that we can at least meet it on equal terms."

We were approaching the wide flight of steps that led up to the vaulted entrance to the great tower. We moved by now in a kind of daze, crushed as we were by the terrific psychic attack that was rapidly conquering our courage.

Then came the climax. The lofty doors of the tower swung slowly open. And from within the building there lurched and shambled out a thing, the sight of which froze us where we stood.

"*That* never came from any part of our own galaxy!" Dril cried hoarsely.

It was black, mountainous in bulk, and of a shape that tore the brain with horror. It was something like a monstrous, squatting toad, its flesh a heaving black slime from which protruded sticky black limbs that were not quite either tentacles or arms.

Its triangle of eyes were three slits of cold green fire that watched us with hypnotic intensity. Beneath that hideous chinless face, its breathing pouch swelled in and out painfully as it lurched, slobbering, down the steps toward us.

Our beams lashed frantically at that looming horror. And they had not the slightest effect on it. It continued to lurch down the steps. And, most ghastly of all, there was in its outlines a subtly hideous suggestion that it was parent, somehow, to the smaller horrors that swarmed in the city behind us.

Dril uttered a cry and turned to flee, and I stumbled around to join him. But from Tharn came a sharp exclamation.

"Wait! Look at the thing! It's *breathing!*"

For a moment, we couldn't understand. And then dimly, I did. The thing was obviously breathing. Yet there was no air here!

Tharn suddenly stepped forward. It was the bravest thing I have ever seen done by a member of the Star Service. He strode right toward the towering, slobbering horror.

And abruptly, as he reached it, the mountainous black obscenity vanished. It disappeared like a clicked-off television scene. And the black swarm in the city behind us disappeared at the same moment.

"Then it wasn't real?" Dril exclaimed.

"It was only a projected hypnotic illusion," Tharn declared. "Like the others we saw back there. The fact that it was breathing here where there is no air, gave me the clue to its unreality."

"But then," I said slowly, "whatever projected those hypnotic attacks is inside this building?"

"Yes, and so are the metals we want," Tharn said grimly. "We're going in."

The ceaseless waves of horror-charged thought beat upon us even more strongly as we went up the steps. Gibbering madness seemed to shriek in my brain as we opened the high doors.

And then, as we stepped into the vast, gleaming white nave of the building, all that oppressive mental assault suddenly ceased.

Our reeling minds were free of horror for the first time since we had entered this dead city. It was like bursting out of one of the great darkness clouds of the galaxy into clear space again.

"Listen!" said Tharn in a whisper. "I hear—"

I heard, too. We didn't really hear, of course. It was not sound, but mental waves that brought the sensation of sound to our brains.

It was music we heard. Faint and distant at first, but swelling in a great crescendo of singing instruments and voices.

The music was alien, like none we had ever heard before. But it gripped our minds as its triumphant strains rose and rose.

There was in those thunderous chords the titanic struggles and hopes and despairs of a race. It held us rigid and breathless as we listened to that supernal symphony of glory and defeat.

"They are coming," said Tharn in a low voice, looking across the white immensity of the great nave.

I saw them. Yet oddly, I was not afraid now, though this was by far the strangest thing that had yet befallen us.

Out into the nave toward us was filing a long procession of moving figures. They were the people of this long-dead world, the people of the past.

They were not like ourselves, though they were bipedal, erect figures with a general resemblance to us in bodily structure. I cannot particularize them, they were so alien to our eyes.

As the music swelled to its final crescendo and then died away, the marching figures stopped a little away from us and looked at us. The foremost, apparently their leader, spoke, and his voice reached our minds.

"Whoever you are, you have nothing more to fear," he said. "There is no life in this city. All the creatures you have seen, all the terror that has attacked you, yes, even we ourselves who speak to you, are but phantoms of the mind projected from telepathic records that are set to start functioning automatically when anyone enters this city."

"I thought so," whispered Tharn. "They could be nothing else."

The leader of the aliens spoke on.

"We are a people who perished long ago, by your reckoning. We originated on this planet"—he called it by an almost unpronounceable alien name—"far back in your past. We rose to power and wisdom and then to glory. Our science bore us out to other worlds, to other stars, finally to exploration and colonization of most of the galaxy.

"And then came disaster. From the abyss of extra-galactic space came invaders so alien that they could never live in amity with us. It was inevitable war between us and them, we to hold our galaxy, they to conquer it.

"They were not creatures of matter. They were creatures made up of photons, particles of force—shifting clouds capable of unimaginable cooperation between themselves and of almost unlimited activities. They swept us from star after star, they destroyed us on a thousand worlds.

"We were finally hemmed in on this star system of our origin, our last citadel. Had there been hope for the future in the photon race, had they been creatures capable of creating a future civilization, we would have accepted defeat and destruction and would have abdicated thus in their favor. But their limitations of intelligence made that impossible. They would never rise to civilization themselves nor allow any other race in the galaxy to do so.

"So we determined that, before we perished, we would destroy them. They were creatures of force who could only be destroyed by force. We converted our sun into a gigantic generator, hurling some of our planets and moons into it to cause the cataclysm we desired. From our sun generator sprang a colossal wave of force that swept out and annihilated the photon race in one cosmic surge of energy.

"It annihilated the last of us also. But we had already prepared this buried city, and in it had gathered all that we knew of science and wisdom to be garnered by future ages. Some day new forms of life will rise to civilization in the galaxy, some day explorers from other stars will come here.

"If they are not intelligent enough to make benign use of the powers we have gathered here, our telepathic attacks should frighten them away. But if they are intelligent enough to discern the clues we leave for them, they will understand that all is but hypnotic illusion and will press forward into this tower of our secrets.

"You, who listen to me, have done this. To you, whoever and whatever future race you may be, we bequeath our wisdom and our power. In this building, and in others throughout the city, you will find all that we have left. Use it wisely for the good of the galaxy and all of its races. And now, from we of the past to you of the future —farewell."

The figures that stood before us vanished. And we three remained standing alone in the silent, shimmering white building.

"Space, what a race they must have been!" breathed Tharn. "To do all that, to die destroying a menace that would have blighted the galaxy forever, and still to contrive to leave all that they had gained to the future!"

"Let's see if we can find the metals," begged Dril, his voice shaky. "All I want now is to get out of here and take a long drink of *sanqua*."

We found more than the metals we needed. In that wonderful storehouse of alien science we found whole wave generators of a type far superior to ours, which could easily be installed in our crippled ship.

I shall not tell of all we found. The Star Service is already carefully exploring that great treasury of ancient science, and in time its findings will be known to all the galaxy.

It took labor to get the generators back up to our ship but when that was done, it was not hard to install them. And when we had fused a patch on our punctured hull, we were ready to depart.

As our ship arrowed up through the eternal dusk of that ice clad world and darted past its smoldering dying sun on our homeward voyage, Dril took down the bottle of *sanqua*.

"Let's get these cursed suits off, and then I'm going to have the longest drink I ever took!" he vowed.

We divested ourselves of the heavy suits at last. It was a wonderful relief to step out of them, to unfold our cramped wings and smooth our ruffled feathers.

We looked at each other, we three tall bird-men of Rigel, as Dril handed us the glasses of pink *sanqua*. On Tharn's beaked face, in his green eyes, was an expression that told me we all were thinking of the same thing.

He raised the glass that he held in his talons.

"To that great dead race to whom our galaxy owes all," he said. "We will drink to their world by their own name for it. We will drink to Earth."

Part Two

Human Threat

Terror implies threat. So it follows that the Gothic story, insofar as it is a tale of terror, is also a tale of threat. But the threat can take many forms, from the explicit threat of torture and death ("The Pit and the Pendulum") through threat of rape and degradation (*The Monk*), threat of transformation to something hideous, such as a vampire (*Dracula*), threat of loss of loved ones (*Frankenstein*), threat of madness or other psychological aberration (*The Turn of the Screw* and "The Yellow Wall Paper"), to a threat whose terror lies precisely in its unknown nature and origins ("The Willows" and "The Horla"). To these must be added the *implied* threat of destruction or death found in such stories as "The Dead Planet," in which the time is subsequent to the death of a world, and only the ultimate revelation of the planet's identity brings about a feeling of potential destruction and that horror for which the Gothic strives.

Threat, in turn, necessarily involves a victim or victims, and Gothic stories abound with such figures. It might even be said that the presence of the victim is, in a special sense, part of the physical setting of the Gothic. For if the setting is used to involve the reader and to make him willingly susceptible to the effects of the Gothic, it is equally true that the empathy, or at least the sympathy, of the reader for the plight of the victim is a powerful means of eliciting his emotional responses. It is not, however, the victim, the threat, nor even the nature of the threat which makes possible a distinction among the approaches to Gothic terror. This distinction is based on the differing *agencies* of terror, most commonly the human one—the threat to one person by another.

The stories in this particular section, illustrating human threat, may, and often do, have another agency such as the supernatural at work, but the major conflict is between humans. A very good example of the use of two agencies is found in *The Monk*. Ambrosio, who threatens the victim Antonia with rape and death, succeeds in carrying out his perverted desires. Eventually caught and condemned, he sells his soul to Satan in exchange for rescue from the Inquisition. Although this reveals the agency of the Satanic supernatural (which has been Ambrosio's ally all along), the major theme throughout has been the monk's threat to Antonia. Therefore, although Lewis incorporates the supernatural into his story, it is of secondary importance to the human threat. It might also be argued that Ambrosio himself is a victim or that there is a psychological threat inherent in the work. Certainly Lewis and many other Gothic writers succeed, while probing man's fears, appetites and drives in anticipating a great many subsequent psychological concerns, but the *principal* device or agency utilized by Lewis is that of human threat, and it is for that reason the selection from *The Monk* is placed in this section.

If the three stories presented here are considered from the point of view of ascending or increasing involvement of the human agency, Poe's "The Pit and the Pendulum" is most impersonal of all, having as it does no active character but that of protagonist. Aside from the terror aroused by descriptions of the situation, there is an added psychological element of fear of the unknown, but the major agency is still an unseen, all but unmentioned, Inquisition. The victim's terrible plight in the pit is not even tempered by the dubious comfort of the presence of his torturers. This impersonal treatment of the victim is quite different from that in stories such as *The Monk* and *The Romance of the Forest*, whose pages abound with confrontations between the victim and the threatening human agency.

In Ann Radcliffe's novel, by way of contrast, the human threat is always imminent and pervasive, and the reader follows Mrs. Radcliffe's victims from one harrowing episode to another. The principal victim, young Adeline, is constantly, perilously, often unsuspectingly close to disaster. But Mrs. Radcliffe gives the reader the added excitement of other victims—Mr. La Motte, who discovers himself a prisoner for no apparent reason in the hands of strangers, and a seventeenth-century victim who has written an account of his confinement in the abbey. Adeline's discovery and reading of the yellowed manuscript is a further touch described to intensify by suggested parallel her own plight. Mrs. Radcliffe prepares her reader for each episode through use of descriptive passages of lonely moors, night, abandoned abbeys, and all the usual embellishments of Gothic atmosphere and then generously compounds each incident of violence, flight, entrapment, betrayal, and despair—all carefully calculated to elicit the desired emotional involvement of the reader.

The Romance of the Forest, with its numerous characters and minimum concern with the supernatural, is the most "human" of all three selections, but Mrs. Radcliffe is less successful in presenting her humans than is Lewis. Her threatening human agencies are never presented with the roundness or wholeness of character that makes it possible to sympathize greatly with them. Lewis, however, succeeds in giving the reader a complete, three-dimensional image of Ambrosio, so that despite the monk's deceptions, lusts, and weaknesses, he is vibrantly human, and it is difficult if not impossible to avoid sympathy for him. It may be a sympathy more akin to that which the reader feels for Frankenstein's hapless monster, but it is sympathy none the less and makes the character credible. Nevertheless, in all three selections the dominant theme remains that of the victim and the human predator, the eternal theme of man's inhumanity to man.

from

𝕿𝖍𝖊 𝕸𝖔𝖓𝖐

𝖇𝖞 𝕸𝖆𝖙𝖙𝖍𝖊𝖜 𝕲. 𝕷𝖊𝖜𝖎𝖘

[*The monk Ambrosio is obsessed with possessing Antonia, an innocent young girl. Through the machinations of the scheming Matilda, Antonia is given a drug which induces a deathlike state and she is buried in the vaults of St. Clare just as the festival to this patron saint has begun.*]

CHAPTER XI.

Great Heaven! How frail thy creature man is made!
How by himself insensibly betrayed!
In our own strength unhappily secure,
Too little cautious of the adverse power,
On pleasure's flowery brink we idly stray,
Masters as yet of our returning way:
Till the strong gusts of raging passion rise,
Till the dire tempest mingles earth and skies,
And, swift into the boundless ocean borne,
Our foolish confidence too late we mourn:
Round our devoted heads the billows beat,
And from our troubled view the lessening lands retreat.
                                                    PRIOR.

All this while Ambrosio was unconscious of the dreadful scenes which were passing so near. The execution of his designs upon Antonia employed his every thought. Hitherto he was satisfied with the success of his plans. Antonia had drunk the opiate, was buried in the vaults of St. Clare, and absolutely in his disposal. Matilda, who was well acquainted with the nature and effects of the soporific medicine, had computed that it would not cease to operate till one in the morning. For that hour he waited with impatience. The festival of St. Clare presented him with a favourable opportunity of consummating his crime. He was certain that the friars and nuns would be engaged in the procession, and that he had no cause to dread an interruption: from appearing himself at the head of his monks, he had desired to be excused. He doubted not, that being beyond the reach of help, cut off from all the world, and totally in his power, Antonia would comply with his desires. The affection which she had ever expressed for him, warranted this persuasion: but he resolved, that should she prove obstinate, no consideration whatever should prevent him from enjoying her. Secure from a discovery, he shuddered not at the idea of employing force; or, if he felt any repugnance, it arose not from a principle of shame or compassion, but from his feeling for Antonia the most sincere and ardent affection, and wishing to owe her favours to no one but herself.

The monks quitted the abbey at midnight. Matilda was among the choristers, and led the chaunt. Ambrosio was left by himself, and at liberty to pursue his own inclinations. Convinced that no one remained behind to watch his motions, or disturb his pleasures, he now hastened to the western aisles. His heart beating with hope not unmingled with anxiety, he crossed the garden, unlocked the door which admitted him into the cemetery, and in a few minutes he stood before the vaults. Here he paused: he looked round with suspicion, conscious that his business was unfit for any other eye. As he stood in hesitation, he heard the melancholy shriek of the screech-owl: the wind rattled loudly against the windows of the adjacent convent, and, as the current swept by him, bore with it the faint notes of the chaunt of choristers. He opened the door cautiously, as if fearing to be overheard; he entered, and closed it again after him. Guided by his lamp, he threaded the long passages, in whose windings Matilda had instructed him, and reached the private vault which contained his sleeping mistress.

Its entrance was by no means easy to discover; but this was no obstacle to Ambrosio, who at the time of Antonia's funeral had observed it too carefully to be deceived. He found the door, which was unfastened, pushed it open, and descended into the dungeon. He approached the humble tomb in which Antonia reposed. He had provided himself with an iron crow and a pick-axe: but this precaution was unnecessary. The grate was slightly fastened on the outside: he raised it, and, placing the lamp upon its ridge, bent silently over the tomb. By the side of three putrid half-corrupted bodies lay the sleeping beauty. A lively red, the forerunner of returning animation, had already spread itself over her cheeks; and as wrapped in her shroud she reclined upon her funeral bier; she seemed to smile at the images of death around her. While he gazed upon their rotting bones and disgusting figures, who perhaps were once as sweet and lovely, Ambrosio thought upon Elvira, by him reduced to the same state. As the memory of that horrid act glanced upon his mind, it was clouded with a gloomy horror; yet it served but to strengthen his resolution to destroy Antonia's honour.

"For your sake, fatal beauty!" murmured the monk, while gazing on his devoted prey, "for your sake have I committed this murder, and sold myself to eternal tortures. Now you are in my power: the produce of my guilt will at last be mine. Hope not that your prayers breathed in tones of unequalled melody, your bright eyes filled with tears, and your hands lifted in supplication, as when seeking in penitence the Virgin's pardon: hope not, that your moving innocence, your beauteous grief, or all your suppliant arts, shall ransom you from my embraces. Before the break of day, mine you must, and mine you shall be!"

He lifted her, still motionless, from the tomb: he seated himself upon a bank of stone, and, supporting her in his arms, watched impatiently for the symptoms of returning animation. Scarcely could he command his passion sufficiently, to restrain himself from enjoying her while yet insensible. His natural lust was increased in ardour by the difficulties which had opposed his satisfying it; as also his long abstinence from woman, since, from the moment of resigning her claim to his love, Matilda had exiled him from her arms for ever.

"I am no prostitute, Ambrosio," had she told him, when, in the fullness of his lust, he demanded her favours with more than usual earnestness; "I am now no more than your friend, and will not be your mistress. Cease then to solicit my complying with desires which insult me. While your heart was mine, I gloried in your embraces. Those happy times are past; my person is become indifferent to you, and 'tis necessity, not love, which makes you seek my enjoyment. I cannot yield to a request so humiliating to my pride."

Suddenly deprived of pleasures, the use of which had made them an absolute want, the monk felt this restraint severely. Naturally addicted to the gratification of the senses, in the full vigour of manhood and heat of blood, he had suffered his temperament to acquire such ascendency, that his lust was become madness. Of his fondness for Antonia, none but the grosser particles remained; he longed for the possession of her person; and even the gloom of the vault, the surrounding silence, and the resistance which he expected from her, seemed to give a fresh edge to his fierce and unbridled desires.

Gradually he felt the bosom which rested against his glow with returning warmth. Her heart throbbed again, her blood flowed swifter, and her lips moved. At length she opened her eyes; but, still oppressed and bewildered by the effects of the strong opiate, she closed them again immediately. Ambrosio watched her narrowly, nor permitted a movement to escape him. Perceiving that she was fully restored to existence, he caught her in rapture to his bosom, and closely pressed his lips to hers. The suddenness of his action sufficed to dissipate the fumes which obscured Antonia's reason. She hastily raised herself and cast a wild look round her. The strange images which presented themselves on every side contributed to confuse her. She put her hand to her head, as if to settle her disordered imagination. At length she took it away, and threw her eyes through the dungeon a second time. They fixed on the abbot's face.

"Where am I?" she said abruptly. "How came I here?—Where is my mother? Methought I saw her! Oh! a dream, a dreadful dreadful dream told me . . . . . . But where am I? Let me go! I cannot stay here!"

She attempted to rise, but the monk prevented her.

"Be calm, lovely Antonia!" he replied; "no danger is near you: confide in my protection. Why do you gaze on me so earnestly? Do you not know me? Not know your friend, Ambrosio?"

"Ambrosio? my friend?—Oh! yes, yes; I remember . . . . . . But why am I here? Who has brought me? Why are you with me?—Oh! Flora bade me beware . . . . . !—Here are nothing but graves, and tombs, and skeletons! This place frightens me! Good Ambrosio, take me away from it, for it recalls my fearful dream!—Methought I was dead, and laid in my grave!—Good Ambrosio, take me from hence!—Will you not? Oh! will you not?—Do

not look on me thus!—Your flaming eyes terrify me!—
Spare me, father! Oh! spare me for God's sake!"

"Why these terrors, Antonia?" rejoined the abbot, fold-
ing her in his arms, and covering her bosom with kisses
which she in vain struggled to avoid. "What fear you
from me, from one who adores you? What matters it
where you are? This sepulchre seems to me Love's bower.
This gloom is the friendly night of Mystery, which he
spreads over our delights! Such do I think it, and such
must my Antonia. Yes, my sweet girl! yes! Your veins
shall glow with the fire which circles in mine, and my
transports shall be doubled by your sharing them!"

While he spoke thus, he repeated his embraces, and
permitted himself the most indecent liberties. Even
Antonia's ignorance was not proof against the freedom
of his behaviour. She was sensible of her danger, forced
herself from his arms, and her shroud being her only
garment, she wrapped it closely around her.

"Unhand me, father!" she cried, her honest indignation
tempered by alarm at her unprotected position: "Why
have you brought me to this place? Its appearance freezes
me with horror! Convey me from hence; if you have
the least sense of pity and humanity! Let me return to the
house, which I have quitted I know not how; but stay
here one moment longer, I neither will nor ought."

Though the monk was somewhat startled by the resolute
tone in which this speech was delivered, it produced
upon him no other effect than surprise. He caught her
hand, forced her upon his knee, and, gazing upon her
with gloating eyes, he thus replied to her:

"Compose yourself, Antonia. Resistance is unavailing,
and I need disavow my passion for you no longer. You are
imagined dead; society is for ever lost to you. I possess you
here alone; you are absolutely in my power, and I burn
with desires which I must either gratify or die: but I
would owe my happiness to yourself. My lovely girl! my
adorable Antonia! let me instruct you in the joys to

which you are still a stranger, and teach you to feel those pleasures in my arms, which I must soon enjoy in yours. Nay, this struggling is childish," he continued, seeing her repel his caresses, and endeavour to escape from his grasp; "no aid is near; neither heaven nor earth shall save you from my embraces. Yet why reject pleasures so sweet, so rapturous? No one observes us; our loves will be a secret to all the world. Love and opportunity invite your giving loose to your passions. Yield to them, my Antonia! yield to them, my lovely girl! Throw your arms thus fondly round me; join your lips thus closely to mine! Amidst all her gifts, has Nature denied her most precious, the sensibility of pleasure? Oh! impossible! Every feature, look, and motion declares you are formed to bless, and to be blessed yourself! Turn not on me those supplicating eyes: consult your own charms; they will tell you that I am proof against entreaty. Can I relinquish these limbs so white, so soft, so delicate! these swelling breasts, round, full, and elastic! these lips fraught with such inexhaustible sweetness? Can I relinquish these treasures, and leave them to another's enjoyment? No, Antonia; never, never! I swear it by this kiss! and this! and this!"

With every moment the friar's passion became more ardent, and Antonia's terror more intense. She struggled to disengage herself from his arms. Her exertions were unsuccessful; and, finding that Ambrosio's conduct became still freer, she shrieked for assistance with all her strength. The aspect of the vault, the pale glimmering of the lamp, the surrounding obscurity, the sight of the tomb, and the objects of mortality which met her eyes on either side, were ill calculated to inspire her with those emotions by which the friar was agitated. Even his caresses terrified her from their fury, and created no other sentiment than fear. On the contrary, her alarm, her evident disgust, and incessant opposition, seemed only to inflame the monk's desires, and supply his brutality with additional strength.

Antonia's shrieks were unheard; yet she continued them, nor abandoned her endeavours to escape, till exhausted and out of breath she sank from his arms upon her knees, and once more had recourse to prayers and supplications. This attempt had no better success than the former. On the contrary, taking advantage of her situation, the ravisher threw himself by her side. He clasped her to his bosom almost lifeless with terror, and faint with struggling. He stifled her cries with kisses, treated her with the rudeness of an unprincipled barbarian, proceeded from freedom to freedom, and, in the violence of his lustful delirium, wounded and bruised her tender limbs. Heedless of her tears, cries, and entreaties, he gradually made himself master of her person, and desisted not from his prey, till he had accomplished his crime and the dishonour of Antonia.

Scarcely had he succeeded in his design, than he shuddered at himself, and the means by which it was effected. The very excess of his former eagerness to possess Antonia now contributed to inspire him with disgust; and a secret impulse made him feel how base and unmanly was the crime which he had just committed. He started hastily from her arms. She, who so lately had been the object of his adoration, now raised no other sentiment in his heart than aversion and rage. He turned away from her; or, if his eyes rested upon her figure involuntarily, it was only to dart upon her looks of hate. The unfortunate had fainted ere the completion of her disgrace: she only recovered life to be sensible of her misfortune. She remained stretched upon the earth in silent despair; the tears chased each other slowly down her cheeks, and her bosom heaved with frequent sobs. Oppressed with grief, she continued for some time in this state of torpidity. At length she rose with difficulty, and, dragging her feeble steps towards the door, prepared to quit the dungeon.

The sound of her foot-steps roused the monk from his sullen apathy. Starting from the tomb against which he reclined, while his eyes wandered over the images of corruption contained in it, he pursued the victim of his brutality, and soon overtook her. He seized her by the arm, and violently forced her back into the dungeon.

"Whither go you?" he cried in a stern voice; "return this instant!"

Antonia trembled at the fury of his countenance.

"What would you more?" she said with timidity: "Is not my ruin completed? Am I not undone, undone for ever? Is not your cruelty contented, or have I yet more to suffer? Let me depart: let me return to my home, and weep unrestrained my shame and my affliction!"

"Return to your home?" repeated the monk, with bitter and contemptuous mockery; then suddenly his eyes flaming with passion, "What? That you may denounce me to the world? that you may proclaim me a hyprocrite, a ravisher, a betrayer, a monster of cruelty, lust, and ingratitude? No, no, no! I know well the whole weight of my offences; well, that your complaints would be too just, and my crimes too notorious! You shall not from hence to tell Madrid that I am a villain; that my conscience is loaded with sins, which make me despair of Heaven's pardon. Wretched girl, you must stay here with me! Here amidst these lonely tombs, these images of death, these rotting, loathsome, corrupted bodies! Here shall you stay, and witness my sufferings; witness what it is to be in the horrors of despondency, and breathe the last groan in blasphemy and curses!—And whom am I to thank for this? What seduced me into crimes, whose bare remembrance makes me shudder? Fatal witch! was it not thy beauty? Have you not plunged my soul into infamy? Have you not made me a perjured hypocrite, a ravisher, an assassin? Nay, at this moment, does not that angel look bid me despair of God's forgiveness? Oh! when I stand before his judgment-throne, that look will suffice to damn me! You will tell my judge, that you were happy, till *I* saw you; that you were innocent, till *I* polluted you!

You will come with those tearful eyes, those cheeks pale and ghastly, those hands lifted in supplication, as when you sought from me that mercy which I gave not! Then will my perdition be certain! Then will come your mother's ghost, and hurl me down into the dwellings of fiends, and flames, and furies, and everlasting torments! And 'tis you who will accuse me! 'tis you who will cause my eternal anguish!—you, wretched girl! you! you!"

As he thundered out these words, he violently grasped Antonia's arm, and spurned the earth with delirious fury.

Supposing his brain to be turned, Antonia sank in terror upon her knees; she lifted up her hands, and her voice almost died away ere she could give it utterance.

"Spare me! spare me!" she murmured with difficulty.

"Silence!" cried the friar madly, and dashed her upon the ground——

He quitted her, and paced the dungeon with a wild and disordered air. His eyes rolled fearfully; Antonia trembled whenever she met their gaze. He seemed to meditate on something horrible, and she gave up all hopes of escaping from the sepulchre with life. Yet in harbouring this idea she did him injustice. Amidst the horror and disgust to which his soul was prey, pity for his victim still held a place in it. The storm of passion once over, he would have given worlds, had he possessed them, to have restored to her that innocence of which his unbridled lust had deprived her. Of the desires which had urged him to the crime, no trace was left in his bosom. The wealth of India would not have tempted him to a second enjoyment of her person. His nature seemed to revolt at the very idea, and fain would he have wiped from his memory the scene which had just passed. As his gloomy rage abated, in proportion did his compassion augment for Antonia. He stopped, and would have spoken to her words of comfort; but he knew not from whence to draw them, and remained gazing upon her with mournful wildness. Her situation seemed so hopeless, so woe-begone, as to baffle mortal power to relieve her. What could he do for her? Her peace of mind was lost, her honour irreparably ruined. She was cut off for ever from society, nor dared he give her back to it. He was conscious that, were she to appear in the world again, his guilt would be revealed, and his punishment inevitable. To one so laden with crimes, death came armed with double terrors. Yet, should he restore Antonia to light, and stand the chance of her betraying him, how miserable a prospect would present itself before her! She could never hope to be creditably established; she would be marked with infamy, and condemned to sorrow and solitude for the remainder of her existence. What was the alternative? A resolution far more terrible for Antonia, but which at least would insure the abbot's safety. He determined to leave the world persuaded of her death, and to retain her a captive in this gloomy prison. There he proposed to visit her every night, to bring her food, to profess his penitence, and mingle his tears with hers. The monk felt that this resolution was unjust and cruel; but it was his only means to prevent Antonia from publishing his guilt and her own infamy. Should he release her, he could not depend upon her silence. His offence was too flagrant to permit his hoping for her forgiveness. Besides, her reappearing would excite universal curiosity, and the violence of her affliction would prevent her from concealing its cause. He determined, therefore, that Antonia should remain a prisoner in the dungeon.

He approached her with confusion painted on his countenance. He raised her from the ground—her hand trembled as he took it, and he dropped it again as if he had touched a serpent. Nature seemed to recoil at the touch. He felt himself at once repulsed from and attracted towards her, yet could account for neither sentiment. There was something in her look which penetrated him with horror; and though his understanding was still ignorant of it, conscience pointed out to him the whole extent of his crime. In hurried accents, yet the gentlest he could find, while his eye was averted, and his voice scarcely audible, he strove to console her under a misfortune which now could not be avoided. He declared himself sincerely penitent, and that he would gladly shed a drop of his blood for every tear which his barbarity had forced from her. Wretched and hopeless, Antonia listened to him in silent grief; but when he announced her confinement in the sepulchre, that dreadful doom, to which even death seemed preferable, roused her from her insensibility at once. To linger out a life of misery in a narrow loathsome cell, known to exist by no human being save her ravisher, surrounded by mouldering corses, breathing the pestilential air of corruption, never more to behold the light, or drink the pure gale of heaven—the idea was more terrible than she could support. It conquered even her abhorrence of the friar. Again she sank upon her knees; she besought his compassion in terms the most pathetic and urgent; she promised, would he but restore her to liberty, to conceal her injuries from the world; to assign any reason for her re-appearance, which he might judge proper; and in order to prevent the least suspicion from falling upon him, she offered to quit Madrid immediately. Her entreaties were so urgent as to make a considerable impression upon the monk. He reflected, that as her person no longer excited his desires, he had no interest in keeping her concealed as he had at first intended; that he was adding a fresh injury to those which she had already suffered; and that if she adhered to her promises, whether she was confined or at liberty, his life and reputation were equally secure. On the other hand, he trembled lest in her affliction Antonia should unintentionally break her engagement, or that her excessive simplicity and ignorance of deceit should permit some one more artful to surprise her secret. However well-founded were these apprehensions, compassion, and sincere wish to repair his fault as much as possible, solicited his complying with the prayers of his suppliant. The difficulty of colouring Antonia's unexpected return to life, after her supposed death and public interment, was the only point which kept him irresolute. He was still pondering on the means of removing this obstacle, when he heard the sound of feet approaching with precipitation. The door of the vault was thrown open, and Matilda rushed in, evidently much confused and terrified.

On seeing a stranger enter, Antonia uttered a cry of joy; but her hopes of receiving succor from him were soon dissipated. The supposed novice, without expressing the least surprise at finding a woman alone with the monk, in so strange a place, and at so late an hour, addressed him thus without losing a moment:

"What is to be done, Ambrosio? We are lost, unless some speedy means is found of dispelling the rioters. Ambrosio, the convent of St. Clare is on fire; the prioress is fallen a victim to the fury of the mob. Already is the abbey menaced with a similar fate. Alarmed at the threats of the people, the monks seek for you every where. They imagine that your authority alone will suffice to calm this disturbance. No one knows what is become of you, and your absence creates universal astonishment and despair. I profited by the confusion, and fled hither to warn you of the danger."

"This will soon be remedied," answered the abbot; "I will hasten back to my cell: a trivial reason will account for my having been missed."

"Impossible!" rejoined Matilda: "The sepulchre is filled with archers. Lorenzo de Medina, with several officers of the Inquisition, searches through the vaults, and pervades every passage. You will be intercepted in your flight; your reasons for being at this late hour in the sepulchre will be examined; Antonia will be found, and then you are undone for ever!"

"Lorenzo de Medina? Officers of the Inquisition? What brings them here? Seek they for me? Am I then suspected? Oh! speak, Matilda! answer me in pity!"

"As yet they do not think of you; but I fear that they will ere long. Your only chance of escaping their notice rests upon the difficulty of exploring this vault. The door is artfully hidden, haply it may not be observed, and we may remain concealed till the search is over."

"But Antonia . . . . Should the inquisitors draw near, and her cries be heard. . . ."

"Thus I remove that danger!" interrupted Matilda.

At the same time drawing a poniard, she rushed upon her devoted prey.

"Hold! hold!" cried Ambrosio, seizing her hand, and wresting from it the already lifted weapon. "What would you do, cruel woman? The unfortunate has already suffered but too much, thanks to your pernicious counsels! Would to God that I had never followed them! Would to God that I had never seen your face!"

Matilda darted upon him a look of scorn.

"Absurd!" she exclaimed with an air of passion and majesty, which impressed the monk with awe. "After robbing her of all that made it dear, can you fear to deprive her of a life so miserable? But 'tis well! Let her live to convince you of your folly. I abandon you to your evil destiny! I disclaim your alliance! Who trembles to commit so insignificant a crime, deserves not my protection. Hark! hark! Ambrosio; hear you not the archers? They come, and your destruction is inevitable!"

At this moment the abbot heard the sound of distant voices. He flew to close the door, on whose concealment his safety depended, and which Matilda had neglected to fasten. Ere he could reach it, he saw Antonia glide suddenly by him, rush through the door, and fly towards the noise with the swiftness of an arrow. She had listened attentively to Matilda: she heard Lorenzo's name mentioned, and resolved to risque every thing to throw herself under his protection. The door was open. The sounds convinced her that the archers could be at no great distance. She mustered up her little remaining strength, rushed by the monk ere he perceived her design, and bent her course rapidly towards the voices. As soon as he recovered from his first surprise, the abbot failed not to pursue her. In vain did Antonia redouble her speed, and stretched every nerve to the utmost. Her enemy gained upon her every moment: she heard his steps close after her, and felt the heat of his breath glow upon her neck. He overtook her; he twisted his hand in the ringlets of her streaming hair, and attempted to drag her back with him to the dungeon. Antonia resisted with all her strength. She folded her arms round a pillar which supported the roof, and shrieked loudly for assistance. In vain did the monk strive to threaten her to silence.

"Help!" she continued to exclaim; "help! help! for God's sake!"

Quickened by her cries, the sound of foot-steps was heard approaching. The abbot expected every moment to see the inquisitors arrive. Antonia still resisted, and he now enforced her silence by means the most horrible and inhuman. He still grasped Matilda's dagger: without allowing himself a moment's reflection, he raised it, and plunged it twice in the bosom of Antonia! She shrieked, and sank upon the ground. The monk endeavoured to bear her away with him, but she still embraced the pillar firmly. At that instant the light of approaching torches flashed upon the walls. Dreading a discovery, Ambrosio was compelled to abandon his victim, and hastily fled back to the vault, where he had left Matilda.

He fled not unobserved. Don Ramirez happening to arrive the first, perceived a female bleeding upon the ground, and a man flying from the spot, whose confusion betrayed him for the murderer. He instantly pursued the fugitive, with some part of the archers, while the others remained with Lorenzo to protect the wounded stranger.

They raised her, and supported her in their arms. She had fainted from excess of pain, but soon gave signs of returning life. She opened her eyes; and on lifting up her head, the quantity of fair hair fell back, which till then had obscured her features.

"God Almighty! it is Antonia!"

Such was Lorenzo's exclamation, while he snatched her from the attendant's arms, and clasped her in his own.

Though aimed by an uncertain hand, the poniard had answered but too well the purpose of its employer. The wounds were mortal, and Antonia was conscious that she never could recover. Yet the few moments which remained for her, were moments of happiness. The concern expressed upon Lorenzo's countenance, the frantic fondness of his complaints, and his earnest enquiries respecting her wounds, convinced her beyond a doubt that his affections were her own. She would not be removed from the vaults, fearing lest motion should only hasten her death; and she was unwilling to lose those moments which she passed in receiving proofs of Lorenzo's love, and assuring him of her own. She told him, that had she still been undefiled she might have lamented the loss of life; but that, deprived of honour and branded with shame, death was to her a blessing: she could not have been his wife; and that hope being denied her, she resigned herself to the grave without one sigh of regret. She bade him take courage, conjured him not to abandon himself to fruitless sorrow, and declared that she mourned to leave nothing in the whole world but him. While every sweet accent increased rather than lightened Lorenzo's grief, she continued to converse with him till the moment of dissolution. Her voice grew faint, and scarcely audible; a thick cloud spread itself over her eyes; her heart beat slow and irregular, and every instant seemed to announce that her fate was near at hand.

She lay, her head reclining upon Lorenzo's bosom, and her lips still murmuring to him words of comfort. She was interrupted by the convent-bell, as, tolling at a distance, it struck the hour. Suddenly Antonia's eyes sparkled with celestial brightness; her frame seemed to have received new strength and animation. She started from her lover's arms.

"Three o'clock!" she cried. "Mother, I come!"

She clasped her hands, and sank lifeless upon the ground. Lorenzo, in agony, threw himself beside her. He tore his hair, beat his breast, and refused to be separated from the corse. At length his force being exhausted, he suffered himself to be led from the vault, and was conveyed to the palace de Medina scarcely more alive than the unfortunate Antonia.

In the mean while, though closely pursued, Ambrosio succeeded in regaining the vault. The door was already fastened when Don Ramirez arrived, and much time elapsed ere the fugitive's retreat was discovered. But nothing can resist perseverance. Though so artfully concealed, the door could not escape the vigilance of the archers. They forced it open, and entered the vault to the infinite dismay of Ambrosio and his companion. The monk's confusion, his attempt to hide himself, his rapid flight, and the blood sprinkled upon his clothes, left no room to doubt his being Antonia's murderer. But when he was recognized for the immaculate Ambrosio "the man of holiness," the idol of Madrid; the faculties of the spectators were chained up in surprise, and scarcely could they persuade themselves that what they saw was no vision. The abbot strove not to vindicate himself, but preserved a sullen silence. He was secured and bound. The same precaution was taken with Matilda. Her cowl being removed, the delicacy of her features and profusion of her golden hair betrayed her sex; and this incident created fresh amazement. The dagger was also found in the tomb, where the monk had thrown it; and the dungeon having undergone a thorough search, the two culprits were conveyed to the prisons of the Inquisition.

from

𝕿𝖍𝖊 𝕽𝖔𝖒𝖆𝖓𝖈𝖊 𝖔𝖋 𝖙𝖍𝖊 𝕱𝖔𝖗𝖊𝖘𝖙

𝖇𝖞 𝕬𝖓𝖓 𝕽𝖆𝖉𝖈𝖑𝖎𝖋𝖋𝖊

[*Monsieur and Madame La Motte have been forced to flee Paris to avoid arrest for debts. They travel hastily by coach, accompanied by their two faithful servants, and in the course of their journey, under threatening circumstances, they accept another passenger, Adeline, a young woman of mysterious background. In a remote woodland a carriage wheel breaks and the party takes refuge in the ruins of a Gothic abbey.*]

CHAPTER II.

He approached, and perceived the Gothic remains of an abbey. It stood on a kind of rude lawn, overshadowed by high and spreading trees which seemed coeval with the building and diffused a romantic gloom around. The greater part of the pile appeared to be sinking into ruins, and that which had withstood the ravages of time showed the remaining features of the fabric more awful in decay. The lofty battlements, thickly enwreathed with ivy, were half demolished, and become

134

the residence of birds of prey. Huge fragments of the eastern tower, which was almost demolished, lay scattered amid the high grass that waved slowly to the breeze. "The thistle shook its lonely head; the moss whistled to the wind." A Gothic gate richly ornamented with fret work, which opened into the main body of the edifice, but which was now obstructed with brush-wood, remained entire. Above the vast and magnificent portal of this gate arose a window of the same order, whose pointed arches still exhibited fragments of stained glass, once the pride of monkish devotion. La Motte, thinking it possible it might yet shelter some human being, advanced to the gate and lifted a massy knocker. The hollow sounds rung through the emptiness of the place. After waiting a few minutes, he forced back the gate, which was heavy with iron-work and creaked harshly on its hinges.

He entered what appeared to have been the chapel of the abbey, where the hymn of devotion had once been raised and the tear of penitence had once been shed: sounds which could now only be recalled by imagination—tears of penitence which had long since fixed in fate. La Motte paused a moment, for he felt a sensation of sublimity rising into terror—a suspension of mingled astonishment and awe! He surveyed the vastness of the place, and as he contemplated its ruins, fancy bore him back to past ages.—"And these walls," said he, "where once superstition lurked and austerity anticipated an earthly purgatory, now tremble over the mortal remains of the beings who reared them!"

* * * * * * * * * * * * * * *

He opened the door of the great hall, and they entered; its extent was lost in gloom.—"Let us stay here," said Madame La Motte, "I will go no farther." La Motte pointed to the broken roof, and was proceeding, when he was interrupted by an uncommon noise which passed along the hall. They were all silent—it was the silence of terror. Madame La Motte spoke first. "Let us quit this spot," said she, "any evil is preferable to the feeling which now oppresses me. Let us retire instantly." The stillness had for some time remained undisturbed, and La Motte, ashamed of the fear he had involuntarily betrayed, now thought it necessary to affect a boldness which he did not feel. He therefore opposed ridicule to the terror of Madame, and insisted upon proceeding. Thus compelled to acquiesce, she traversed the hall with trembling steps. They came to a narrow passage, and Peter's sticks being nearly exhausted, awaited here while he went in search of more.

The almost expiring light flashed faintly upon the walls of the passage, showing the recess more horrible. Across the hall, the greater part of which was concealed in shadow, the feeble ray spread a tremulous gleam, exhibiting the chasm in the roof, while many nameless objects were seen imperfectly through the dusk. Adeline with a smile inquired of La Motte if he believed in spirits. The question was ill-timed, for the present scene impressed its terrors upon La Motte, and in spite of endeavour he felt a superstitious dread stealing upon him. He was now, perhaps, standing over the ashes of the dead. If spirits were ever permitted to revisit the earth, this seemed the hour and the place most suitable for their appearance. La Motte remaining silent, Adeline said, "Were I inclined to superstition"—she was interrupted by a return of the noise which had been lately heard. It sounded down the passage at whose entrance they stood, and sunk gradually away. Every heart palpitated, and they remained listening in silence. A new subject of apprehension seized La Motte:—the noise might proceed from banditti, and he hesitated whether it would be safe to proceed. Peter now came with the light. Madame refused to enter the passage—

La Motte was not much inclined to it; but Peter, in whom curiosity was more prevalent than fear, readily offered his services. La Motte, after some hesitation, suffered him to go, while he awaited at the entrance the result of the inquiry. The extent of the passage soon concealed Peter from view, and the echoes of his footsteps were lost in a sound which rushed along the avenue and became fainter and fainter till it sunk into silence. La Motte now called aloud to Peter, but no answer was returned; at length, they heard the sound of a distant footstep, and Peter soon after appeared, breathless, and pale with fear.

When he came within hearing of La Motte, he called out, "An please your honour, I've done for them, I believe, but I've had a hard bout. I thought I was fighting with the devil."—"What are you speaking of?" said La Motte.

"They were nothing but owls and rooks after all," continued Peter; "but the light brought them all about my ears, and they made such a confounded clapping with their wings that I thought at first I had been beset with a legion of devils. But I have driven them all out, master, and you have nothing to fear now."

The latter part of the sentence, intimating a suspicion of his courage, La Motte could have dispensed with, and to retrieve in some degree his reputation, he made a point of proceeding through the passage. They now moved on with alacrity, for, as Peter said, they had nothing to fear.

The passage led into a large area, on one side of which, over a range of cloisters, appeared the west tower, and a lofty part of the edifice; the other side was open to the woods. La Motte led the way to a door of the tower, which he now perceived was the same he had formerly entered; but he found some difficulty in advancing, for the area was overgrown with brambles and nettles, and the light which Peter carried afforded only an uncertain gleam. When he unclosed the door, the dismal aspect of the place revived the apprehensions of Madame La Motte, and extorted from Adeline an inquiry whither they were going. Peter held up the light to shew the narrow staircase that wound round the tower; but La Motte, observing the second door, drew back the rusty bolts, and entered a spacious apartment which from its style and condition was evidently of a much later date that the other part of the structure. Though desolate and forlorn, it was very little impaired by time; the walls were damp, but not decayed; and the glass was yet firm in the windows.

They passed on to a suite of apartments resembling the first they had seen, and expressed their surprise at the incongruous appearance of this part of the edifice with the mouldering walls they had left behind. These apartments conducted them to a winding passage, that received light and air through narrow cavities placed high in the wall, and was at length closed by a door barred with iron, which being with some difficulty opened, they entered a vaulted room. La Motte surveyed it with a scrutinizing eye, and endeavoured to conjecture for what purpose it had been guarded by a door of such strength; but he saw little within to assist his curiosity. The room appeared to have been built in modern times upon a Gothic plan. Adeline approached a large window that formed a kind of recess raised by one step over the level of the floor. She observed to La Motte that the whole floor was inlaid with Mosaic work, which drew from him a remark that the style of this apartment was not strictly Gothic. He passed on to a door which appeared on the opposite side of the apartment, and unlocking it, found himself in the great hall by which he had entered the fabric.

He now perceived, what the gloom had before concealed, a spiral staircase which led to a gallery above, and which from its present condition seemed to have been built with the more modern part of the fabric, though this also affected the Gothic mode of architecture. La Motte had little doubt that these stairs led to apartments corresponding with those he had passed below, and hesitated whether to explore them; but the entrances of Madame, who was much fatigued, prevailed with him to defer all farther examination. After some deliberation in which of the rooms they should pass the night, they determined to return to that which opened from the tower.

* * * * * * * * * * * * * * * *

[*In the chambers adjoining hers, Adeline finds an old manuscript.*]

CHAPTER IX.

The MS. found by Adeline the preceding night had several times occurred to her recollection in the course of the day, but she had then been either too much interested by the events of the moment, or too apprehensive of interruption, to attempt a perusal of it. She now took it from the drawer in which it had been deposited, and intending only to look cursorily over the first few pages, sat down with it by her bedside.

She opened it with an eagerness of inquiry which the discoloured and almost obliterated ink but slowly gratified. The first words on the page were entirely lost, but those that appeared to commence the narrative were as follows.

"O! ye, whoever ye are, whom chance or misfortune may hereafter conduct to this spot—to you I speak— to you reveal the story of my wrongs, and ask you to avenge them. Vain hope! yet it imparts some comfort to believe it possible that what I now write may one day meet the eye of a fellow-creature, that the words which tell my sufferings may one day draw pity from the feeling heart.

"Yet stay your tears—your pity now is useless. Long since have the pangs of misery ceased; the voice of complaining is passed away. It is weakness to wish for compassion which cannot be felt till I shall sink in the repose of death, and taste, I hope, the happiness of eternity!

"Know, then, that on the night of the twelfth of October, in the year 1642, I was arrested on the road to Caux, and on the very spot where a column is erected to the memory of the immortal Henry, by four ruffians who, after disabling my servant, bore me through wilds and woods to this abbey. Their demeanour was not that of common banditti, and I soon perceived they were employed by a superior power to perpetrate some dreadful purpose. Entreaties and bribes were vainly offered them to discover their employer and abandon their design. They would not reveal even the least circumstance of their intentions.

"But when after a long journey they arrived at this edifice, their base employer was at once revealed, and his horrid scheme but too well understood. What a moment was that! All the thunders of heaven seemed launched at this defenceless head! O! fortitude! nerve my heart to——

*   *   *   *   *   *   *   *   *   *   *   *   *   *   *

"The ruffians unbound me from my horse and led me through the hall up the spiral staircase of the abbey. Resistance was useless, but I looked around in the hope of seeing some person less obdurate than the men who brought me hither, some one who might be sensible to pity and capable at least of civil treatment. I looked in vain; no person appeared, and this circumstance confirmed my worst apprehensions. The secrecy of the business foretold a horrible conclusion. Having passed some chambers, they stopped in one hung with old tapestry. I inquired why we did not go on, and was told I should soon know.

"At that moment I expected to see the instrument of death uplifted and silently recommended myself to God. But death was not then designed for me; they raised the arras and discovered a door, which they then opened. Seizing my arms, they led me through a suite of dismal chambers beyond. Having reached the farthest of these, they again stopped. The horrid gloom of the place seemed congenial to murder, and inspired deadly thoughts. Again I looked round for the instrument of destruction, and again I was respited. I supplicated to know what was designed me. It was now unnecessary to ask who was the author of the design. They were silent to my question, but at length told me this chamber was my prison. Having said this and set down a jug of water, they left the room, and I heard the door barred upon me.

"O sound of despair! O moment of unutterable anguish! The pang of death itself is surely not superior to that I then suffered. Shut out from day, from friends, from life—*for such I must foretell it*—in the prime of my years, in the height of my transgressions, and left to imagine horrors more terrible than any, perhaps, which certainty could give—I sink beneath the——"

Here several pages of the manuscript were decayed with damp and totally illegible. With much difficulty Adeline made out the following lines:

"Three days have now passed in solitude and silence: the horrors of death are ever before my eyes, let me endeavour to prepare for the dreadful change! When I awake in the morning I think I shall not live to see another night; and when night returns, that I must never more unclose my eyes on morning. Why am I brought hither—why confined thus rigorously—but for death! Yet what action of my life has deserved this at the hand of a fellow creature?—Of———"

* * *

"O my children! O friends far distant! I shall never see you more—never more receive the parting look of kindness—never bestow a parting blessing! Ye know not my wretched state—alas! ye cannot know it by human means. Ye believe me happy, or ye would fly to my relief. I know that what I now write cannot avail me, yet there is comfort in pouring forth my griefs; and I bless that man, less savage than his fellows, who has supplied me these means of recording them. Alas! he knows full well that from this indulgence he has nothing to fear. My pen can call no friends to succour me, nor reveal my danger ere it is too late. O! ye who may hereafter read what I now write, give a tear to my sufferings; I have wept often for the distresses of my fellow creatures!"

Adeline paused. Here the wretched writer appealed directly to her heart; he spoke in the energy of truth, and by a strong illusion of fancy it seemed as if his past sufferings were at this moment present. She was for some time unable to proceed, and sat in musing sorrow. "In these very apartments," said she, "this poor sufferer was confined—here he"—Adeline started, and thought she heard a sound, but the stillness of the night was undisturbed.—"In these very chambers," said she, "these lines were written—these lines, from which he then derived a comfort in believing they would hereafter be read by some pitying eye. This time is now come. Your miseries, O injured being! are lamented, where they were endured. *Here,* where you suffered, I weep for your sufferings!"

Her imagination was now strongly impressed, and to her distempered senses the suggestion of a bewildered mind appeared with the force of reality. Again she started and listened, and thought she heard *Here* distinctly repeated by a whisper immediately behind her. The terror of the thought, however, was but momentary; she knew it could not be. Convinced that her fancy had deceived her, she took up the MS. and again began to read.

"For what am I reserved! Why this delay? If I am to die—why not quickly? Three weeks have I now passed within these walls, during which time no look of pity has softened my afflictions; no voice save my own has met my ear. The countenances of the ruffians who attend me are stern and inflexible, and their silence is obstinate. This stillness is dreadful! O! ye who have known what it is to live in the depths of solitude, who have passed your dreary days without one sound to cheer you, ye, and ye only, can tell what now I feel; and ye may know how much I would endure to hear the accents of a human voice.

"O dire extremity! O state of living death! What dreadful stillness! All around me is dead; and do I really exist, or am I but a statue? Is this a vision? Are these things real? Alas, I am bewildered!—this death-like and perpetual silence, this dismal chamber, the dread of farther sufferings, have disturbed my fancy. O for some friendly breast to lay my weary head on! some cordial accents to revive my soul!

● ● ●

"I write by stealth. He who furnished me with the means, I fear, has suffered for some symptoms of pity he may have discovered for me; I have not seen him for several days. Perhaps he is inclined to help me, and for that reason is forbid to come. O that hope! but how vain. Never more must I quit these walls while life remains. Another day is gone, and yet I live; at this time tomorrow night my sufferings may be sealed in death. I will continue my journal nightly, till the hand that writes shall be stopped by death. When the journal ceases, the reader will know I am no more. Perhaps these are the last lines I shall ever write."

● ● ●

CHAPTER X.

"Again I return to this poor consolation—again I have been permitted to see another day. It is now midnight! My solitary lamp burns beside me; the time is awful, but to me the silence of noon is as the silence of midnight: a deeper gloom is all in which they differ. The still, unvarying hours are numbered only by my sufferings! Great God! when shall I be released!

● ● ●

"But whence this strange confinement? I have never injured him. If death is designed me, why this delay; and for what but death am I brought hither? This abbey—alas!"—Here the MS. was again illegible, and for several pages Adeline could only make out disjointed sentences.

"O bitter draught! When, when shall I have rest! O my friends! will none of ye fly to aid me; will none of ye avenge my sufferings? Ah! when it is too late—when I am gone for ever, ye will endeavour to avenge them.

"Once more is night returned to me. Another day has passed in solitude and misery. I have climbed to the casement, thinking the view of nature would refresh my soul, and somewhat enable me to support these afflictions. Alas! even this small comfort is denied me; the windows open towards other parts of this abbey, and admit only a portion of that day which I must never more fully behold. Last night! last night! O scene of horror!"

Adeline shuddered. She feared to read the coming sentence, yet curiosity prompted her to proceed. Still she paused: an unaccountable dread came over her. "Some horrid deed has been done here," said she; "the reports of the peasants are true. Murder has been committed." The idea thrilled her with horror. She recollected the dagger which had impeded her steps in the secret chamber, and this circumstance served to confirm her most terrible conjectures. She wished to examine it, but it lay in one of these chambers, and she feared to go in quest of it.

"Wretched, wretched victim!" she exclaimed, "could no friend rescue thee from destruction! O that I had been near! yet what could I have done to save thee? Alas! nothing. I forget that even now, perhaps, I am like thee abandoned to dangers from which I have no friend to succour me. Too surely I guess the author of thy miseries!" She stopped, and thought she heard a sigh such as on the preceeding night had passed along the chamber. Her blood was chilled, and she sat motionless. The lonely situation of her room, remote from the rest of the family, (for she was now in her old apartment, from which Madame La Motte had removed) who were almost beyond call, struck so forcibly upon her imagination that she with difficulty preserved herself from fainting. She sat for a considerable time, but all was still. When she was somewhat recovered, her first design was to alarm the family; but farther reflection again withheld her.

She endeavoured to compose her spirits, and addressed a short prayer to that Being who had hitherto protected her in every danger. While she was thus employed, her mind gradually became elevated and reassured; a sublime complacency filled her heart, and she sat down once more to pursue the narrative.

Several lines that immediately followed were obliterated.—

• • •

"He had told me I should not be permitted to live
long, not more than three days, and bade me choose
whether I would die by poison or by the sword. O the
agonies of that moment! Great God! thou seest my
sufferings! I often viewed, with a momentary hope of
escaping, the high grated windows of my prison—all
things within the compass of possibility I was resolved
to try, and with an eager desperation I climbed towards
the casements, but my foot slipped, and falling back
to the floor, I was stunned by the blow. On recovering,
the first sounds I heard were the steps of a person entering my prison. A recollection of the past returned, and
deplorable was my condition. I shuddered at what was
to come. The same man approached; he looked at me at
first with pity; but his countenance soon recovered its
natural ferocity. Yet he did not then come to execute the
purposes of his employer. I am reserved to another day
—Great God, thy will be done!"

from

The Pit and the Pendulum

by Edgar Allan Poe

Impia tortorum longas, hic turbas furores
Sanguinis innocui, non satiata, aluit.
Sospite nunc patria, fracto nuc funeris antro,
Mors ubi dira fuit vita salusque patent.
  Quatrain composed for the gates of a market to be
  erected upon the site of the Jacobin Club House at Paris.

I was sick—sick unto death with that long agony; and
when they at length unbound me, and I was permitted to
sit, I felt that my senses were leaving me. The sentence
—the dread sentence of death—was the last of distinct
accentuation which reached my ears. After that the sound
of the inquisitorial voices seemed merged in one dreamy
indeterminate hum. It conveyed to my soul the idea of
revolution—perhaps from its association in fancy with
the burr of a millwheel. This only for a brief period, for
presently I heard no more. Yet, for a while, I saw—but
with how terrible an exaggeration! I saw the lips of the
black-robed judges. They appeared to me white—whiter
than the sheet upon which I trace these words—and thin
even to grotesqueness; thin with the intensity of their

expression of firmness—of immovable resolution—of
stern contempt of human torture. I saw that the decrees
of what to me was Fate were still issuing from those lips.
I saw them writhe with a deadly locution. I saw them
fashion the syllables of my name; and I shuddered because no sound succeeded. I saw, too, for a few moments
of delirious horror, the soft and nearly imperceptible
waving of the sable draperies which enwrapped the walls
of the apartment. And then my vision fell upon the seven
tall candles upon the table. At first they wore the aspect
of charity, and seemed white slender angels who would
save me; but then, all at once, there came a most deadly
nausea over my spirit, and I felt every fiber in my frame
thrill as if I had touched the wire of a galvanic battery,
while the angel forms became meaningless specters, with
heads of flame, and I saw that from them there would
be no help. And then there stole into my fancy, like
a rich musical note, the thought of what sweet rest there
must be in the grave. The thought came gently and
stealthily, and it seemed long before it attained full
appreciation; but just as my spirit came at length properly
to feel and entertain it, the figures of the judges vanished,
as if magically, from before me; the tall candles sank
into nothingness; their flames went out utterly; the
blackness of darkness supervened; all sensations appeared swallowed up in a mad rushing descent as of the
soul into Hades. Then silence, and stillness, and night
were the universe.

I had swooned; but still will not say that all of consciousness was lost. What of it remained I will not attempt to define, or even to describe; yet all was not lost.
In the deepest slumber—no! In delirium—no! In a
swoon—no! In death—no! even in the grave all *is not*
lost. Else there is no immortality for man. Arousing from
the most profound of slumbers, we break the gossamer
web of *some* dream. Yet in a second afterward (so frail
may that web have been) we remember not that we have

dreamed. In the return to life from the swoon there are two stages; first, that of the sense of mental or spiritual; secondly, that of the sense of physical, existence. It seems probable that if, upon reaching the second stage, we could recall the impressions of the first, we should find these impressions eloquent in memories of the gulf beyond. And that gulf is—what? How at least shall we distinguish its shadows from those of the tomb? But if the impressions of what I have termed the first stage, are not at will, recalled, yet, after long interval, do they not come unbidden, while we marvel whence they come? He who has never swooned, is not he who finds strange palaces and wildly familiar faces in coals that glow; is not he who beholds floating in mid-air the sad visions that the many may not view; it not he who ponders over the perfume of some novel flower; is not he whose brain grows bewildered with the meaning of some musical cadence which has never before arrested his attention.

Amid frequent and thoughtful endeavors to remember, amid earnest struggles to regather some token of the state of seeming nothingness into which my soul had lapsed, there have been moments when I have dreamed of success; there have been brief, very brief periods when I conjured up remembrances which the lucid reason of a later epoch assures me could have had reference only to that condition of seeming unconsciousness. These shadows of memory tell, indistinctly, of tall figures that lifted and bore me in silence down—down—still down —till a hideous dizziness oppressed me at the mere idea of the interminableness of the descent. They tell also of a vague horror at my heart, on account of that heart's unnatural stillness. Then comes a sense of sudden motionlessness throughout all things; as if those who bore me (a ghastly train!) had outrun, in their descent, the limits of the limitless, and paused from the wearisomeness of their toil. After this I call to mind flatness and dampness; and then all is *madness*—the madness of a memory which busies itself among forbidden things.

Very suddenly there came back to my soul motion and sound—the tumultuous motion of my heart, and, in my ears, the sound of its beating. Then a pause in which all is blank. Then again sound, and motion, and touch—a tingling sensation pervading my frame. Then the mere consciousness of existence, without thought, a condition which lasted long. Then very suddenly, *thought,* and shuddering terror, and earnest endeavor to comprehend my true state. Then a strong desire to lapse into insensibility. Then a rushing revival of soul and successful effort to move. And now a full memory of the trial, of the judges, of the sable draperies, of the sentence, of the sickness, of the swoon. Then entire forgetfulness of all that followed; of all that a later day and much earnestness of endeavor have enabled me vaguely to recall.

So far, I had not opened my eyes. I felt that I lay upon my back, unbound. I reached out my hand, and it fell heavily upon something damp and hard. There I suffered it to remain for many minutes, while I strove to imagine where and *what* I could be. I longed, yet dared not, to employ my vision. I dreaded the first glance at objects around me. It was not that I feared to look upon things horrible, but that I grew aghast lest there should be *nothing* to see. At length, with a wild desperation at heart, I quickly unclosed my eyes. My worst thoughts, then, were confirmed. The blackness of eternal night encompassed me. I struggled for breath. The intensity of the darkness seemed to oppress and stifle me. The atmosphere was intolerably close. I still lay quietly, and made effort to exercise my reason. I brought to mind the inquisitorial proceedings, and attempted from that point to deduce my real condition. The sentence had passed; and it appeared to me that a very long interval of time had since elapsed. Yet not for a moment did I suppose myself actually dead. Such a supposition, notwithstanding what we read in fiction, is altogether inconsistent with real existence;—but where and in what state was I? The condemned to death, I knew, perished usually at the *auto-da-fès*, and one of these had been held on the very night of the day of my trial. Had I been remanded to my dungeon, to await the next sacrifice, which would not take place for many months? This I at once saw could not be. Victims had been in immediate demand. Moreover, my dungeon, as well as all the condemned cells at Toledo, had stone floors, and light was not altogether excluded.

A fearful idea now suddenly drove the blood in torrents upon my heart, and for a brief period I once more relapsed into insensibility. Upon recovering, I at once started to my feet, trembling convulsively in every fiber. I thrust my arms wildly above and around me in all directions. I felt nothing; yet dreaded to move a step, lest I should be impeded by the walls of a *tomb*. Perspiration burst from every pore, and stood in cold big beads upon my forehead. The agony of suspense grew at length intolerable, and I cautiously moved forward, with my arms extended, and my eyes straining from their sockets in the hope of catching some faint ray of light. I proceeded for many paces; but still all was blackness and vacancy. I breathed more freely. It seemed evident that mine was not, at least, the most hideous of fates.

And now, as I still continued to step cautiously onward, there came thronging upon my recollection a thousand vague rumors of the horrors of Toledo. Of the dungeons there had been strange things narrated—fables I had always deemed them—but yet strange, and too ghastly to repeat, save in a whisper. Was I left to perish of starvation in this subterranean world of darkness; or what fate, perhaps even more fearful, awaited me? That the result would be death, and a death of more than customary bitterness, I knew too well the character of my judges to doubt. The mode and the hour were all that occupied or distracted me.

My outstretched hands at length encountered some solid obstruction. It was a wall, seemingly of stone masonry—very smooth, slimy, and cold. I followed it up; stepping with all the careful distrust with which certain antique narratives had inspired me. This process, however, afforded me no means of ascertaining the dimensions of my dungeon, as I might make its circuit and return to the point whence I set out without being aware of the fact, so perfectly uniform seemed the wall. I therefore sought the knife which had been in my pocket when led into the inquisitorial chamber; but it was gone; my clothes had been exchanged for a wrapper of coarse serge. I had thought of forcing the blade in some minute crevice of the masonry, so as to identify my point of departure. The difficulty, nevertheless, was but trivial; although, in the disorder of my fancy, it seemed at first insuperable. I tore a part of the hem from the robe and placed the fragment at full length, and at right angles to the wall. In groping my way around the prison, I could not fail to encounter this rag upon completing the circuit. So, at least, I thought; but I had not counted upon the extent of the dungeon, or upon my own weakness. The ground was moist and slippery. I staggered onward for some time, when I stumbled and fell. My excessive fatigue induced me to remain prostrate; and sleep soon overtook me as I lay.

Upon awakening, and stretching forth an arm, I found beside me a loaf and a pitcher with water. I was too much exhausted to reflect upon this circumstance, but ate and drank with avidity. Shortly afterward, I resumed my tour around the prison, and with much toil, came at last upon the fragment of the serge. Up to the period when I fell, I had counted fifty-two paces, and, upon resuming my walk, I had counted forty-eight more—when I arrived at the rag. There were in all, then, a hundred paces; and, admitting two paces to the yard, I presumed the dungeon to be fifty yards in circuit. I had met, however, with many angles in the wall, and thus I could form no guess at the shape of the vault, for vault I could not help supposing it to be.

I had little object—certainly no hope—in these researches; but a vague curiosity prompted me to continue them. Quitting the wall, I resolved to cross the area of the enclosure. At first, I proceeded with extreme caution, for the floor, although seemingly of solid material, was treacherous with slime. At length, however, I took courage, and did not hesitate to step firmly—endeavouring to cross in as direct a line as possible. I had advanced some ten or twelve paces in this manner, when the remnant of the torn hem of my robe became entangled between my legs. I stepped on it, and fell violently on my face.

In the confusion attending my fall, I did not immediately apprehend a somewhat startling circumstance, which yet, in a few seconds afterward, and while I still lay prostrate, arrested my attention. It was this: my chin rested upon the floor of the prison, but my lips, and the upper portion of my head, although seemingly at a less elevation than the chin, touched nothing. At the same time, my forehead seemed bathed in a clammy vapor, and the peculiar smell of decayed fungus arose to my nostrils. I put forward my arm, and shuddered to find that I had fallen at the very brink of a circular pit, whose extent, of course, I had no means of ascertaining at the moment. Groping about the masonry just below the margin, I succeeded in dislodging a small fragment, and let it fall into the abyss. For many seconds I harkened to its reverberations as it dashed against the sides of the chasm in its descent; at length, there was a sullen plunge into water, succeeded by loud echoes. At the same moment, there came a sound resembling the quick opening and as rapid closing of a door overhead, while a faint gleam of light flashed suddenly through the gloom, and as suddenly faded away.

I saw clearly the doom which had been prepared for me, and congratulated myself upon the timely accident by which I had escaped. Another step before my fall, and the world had seen me no more. And the death just avoided was of that very character which I had regarded as fabulous and frivolous in the tales respecting the Inquisition. To the victims of its tyranny, there was the choice of death with its direst physical agonies, or death with its most hideous moral horrors. I had been reserved for the latter. By long suffering my nerves had been unstrung, until I trembled at the sound of my own voice, and had become in every respect a fitting subject for the species of torture which awaited me.

Shaking in every limb, I groped my way back to the wall—resolving there to perish rather than risk the terrors of the wells, of which my imagination now pictured many in various positions about the dungeons. In other conditions of mind, I might have had the courage to end my misery at once, by a plunge into one of these abysses; but now I was the veriest of cowards. Neither could I forget what I had read of these pits—that the *sudden* extinction of life formed no part of their most horrible plan.

Agitation of spirit kept me awake for many long hours, but at length I again slumbered. Upon arousing, I found by my side, as before, a loaf and a pitcher of water. A burning thirst consumed me, and I emptied the vessel at a draught. It must have been drugged—for scarcely had I drunk, before I became irresistibly drowsy. A deep sleep fell upon me—a sleep like that of death. How long it lasted, of course I know not; but when, once again, I unclosed my eyes, the objects around me were visible. By a wild, sulphurous luster, the origin of which I could not at first determine, I was enabled to see the extent and aspect of the prison.

In its size I had been greatly mistaken. The whole circuit of its walls did not exceed twenty-five yards. For some minutes this fact occasioned me a world of vain trouble; vain indeed—for what could be of less importance, under the terrible circumstances which environed me, than the mere dimensions of my dungeon? But my soul took a wild interest in trifles, and I busied myself in endeavours to account for the error I had committed in my measurement. The truth at length flashed upon me. In my first attempt at exploration I had counted fifty-two paces, up to the period when I fell: I must then have been within a pace of the fragment of serge; in fact, I had nearly performed the circuit of the vault. I then slept—and upon awaking, I must have turned upon my steps—thus supposing the circuit nearly double what it actually was. My confusion of mind prevented me from observing that I began my tour with the wall to the left, and ended with the wall to the right.

I had been deceived, too, in respect to the shape of the enclosure. In feeling my way I had found many angles, and thus deduced an idea of great irregularity; so potent is the effect of total darkness upon one arousing from lethargy or sleep! The angles were simply those of a few slight depressions, or niches at odd intervals. The general shape of the prison was square. What I had taken for masonry seemed now to be iron, or some other metal, in huge plates, whose sutures or joints occasioned the depression. The entire surface of this metallic enclosure was rudely daubed in all the hideous and repulsive devices to which the charnel superstition of the monks has given rise. The figures of fiends in aspects of menace, with skeleton forms, and other more really fearful images, overspread and disfigured the walls. I observed that the outlines of these monstrosities were sufficiently distinct, but that the colors seemed faded and blurred, as if from the effects of a damp atmosphere. I now noticed the floor, too, which was of stone. In the center yawned the circular pit from whose jaws I had escaped; but it was the only one in the dungeon.

All this I saw indistinctly and by much effort—for my personal condition had been greatly changed during slumber. I now lay upon my back, and at full length, on a species of low framework of wood. To this I was securely bound by a long strap resembling a surcingle. It passed in many convolutions about my limbs and body, leaving at liberty only my head, and my left arm to such extent, that I could, by dint of much exertion, supply myself with food from an earthen dish which lay by my side on the floor. I saw, to my horror, that the pitcher had been removed. I say to my horror—for I was consumed with intolerable thirst. This thirst it appeared to be the design of my persecutors to stimulate —for the food in the dish was meat pungently seasoned.

Looking upward, I surveyed the ceiling of my prison. It was some thirty or forty feet overhead, and constructed much as the side walls. In one of its panels a very singular figure riveted my whole attention. It was the painted figure of Time as he is commonly represented, save that, in lieu of a scythe, he held what, at a casual glance, I supposed to be the pictured image of a huge pendulum, such as we see on antique clocks. There was something, however, in the appearance of this machine which caused me to regard it more attentively. While I gazed directly upward at it (for its position was immediately over my own) I fancied that I saw it in motion. In an instant afterward the fancy was confirmed. Its sweep was brief, and of course slow. I watched it for some minutes somewhat in fear, but more in wonder. Wearied at length with observing its dull movement, I turned my eyes upon the other objects in the cell.

A slight noise attracted my notice, and, looking to the floor, I saw several enormous rats traversing it. They had issued from the well which lay just within view to my right. Even then, while I gazed, they came up in troops, hurriedly, with ravenous eyes, allured by the scent of the meat. From this it required much effort and attention to scare them away.

It might have been half an hour, perhaps even an hour (for I could take but imperfect note of time), before I again cast my eyes upward. What I then saw confounded and amazed me. The sweep of the pendulum had increased in extent by nearly a yard. As a natural consequence its velocity was also much greater. But what mainly disturbed me was the idea that it had perceptibly *descended*. I now observed—with what horror it is needless to say—that its nether extremity was formed of a crescent of glittering steel, about a foot in length from horn to horn; the horns upward, and the under edge evidently as keen as that of a razor. Like a razor, also, it seemed massive and heavy, tapering from the edge into a solid and broad structure above. It was appended to a weighty rod of brass, and the whole *hissed* as it swung through the air.

I could no longer doubt the doom prepared for me by monkish ingenuity in torture. My cognizance of the pit had become known to the inquisitorial agents—*the pit,* whose horrors had been destined for so bold a recusant as myself—*the pit,* typical of hell and regarded by rumor as the Ultima Thule of all their punishments. The plunge into this pit I had avoided by the merest of accidents, and I knew that surprise, or entrapment into torment, formed an important portion of all the grotesquerie of these dungeon deaths. Having failed to fall, it was no part of the demon plan to hurl me into the abyss; and thus (there being no alternative) a different and a milder destruction awaited me. Milder! I half smiled in my agony as I thought of such application of such a term.

What boots it to tell of the long, long hours of horror more than mortal, during which I counted the rushing oscillations of the steel! Inch by inch—line by line—with a descent only appreciable at intervals that seemed ages

—down and still down it came! Days passed—it might have been that many days passed—ere it swept so closely over me as to fan me with its acrid breath. The odor of the sharp steel forced itself into my nostrils. I prayed—I wearied heaven with my prayer for its more speedy descent. I grew frantically mad, and struggled to force myself upward against the sweep of the fearful scimitar. And then I fell suddenly calm, and lay smiling at the glittering death, as a child at some rare bauble.

There was another interval of utter insensibility; it was brief; for upon again lapsing into life, there had been no perceptible descent in the pendulum. But it might have been long—for I knew there were demons who took note of my swoon, and who could have arrested the vibration at pleasure. Upon my recovery, too, I felt very—oh! inexpressibly—sick and weak, as if through long inanition. Even amid the agonies of that period the human nature craved food. With painful effort I outstretched my left arm as far as my bonds permitted, and took possession of the small remnant which had been spared me by the rats. As I put a portion of it within my lips, there rushed to my mind a half-formed thought of joy—of hope. Yet what business had *I* with hope? It was, as I say, a half-formed thought—man has many such, which are never completed. I felt that it was of joy—of hope; but I felt also that it had perished in its formation. In vain I struggled to perfect—to regain it. Long suffering had nearly annihilated all my ordinary powers of mind. I was an imbecile—an idiot.

The vibration of the pendulum was at right angles to my length. I saw that the crescent was designed to cross the region of the heart. It would fray the serge of my robe —it would return and repeat its operations—again—and again. Notwithstanding its terrifically wide sweep (some thirty feet or more), and the hissing vigor of its descent, sufficient to sunder these very walls of iron, still the fraying of my robe would be all that, for several minutes, it would accomplish. And at this thought I paused. I dared not go further than this reflection. I dwelt upon it with a pertinacity of attention—as if, in so dwelling, I could arrest *here* the descent of the steel. I forced myself to ponder upon the sound of the crescent as it should pass across the garment—upon the peculiar thrilling sensation which the friction of cloth produces on the nerves. I pondered over all this frivolity until my teeth were on edge.

Down—steadily down it crept. I took a frenzied pleasure in contrasting its downward with its lateral velocity. To the right—to the left—far and wide—with the shriek of a dammed spirit! to my heart, with the stealthy pace of the tiger! I alternately laughed and howled, as the one or the other idea grew predominant.

Down—certainly, relentlessly down! It vibrated within three inches of my bosom! I struggled violently—furiously —to free my left arm. This was free only from the elbow to the hand. I could reach the latter, from the platter beside me, to my mouth, with great effort, but no farther. Could I have broken the fastening above the elbow, I would have seized and attempted to arrest the pendulum. I might as well have attempted to arrest an avalanche!

Down—still unceasingly—still inevitably down! I gasped and struggled at each vibration. I shrunk convulsively at its every sweep. My eyes followed its outward or upward whirls with the eagerness of the most unmeaning despair; they closed themselves spasmodically at the descent, although death would have been a relief, oh, how unspeakable! Still I quivered in every nerve to think how slight a sinking of the machinery would precipitate that keen, glistening axe upon my bosom. It was *hope* that prompted the nerve to quiver—the frame to shrink. It was *hope*—the hope that triumphs on the rack—that whispers to the death-condemned even in the dungeons of the Inquisition.

I saw that some ten or twelve vibrations would bring

the steel in actual contact with my robe—and with this observation there suddenly came over my spirit all the keen, collected calmness of despair. For the first time during many hours—or perhaps days—I *thought*. It now occurred to me, that the bandage, or surcingle, which enveloped me, was *unique*. I was tied by no separate cord. The first stroke of the razorlike crescent athwart any portion of the band would so detach it that it might be unwound from my person by means of my left hand. But how fearful, in that case, the proximity of the steel! The result of the slightest struggle, how deadly! Was it likely, moreover, that the minions of the torturer had not foreseen and provided for this possibility? Was it probable that the bandage crossed my bosom in the track of the pendulum? Dreading to find my faint and, as it seemed, my last hope frustrated, I so far elevated my head as to obtain a distinct view of my breast. The surcingle enveloped my limbs and body close in all directions—*save in the path of the destroying crescent.*

Scarcely had I dropped my head back into its original position, when there flashed upon my mind what I cannot better describe than as the unformed half of that idea of deliverance to which I have previously alluded, and of which a moiety only floated indeterminately through my brain when I raised food to my burning lips. The whole thought was now present—feeble, scarcely sane, scarcely definite—but still entire. I proceeded at once, with the nervous energy of despair, to attempt its execution.

For many hours the immediate vicinity of the low framework upon which I lay had been literally swarming with rats. They were wild, bold, ravenous—their red eyes glaring upon me as if they waited but for motionlessness on my part to make me their prey. "To what food," I thought, "have they been accustomed in the well?"

They had devoured, in spite of all my efforts to prevent them, all but a small remnant of the contents of the dish. I had fallen into an habitual see-saw or wave of the hand about the platter; and, at length, the unconscious uniformity of the movement deprived it of effect. In their voracity, the vermin frequently fastened their sharp fangs in my fingers. With the particles of the oily and spicy viand which now remained, I thoroughly rubbed the bandage wherever I could reach it; then, raising my hand from the floor, I lay breathlessly still.

At first, the ravenous animals were startled and terrified at the change—at the cessation of movement. They shrank alarmedly back; many sought the well. But this was only for a moment. I had not counted in vain upon their voracity. Observing that I remained without motion, one or two of the boldest leaped upon the framework, and smelt at the surcingle. This seemed the signal for a general rush. Forth from the well they hurried in fresh troops. They clung to the wood—they overran it, and leaped in hundreds upon my person. The measured movement of the pendulum disturbed them not at all. Avoiding its strokes, they busied themselves with the anointed bandage. They pressed—they swarmed upon me in ever accumulating heaps. They writhed upon my throat; their cold lips sought my own; I was half stifled by their thronging pressure; disgust, for which the world has no name, swelled my bosom, and chilled, with a heavy clamminess, my heart. Yet one minute, and I felt that the struggle would be over. Plainly I perceived the loosening of the bandage. I knew that in more than one place it must be already severed. With a more than human resolution I lay *still*.

Nor had I erred in my calculations—nor had I endured in vain. I at length felt that I was *free*. The surcingle hung in ribands from my body. But the stroke of the pendulum already pressed upon my bosom. It had divided the serge of the robe. It had cut through the linen beneath. Twice again it swung, and a sharp sense of pain shot through every nerve. But the moment of escape had arrived. At a wave of my hand my deliverers hurried tumultuously away. With a steady movement—cautious, sidelong, shrinking, and slow—I slid from the embrace of the bandage and beyond the reach of the scimitar. For the moment, at least, *I was free.*

Free!—and in the grasp of the Inquisition! I had scarcely stepped from my wooden bed of horror upon the stone floor of the prison, when the motion of the hellish machine ceased, and I beheld it drawn up, by some invisible force, through the ceiling. This was a lesson which I took desperately to heart. My every motion was undoubtedly watched. Free!—I had but escaped death in one form of agony, to be delivered unto worse than death in some other. With that thought I rolled my eyes nervously around on the barriers of iron that hemmed me in. Something unusual—some change, which, at first, I could not appreciate distinctly—it was obvious, had taken place in the apartment. For many minutes of a dreamy and trembling abstraction, I busied myself in vain, unconnected conjecture. During this period, I became aware, for the first time, of the origin of the sulphurous light which illumined the cell. It proceeded from a fissure, about half an inch in width, extending around the prison at the base of the walls, which thus appeared, and were completely separated from the floor. I endeavored, but of course in vain, to look through the aperture.

As I arose from the attempt, the mystery of the alteration in the chamber broke at once upon my understanding. I have observed that, although the outlines of the figures upon the walls were sufficiently distinct, yet the colors seemed blurred and indefinite. These colors had now assumed, and were momentarily assuming, a startling and most intense brilliancy, that gave to the spectral and fiendish portraitures an aspect that might have thrilled even firmer nerves than my own. Demon eyes, of a wild and ghastly vivacity, glared upon me in a thousand directions, where none had been visible before, and gleamed with the lurid luster of a fire that I could not force my imagination to regard as unreal.

Unreal!—Even while I breathed there came to my nostrils the breath of the vapor of heated iron! A suffocating odor pervaded the prison! A deeper glow settled each moment in the eyes that glared at my agonies! A richer tint of crimson diffused itself over the pictured horrors of blood. I panted! I gasped for breath! There could be no doubt of the design of my tormentors—oh! most unrelenting! oh! most demoniac of men! I shrank from the glowing metal to the center of the cell. Amid the thought of the fiery destruction that impended, the idea of the coolness of the well came over my soul like balm. I rushed to its deadly brink. I threw my straining vision below. The glare from the enkindled roof illumined its inmost recesses. Yet, for a wild moment, did my spirit refuse to comprehend the meaning of what I saw. At length it forced—it wrestled its way into my soul—it burned itself in upon my shuddering reason. Oh, for a voice to speak!—oh! horror!—oh! any horror but this! With a shriek, I rushed from the margin, and buried my face in my hands—weeping bitterly.

The heat rapidly increased, and once again I looked up, shuddering as with a fit of the ague. There had been a second change in the cell—and now the change was obviously in the *form*. As before, it was in vain that I at first endeavored to appreciate or understand what was taking place. But not long was I left in doubt. The Inquisitorial vengeance had been hurried by my two-fold escape, and there was to be no more dallying with the King of Terrors. The room had been square. I saw that two of its iron angles were now acute—two, consequently, obtuse. The fearful difference quickly increased with a low rumbling or moaning sound. In an instant the apartment had shifted its form into that of a lozenge. But the alteration stopped not here—I neither hoped nor desired it to stop. I could have clasped the red walls to my bosom as a garment of eternal peace. "Death," I said, "any

death but that of the pit!" Fool! might I not have known
that *into the pit* it was the object of the burning iron to
urge me? Could I resist its glow? or if even that, could I
withstand its pressure? And now, flatter and flatter grew
the lozenge, with a rapidity that left me no time for
contemplation. Its center, and of course its greatest width,
came just over the yawning gulf. I shrank back—but the
closing walls pressed me resistlessly onward. At length for
my seared and writhing body there was no longer an
inch of foothold on the firm floor of the prison. I struggled
no more, but the agony of my soul found vent in one
loud, long, and final scream of despair. I felt that I tottered
upon the brink—I averted my eyes—

There was a discordant hum of human voices! There
was a loud blast as of many trumpets! There was a harsh
grating as of a thousand thunders! The fiery walls
rushed back! An outstretched arm caught my own as
I fell, fainting, into the abyss. It was that of General
Lasalle. The French army had entered Toledo. The inquisition was in the hands of its enemies.

Part Three

Supernatural Threat

The use of a supernatural agency in Gothic literature places heavy emphasis on the mysterious side of life, on all that lies beyond man's rational ability to understand and explain. The avenues are so varied that it is all but impossible to view the supernatural as a single concept, particularly as the supernatural is often explained away in terms of mental aberration or of natural phenomena improperly understood, as it is in the writings of Ann Radcliffe. Within the perimeter of the truly supernatural are the appearances and actions of ghosts, wraiths, ectoplasmic forms, and all other such nonnatural or noncorporeal beings (including manifestations of Satan and his minions), as well as curses wreaked through supernatural agencies of witchcraft and other unknown powers. However, the supernatural threat should not be confused with monsters of unnatural human origin (Melmoth, Hyde, Dracula, Wagner) nor with monsters of unknown or extraterrestrial origin (Wells's creatures from Mars and Wyndham's mobile, thinking plants), since the supernatural involves a force or forces whose origins are beyond man's comprehension and whose existence is beyond man's powers of destruction.

In "The Haunted and the Haunters," for example, there is an ancient curse on the house and its inhabitants, but there is no mundane or rational accounting for the events. The manuscript explains the reason for the curse, and the finding of the dish of mysterious fluid reveals the use of witchcraft in carrying out the curse, yet the potent fluid remains a mystery, and the actual supernatural power remains beyond man's destruction. Likewise, the origin of the disembodied hand that rises and "very softly closed on the two letters" and the footprints that suddenly appear in the garden cannot be explained. Similarly, in Hawthorne's *The House of the Seven Gables,* Maule's curse that "God will give them blood to drink!" is fulfilled in a manner beyond any possible explanation, except that it is a supernatural agent operating from beyond the grave.

A similar force beyond explanation is found in Poe's frenetic "The Fall of the House of Usher." The house of Usher (that is to say, both the edifice and the family line, or "house"), is doomed. Nothing can save it. But the doom, Roderick Usher believes, is the disruptive power of the old mansion itself and the waters of the still, black tarn beside it. No further explanation is possible. The same is true of Dicken's "The Signal-Man," although a quite different approach to the supernatural is found in it. Again, as in the other stories in this category, there is no rational explanation for the appearance of the ghost which warns of the railroad man's inescapable doom. The ghost, unallied with any other agency, is truly a supernatural phenomenon.

The difference between the "supernatural" of this section and the "unknown" of the final section is one fundamentally related to man's possible degree of control. Man may not be able to explain the supernatural or destroy it, but he can often, as in the case of witchcraft, control it or manipulate it to some degree. No such manipulation is possible with the unknown. One most readily sees this with reference to specific stories. In both "The Haunted and the Haunters" and *The House of the Seven Gables,* the supernatural has been called upon to wreak vengeance on the inhabitants of a house or the members of a family for generations to come. Man's intervention is required to implement the curse and, as in *The Castle of Otranto,* the supernatural becomes an agent of retribution. In "The Willows" and "The Horla," on the contrary, the unknown agency acts apparently of its own volition, without the intervention of man, and, in most cases, it acts in direct opposition to his wishes.

Other considerations emerge as corollaries of control. One is the idea of "containment." In both "The Haunted and the Haunters" and *The House of the Seven Gables,* there is a limit to the operation of the supernatural force. It is possible for the members of the Pyncheon family to remove Maule's curse; it is possible in "The Haunted and the Haunters," through discovery of the witchcraft mechanism, to remove the curse on the house and its inhabitants. Once this is done, the supernatural forces involved cease to operate in these spheres. The same is true in Poe's "The Fall of the House of Usher"; once the house, and this includes the use of the term "house" to mean the family as well, has come to destruction, the operating force passes from the scene; it does not move on to destroy another "house." In "The Willows" and "The Horla," on the other hand, potential victims may escape the threat, but the threat continues in pursuit of new victims.

This latter type of threat, therefore, includes a further consideration—that of hostility. It conveys a sense of destruction and malignancy which the supernatural does not necessarily contain. In this sense, it represents one of the earliest, one might almost say primordial, meanings of "Gothic"—wanton destruction. The supernatural, on the contrary, may be either malignant or beneficent or a combination of both.

from

The Haunted and the Haunters;
or,
The House and the Brain

by E. Bulwer-Lytton

A friend of mine, who is a man of letters and a philosopher, said to me one day, as if between jest and earnest, "Fancy! since we last met I have discovered a haunted house in the midst of London."

"Really haunted? and by what—ghosts?"

"Well, I can't answer these questions; all I know is this: six weeks ago I and my wife were in search of a furnished apartment. Passing a quiet street, we saw on the window of one of the houses a bill, 'Apartments Furnished.' The situation suited us; we entered the house, liked the rooms, engaged them by the week, and left them the third day. No power on earth could have reconciled my wife to stay longer; and I don't wonder at it."

"What did you see?"

"Excuse me; I have no desire to be ridiculed as a superstitious dreamer, nor, on the other hand, could I ask you to accept on my affirmation what you would hold to be incredible, without the evidence of your own

169

senses. Let me only say this: it was not so much what we saw or heard (in which you might fairly suppose that we were the dupes of our own excited fancy, or the victims of imposture in others) that drove us away, as it was an undefinable terror which seized both of us whenever we passed by the door of a certain unfurnished room, in which we neither saw nor heard anything; and the strangest marvel of all was that for once in my life I agreed with my wife, silly woman though she be, and allowed after the third night it was impossible to stay a fourth in that house.

"Accordingly, on the fourth morning I summoned the woman who kept the house and attended on us, and told her that the rooms did not quite suit us, and we would not stay out our week. She said dryly:

" 'I know why; you have stayed longer than any other lodger. Few ever stayed a second night; none before you a third. But I take it that they have been very kind to you.'

" 'They who?' I asked, affecting a smile.

" 'Why, they who haunt the house, whoever they are; I don't mind them; I remember them many years ago, when I lived in this house not as a servant; but I know they will be the death of me some day. I don't care—I'm old and must die soon anyhow; and then I shall be with them, and in this house still.'

"The woman spoke with so dreary a calmness that really it was a sort of awe that prevented my conversing with her further. I paid for my week, and too happy were I and my wife to get off so cheaply."

"You excite my curiosity," said I; "nothing I should like better than to sleep in a haunted house. Pray give me the address of the one which you left so ignominiously."

My friend gave me the address; and when we parted I walked straight toward the house thus indicated.

It is situated on the north side of Oxford street, in a dull but respectable thoroughfare. I found the house shut up; no bill on the window, and no response to my knock. As I was turning away, a beer-boy, collecting pewter pots at the neighboring areas, said to me, "Do you want any one at that house, sir?

"Yes; I heard it was to be let."

"Let! Why, the woman who kept it is dead; has been dead these three weeks; and no one can be found to stay there, though Mr. J—— offered ever so much. He offered mother, who chars for him, one pound a week just to open and shut the windows, and she would not."

"Would not! and why?"

"The house is haunted; and the old woman who kept it was found dead in her bed with her eyes wide open. They say the devil strangled her."

"Pooh! You speak of Mr. J——. Is he the owner of the house?"

"Yes."

"Where does he live?"

"In G—— Street, No.——."

"What is he—in any business?"

"No, sir, nothing particular; a single gentleman."

I gave the pot-boy the gratuity earned by his liberal information, and proceeded to Mr. J—— in G—— Street, which was close by the street that boasted the haunted house. I was lucky enough to find Mr. J—— at home; an elderly man with intelligent countenance and prepossessing manners.

I communicated my name and my business frankly. I said I heard the house was considered to be haunted; that I had a strong desire to examine a house with so equivocal a reputation; that I should be greatly obliged if he would allow me to hire it, though only for a night. I was willing to pay for that privilege whatever he might be inclined to ask.

"Sir," said Mr. J——, with great courtesy, "the house is at your service for as short or as long a time as you please. Rent is out of the question; the obligation will be on my side, should you be able to discover the cause of the strange phenomena which at present deprive it of all value. I cannot let it, for I cannot even get a servant to keep it in order or answer the door.

"Unluckily, the house is haunted, if I may use that expression, not only by night but by day; though at night the disturbances are of a more unpleasant and sometimes of a more alarming character. The poor old woman who died in it three weeks ago was a pauper whom I took out of a workhouse; for in her childhood she had been known to some of my family, and had once been in such good circumstances that she had rented that house of my uncle. She was a woman of superior education and strong mind, and was the only person I could ever induce to remain in the house. Indeed, since her death, which was sudden, and the coroner's inquest, which gave it a notoriety in the neighborhood, I have so despaired of finding any person to take charge of it, much more a tenant, that I would most willingly let it rent free for a year to any one who would pay its rates and taxes."

"How long ago did the house acquire this character?"

"That I can scarcely tell you, but many years since; the old woman I spoke of said it was haunted when she rented it, between thirty and forty years ago. The fact is that my life has been spent in the East Indies, and in the civil service of the East India Company.

"I returned to England last year, on inheriting the fortune of an uncle, among whose possessions was the house in question. I found it shut up and uninhabited. I was told that it was haunted, and no one would inhabit it. I smiled at what seemed to me so idle a story.

"I spent some money in repainting and roofing it, added to its old-fashioned furniture a few modern articles, advertised it, and obtained a lodger for a year. He was a colonel retired on half pay. He came in with his family, a son and a daughter, and four or five servants; they all left the house the next day; and although they deponed that they had all seen something different, that something was equally terrible to all. I really could not in conscience sue, or even blame, the colonel for breach of agreement.

"Then I put in the old woman I have spoken of, and she was empowered to let the house in apartments. I never had one lodger who stayed more than three days. I do not tell you their stories; to no two lodgers have exactly the same phenomena been repeated. It is better that you should judge for yourself than enter the house with an imagination influenced by previous narratives; only be prepared to see and to hear something or other, and take whatever precautions you yourself please."

"Have you never had a curiosity yourself to pass a night in that house?"

"Yes; I passed, not a night, but three hours in broad daylight alone in that house. My curiosity is not satisfied, but it is quenched. I have no desire to renew the experiment. You cannot complain, you see, sir, that I am not sufficiently candid; and unless your interest be exceedingly eager and your nerves unusually strong, I honestly add that I advise you *not* to pass a night in that house."

"My interest *is* exceedingly keen," said I; "and though only a coward will boast of his nerves in situations wholly unfamiliar to him, yet my nerves have been seasoned in such variety of danger that I have the right to rely on them, even in a haunted house."

Mr. J—— said very little more; he took the keys of the house out of his bureau, and gave them to me; and, thanking him cordially for his frankness and his urbane concession to my wish, I carried off my prize.

Impatient for the experiment, as soon as I reached home I summoned my confidential servant—a young man of gay spirits, fearless temper, and as free from superstitious prejudice as any one I could think of.

"F——," said I, "you remember in Germany how disappointed we were at not finding a ghost in that old castle which was said to be haunted by a headless apparition? Well, I have heard of a house in London which, I have reason to hope, is decidedly haunted. I mean to sleep there to-night. From what I hear, there is no doubt that something will allow itself to be seen or to be heard—something perhaps excessively horrible. Do you think, if I take you with me, I may rely on your presence of mind, whatever may happen?"

"Oh, sir; pray trust me!" said he, grinning with delight.

"Very well, then, here are the keys of the house; this is the address. Go now, select for me any bedroom you please; and since the house has not been inhabited for weeks, make up a good fire, air the bed well; see, of course, that there are candles as well as fuel. Take with you my revolver and my dagger—so much for my weapons —arm yourself equally well; and if we are not a match for a dozen ghosts, we shall be but a sorry couple of Englishmen."

I was engaged for the rest of the day on business so urgent that I had not leisure to think much on the nocturnal adventure to which I had plighted my honor. I dined alone and very late, and while dining read, as is my habit. The volume I selected was one of Macaulay's essays. I thought to myself that I would take the book with me; there was so much of healthfulness in the style, and practical life in the subjects, that it would serve as an antidote against the influence of superstitious fancy.

Accordingly, about half-past nine I put the book into my pocket and strolled leisurely toward the haunted house. I took with me a favorite dog—an exceedingly sharp, bold, and vigilant bull-terrier, a dog fond of prowling about strange ghostly corners and passages at night in search of rats, a dog of dogs for a ghost.

It was a summer night, but chilly, the sky somewhat gloomy and overcast; still there was a moon—faint and sickly, but still a moon—and if the clouds permitted, after midnight it would be brighter.

I reached the house, knocked, and my servant opened with a cheerful smile.

"All right, sir, and very comfortable."

"Oh!" said I, rather disappointed; "have you not seen nor heard anything remarkable?"

"Well, sir, I must own that I have heard something queer."

"What?—what?"

"The sound of feet pattering behind me; and once or twice small noises like whispers close at my ear; nothing more."

"You are not at all frightened?"

"I! Not a bit of it, sir!"

And the man's bold look reassured me on one point, namely, that, happen what might, he would not desert me.

We were in the hall, the street-door closed, and my attention was now drawn to my dog. He had first run in eagerly enough, but had sneaked back to the door, and was scratching and whining to get out. After I had patted him on the head and encouraged him gently, the dog seemed to reconcile himself to the situation, and followed me and F—— through the house, but keeping close at my heels, instead of hurrying inquisitively in advance, which was his usual and normal habit in all strange places.

We first visited the subterranean apartments, the kitchen and other offices, and especially the cellars, in which last were two or three bottles of wine still left in a bin, covered with cobwebs, and evidently, by their appearance, undisturbed for many years. It was clear that the ghosts were not wine-bibbers.

For the rest, we discovered nothing of interest. There was a gloomy little back-yard, with very high walls. The stones of this yard were very damp; and what with the damp and what with the dust and smoke-grime on the pavement, our feet left a slight impression where we passed.

And now appeared the first strange phenomenon witnessed by myself in this strange abode.

I saw, just before me, the print of a foot suddenly form itself, as it were. I stopped, caught hold of my servant, and pointed to it. In advance of that footprint as suddenly dropped another. We both saw it. I advanced quickly to the place; the footprint kept advancing before me; a small footprint—the foot of a child; the impression was too faint thoroughly to distinguish the shape, but it seemed to us both that it was the print of a naked foot.

This phenomenon ceased when we arrived at the opposite wall, nor did it repeat itself when we returned. We remounted the stairs and entered the rooms on the ground floor—a dining-parlor, a small back-parlor, and a still smaller third room that had probably been appropriated to a footman—all still as death.

We then visited the drawing-rooms which seemed fresh and new. In the front room I seated myself in an armchair. F—— placed on the table the candlestick with which he had lighted us. I told him to shut the door. As he turned to do so, a chair opposite to me moved from the wall quickly and noiselessly, and dropped itself about a yard from my own chair, immediately fronting it.

"Why, this is better than the turning-tables," said I laughing; and as I laughed, my dog put back his head and howled.

F——, coming back, had not observed the movement of the chair. He employed himself now in stilling the dog. I continued to gaze on the chair, and fancied I saw on it a pale, blue, misty outline of a human figure; but an outline so indistinct that I could only distrust my own vision. The dog was now quiet.

"Put back the chair opposite to me," said I to F——; "put it back to the wall."

F—— obeyed.

"Was that you, sir?" said he, turning abruptly.

"I—what?"

"Why, something struck me. I felt it sharply on the shoulder, just here."

"No," said I; "but we have jugglers present, and though we may not discover their tricks, we shall catch *them* before they frighten *us*."

We did not stay long in the drawing-rooms; in fact, they felt so damp and so chilly that I was glad to get to the fire up-stairs. We locked the doors of the drawing-rooms—a precaution which, I should observe, we had taken with all the rooms we had searched below.

The bedroom my servant had selected for me was the best on the floor; a large one, with two windows fronting the street. The four-posted bedstead, which took up no inconsiderable space, was opposite to the fire, which burned clear and bright; a door in the wall to the left, between the bed and the window, communicated with the room which my servant appropriated to himself. This last was a small room with a sofa-bed, and had no communication with the landing-place; no other door but that which conducted to the bedroom I was to occupy.

On either side of my fireplace was a cupboard; without locks, flush with the wall, and covered with the same dull-brown paper. We examined these cupboards; only hooks to suspend female dresses—nothing else. We sounded the walls; evidently solid—the outer walls of the building.

Having finished the survey of these apartments, warmed myself a few moments, and lighted my cigar, I then, still accompanied by F——, went forth to complete my reconnoiter. In the landing-place there was another door; it was closed firmly.

"Sir," said my servant in surprise, "I unlocked this door with all the others when I first came in; it cannot have got locked from the inside, for it is a——"

Before he had finished his sentence, the door, which neither of us was then touching, opened quietly of itself. We looked at each other a single instant. The same thought seized both: some human agency might be detected here. I rushed in first, my servant followed. A small, black, dreary room without furniture, a few empty boxes and hampers in a corner, a small window, the shutters closed —not even a fire-place—no other door but that by which we had entered, no carpet on the floor, and the floor seemed very old, uneven, worm-eaten, mended here and there, as was shown by the whiter patches on the wood; but no living being, and no visible place in which a living being could have hidden.

As we stood gazing round, the door by which we had entered closed as quietly as it had before opened; we were imprisoned.

For the first time I felt a creep of undefinable horror. Not so my servant.

"Why, they don't think to trap us, sir; I could break that trumpery door with a kick of my foot."

"Try first if it will open to your hand," said I, shaking off the vague apprehension that had seized me, "while I open the shutters and see what is without."

I unbarred the shutters; the window looked on the little back-yard I have before described; there was no ledge without, nothing but sheer descent. No man getting out of that window would have found any footing till he had fallen on the stones below.

F—— meanwhile was vainly attempting to open the door. He now turned round to me and asked my permission to use force. And I should here state, in justice to the servant, that, far from evincing any superstitious terror, his nerve, composure, and even gaiety amid circumstances so extraordinary, compelled my admiration and made me congratulate myself on having secured a companion in every way fitted to the occasion. I willingly gave him the permission he required. But, though he was a remarkably strong man, his force was as idle as his milder efforts; the door did not even shake to his stoutest kick.

Breathless and panting, he desisted. I then tried the door myself, equally in vain. As I ceased from the effort, again that creep of horror came over me; but this time it was more cold and stubborn. I felt as if some strange and ghastly exhalation were rising from the chinks of that rugged floor and filling the atmosphere with a venomous influence hostile to human life.

The door now very slowly and quietly opened as of its own accord. We precipitated ourselves onto the landing-place. We both saw a large, pale light—as large as the human figure, but shapeless and unsubstantial—move before us and ascend the stairs that led from the landing into the attics.

I followed the light, and my servant followed me. It entered, to the right of the landing, a small garret, of which the door stood open. I entered in the same instant. The light then collapsed into a small globule, exceedingly brilliant and vivid; rested a moment on a bed in the corner, quivered, and vanished.

We approached the bed and examined it—a half-tester, such as is commonly found in attics devoted to servants. On the drawers that stood near it we perceived an old faded silk kerchief, with the needle still left in the rent half repaired. The kerchief was covered with dust; probably it had belonged to the old woman who had last died there, and this might have been her sleeping room.

I had sufficient curiosity to open the drawers; there were a few odds and ends of female dress, and two letters tied round with a narrow ribbon of faded yellow. I took the liberty to possess myself of the letters. We found nothing else in the room worth noticing, nor did the light reappear; but we distinctly heard, as we turned to go, a pattering footfall on the floor just before us.

We went through the other attics (in all four), the footfall still preceding us. Nothing to be seen, nothing but the footfall heard. I had the letters in my hand; just as I was descending the stairs I distinctly felt my wrist seized, and a faint, soft effort made to draw the letters from my clasp. I only held them the more tightly, and the effort ceased.

We regained the bedchamber appropriated to myself, and I then remarked that my dog had not followed us when we had left it. He was thrusting himself close to the fire and trembling. I was impatient to examine the letters; and while I read them my servant opened a little box in which he had deposited the weapons I had ordered him to bring, took them out, placed them on a table close at my bed-head, and then occupied himself in soothing the dog, who, however, seemed to heed him very little.

The letters were short; they were dated—the dates exactly thirty-five years ago. They were evidently from a lover to his mistress, or a husband to some young wife. Not only the terms of expression, but a distinct reference to a former voyage indicated the writer to have been a seafarer. The spelling and handwriting were those of a man imperfectly educated; but still the language itself was forcible. In the expressions of endearment there was a kind of rough, wild love; but here and there were dark, unintelligible hints at some secret not of love— some secret that seemed of crime.

"We ought to love each other," was one of the sentences I remember, "for how every one else would execrate us if all was known."

Again: "Don't let any one be in the same room with you at night—you talk in your sleep."

And again: "What's done can't be undone; and I tell you there's nothing against us, unless the dead should come to life."

Here was interlined, in a better handwriting (a female's), "They do!"

At the end of the letter latest in date the same female hand had written these words:

"Lost at sea the 4th of June, the same day as——"

I put down the letters, and began to muse over their contents.

Fearing, however, that the train of thought into which I fell might unsteady my nerves, I fully determined to keep my mind in a fit state to cope with whatever of the marvelous the advancing night might bring forth. I roused myself, laid the letters on the table, stirred up the fire, which was still bright and cheering, and opened my volume of Macaulay.

I read quietly enough till about half-past eleven. I then threw myself dressed upon the bed, and told my servant he might retire to his own room, but must keep himself awake. I bade him leave open the doors between the two rooms. Thus alone I kept two candles burning on the table by my bed-head. I placed my watch beside the weapons, and calmly resumed my Macaulay. Opposite to me the fire burned clear, and on the hearth-rug, seemingly asleep, lay the dog. In about twenty minutes I felt an exceedingly cold air pass by my cheek, like a sudden draft. I fancied the door to my right, communicating with the landing-place, must have got open; but no, it was closed.

I then turned my glance to the left, and saw the flames of the candles violently swayed as by a wind. At the same moment the watch beside the revolver softly slid from the table—softly, softly—no visible hand—it was gone. I sprang up, seizing the revolver with the one hand, the dagger with the other: I was not willing that my weapons should share the fate of the watch.

Thus armed, I looked round the floor: no sign of the watch. Three slow, loud, distinct knocks were now heard at the bed-head; my servant called out:

"Is that you, sir?"

"No; be on your guard."

The dog now roused himself and sat on his haunches, his ears moving quickly backward and forward. He kept his eyes fixed on me with a look so strange that he concentrated all my attention on himself. Slowly he rose, all his hair bristling, and stood perfectly rigid, and with the same wild stare.

I had no time, however, to examine the dog. Presently my servant emerged from his room; and if I ever saw horror in the human face, it was then. I should not have recognized him had we met in the streets, so altered was every lineament. He passed by me quickly, saying, in a whisper that seemed scarcely to come from his lips:

"Run! run! It is after me!"

He gained the door to the landing, pulled it open, and rushed forth. I followed him to the landing involuntarily, calling him to stop; but, without heeding me, he bounded down the stairs, clinging to the balusters and taking several steps at a time. I heard, where I stood, the street-door open, heard it again clap to.

I was left alone in the haunted house.

It was but for a moment that I remained undecided whether or not to follow my servant; pride and curiosity alike forbade so dastardly a flight. I re-entered my room, closing the door after me, and proceeded cautiously into the interior chamber. I encountered nothing to justify my servant's terror.

I again carefully examined the walls, to see if there were any concealed door. I could find no trace of one—not even a seam in the dull-brown paper with which the room was hung. How then had the THING, whatever it was, which had so scared him, obtained ingress, except through my own chamber?

I returned to my room, shut and locked the door that opened upon the interior one, and stood on the hearth, expectant and prepared.

I now perceived that the dog had slunk into an angle

of the wall, and was pressing close against it, as if literally striving to force his way into it. I approached the animal and spoke to it; the poor brute was evidently beside itself with terror. It showed all its teeth, the slaver dropping from its jaws, and would certainly have bitten me if I had touched it. It did not seem to recognize me. Whoever has seen at the Zoological Gardens a rabbit fascinated by a serpent, cowering in a corner, may form some idea of the anguish which the dog exhibited.

Finding all efforts to soothe the animal in vain, and fearing that his bite might be as venomous in that state as if in the madness of hydrophobia, I left him alone, placed my weapons on the table beside the fire, seated myself, and recommenced my Macaulay.

Perhaps, in order not to appear seeking credit for a courage, or rather a coolness, which the reader may conceive I exaggerate, I may be pardoned if I pause to indulge in one or two egotistical remarks.

As I hold presence of mind, or what is called courage, to be precisely proportioned to familiarity with the circumstances that lead to it, so I should say that I had been long sufficiently familiar with all experiments that appertain to the marvelous. I had witnessed many very extraordinary phenomena in various parts of the world—phenomena that would be either totally disbelievable if I stated them, or ascribed to supernatural agencies.

Now, my theory is that the supernatural is the impossible, and that what is called supernatural is only a something in the laws of nature of which we have been hitherto ignorant. Therefore, if a ghost rise before me, I have not the right to say, "So, then, the supernatural is possible," but rather, "So, then, the apparition of a ghost is, contrary to received opinion, within the laws of nature, namely, not supernatural."

Now, in all that I had hitherto witnessed, and indeed in all the wonders which the amateurs of mystery in our age record as facts, a material living agency is always required. On the Continent you will still find magicians who assert that they can raise spirits. Assume for a moment that they assert truly, still the living material form of the magician is present; he is the material agency by which, from some constitutional peculiarities, certain strange phenomena are represented to your natural senses.

Accept, again, as truthful the tales of spirit manifestation in America—musical or other sounds, writings on paper, produced by no discernible hand, articles of furniture moved without apparent human agency, or the actual sight and touch of hands, to which no bodies seem to belong—still there must be found the medium, or living being, with constitutional peculiarities capable of obtaining these signs.

In fine, in all such marvels, supposing even that there is no imposture, there must be a human being like ourselves, by whom or through whom the effects presented to human beings are produced. It is so with the now familiar phenomena of mesmerism or electro-biology; the mind of the person operated on is affected through a material living agent.

Nor, supposing it true that a mesmerized patient can respond to the will or passes of a mesmerizer a hundred miles distant, is the response less occasioned by a material being. It may be through a material fluid, call it Electric, call it Odic, call it what you will, which has the power of traversing space and passing obstacles, that the material effect is communicated from one to the other.

Hence, all that I had hitherto witnessed, or expected to witness, in this strange house, I believed to be occasioned through some agency or medium as mortal as myself; and this idea necessarily prevented the awe with which those who regard as supernatural things that are not within the ordinary operations of nature might have been impressed by the adventures of that memorable night.

As, then, it was my conjecture that all that was presented, or would be presented, to my senses, must originate in some human being gifted by constitution with the powers so to present them, and having some motive so to do, I felt an interest in my theory which, in its way, was rather philosophical than superstitious. And I can sincerely say that I was in as tranquil a temper for observation as any practical experimentalist could be in awaiting the effects of some rare though perhaps perilous chemical combination. Of course, the more I kept my mind detached from fancy the more temper fitted for observation would be obtained; and I therefore riveted eye and thought on the strong daylight sense in the page of my Macaulay.

I now became aware that something interposed between the page and the light: the page was overshadowed. I looked up and saw what I shall find very difficult, perhaps impossible, to describe.

It was a darkness shaping itself out of the air in very undefined outline. I cannot say it was of a human form, and yet it had more of a resemblance to a human form, or rather shadow, than anything else. As it stood, wholly apart and distinct from the air and the light around it, its dimensions seemed gigantic; the summit nearly touched the ceiling.

While I gazed, a feeling of intense cold seized me. An iceberg before me could not more have chilled me; nor could the cold of an iceberg have been more purely physical. I feel convinced that it was not the cold caused by fear. As I continued to gaze, I thought— but this I cannot say with precision—that I distinguished two eyes looking down on me from the height. One moment I seemed to distinguish them clearly, the next they seemed gone; but two rays of a pale, blue light frequently shot through the darkness, as from the height on which I half believed, half doubted, that I had encountered the eyes.

I strove to speak; my voice utterly failed me. I could only think to myself, "Is this fear? it is *not* fear!" I strove to rise, in vain; I felt as weighed down by an irresistible force. Indeed, my impression was that of an immense and overwhelming power opposed to my volition; that sense of utter inadequacy to cope with a force beyond man's, which one may feel *physically* in a storm at sea, in a conflagration, or when confronting some terrible wild beast, or rather, perhaps, the shark of the ocean, I felt *morally*. Opposed to my will was another will, as far superior to its strength as storm, fire, and shark are superior in material force to the force of man.

And now, as this impression grew on me, now came, at last, horror—horror to a degree that no words can convey. Still I retained pride, if not courage; and in my own mind I said, "This is horror, but it is not fear, unless I fear I cannot be harmed; my reason rejects this thing; it is an illusion, I do not fear."

With a violent effort I succeeded at last in stretching out my hand toward the weapon on the table; as I did so, on the arm and shoulder I received a strange shock, and my arm fell to my side powerless. And now, to add to my horror, the light began slowly to wane from the candles; they were not, as it were, extinguished, but their flame seemed very gradually withdrawn; it was the same with the fire, the light was extracted from the fuel; in a few minutes the room was in utter darkness.

The dread that came over me thus in the dark with that dark thing, whose power was so intensely felt, brought a reaction of nerve. In fact, terror had reached that climax that either my senses must have deserted me, or I must have burst through the spell.

I did burst through it.

I found voice, though the voice was a shriek. I remember that I broke forth with words like these, "I do not fear, my soul does not fear"; and at the same time I found strength to rise.

Still in that profound gloom, I rushed to one of the windows, tore aside the curtain, flung open the shutters; my first thought was LIGHT.

And when I saw the moon, high, clear, and calm, I felt a joy that almost compensated for the previous terror. There was the moon, there was also the light from the gas-lamps in the deserted, slumberous street. I turned to look back into the room; the moon penetrated its shadow very palely and partially, but still there was light. The dark thing, whatever it might be, was gone; except that I could yet see a dim shadow of that shade, against the opposite wall.

My eye now rested on the table, and from under the table (which was without cloth or cover, an old mahogany round table) rose a hand, visible as far as the wrist. It was a hand, seemingly, as much of flesh and blood as my own, but the hand of an aged person, lean, wrinkled, small too, a woman's hand. That hand very softly closed on the two letters that lay on the table; hand and letters both vanished. Then came the same three loud measured knocks I had heard at the bed-head before this extraordinary drama had commenced.

As these sounds slowly ceased, I felt the whole room vibrate sensibly; and at the far end rose, as from the floor, sparks or globules like bubbles of light, many-colored—green, yellow, fire-red, azure—up and down, to and fro, hither, thither, as tiny will-o'-the-wisps the sparks moved, slow or swift, each at its own caprice. A chair (as in the drawing-room below) was now advanced from the wall without apparent agency, and placed at the opposite side of the table.

Suddenly, as forth from the chair, grew a shape, a woman's shape. It was distinct as a shape of life, ghastly as a shape of death. The face was that of youth, with a strange, mournful beauty; the throat and shoulders were bare, the rest of the form in a loose robe of cloudy white.

It began sleeking its long yellow hair, which fell over its shoulders; its eyes were not turned toward me, but to the door; it seemed listening, watching, waiting. The shadow of the shade in the background grew darker, and again I thought I beheld the eyes gleaming out from the summit of the shadow, eyes fixed upon that shape.

As if from the door, though it did not open, grew another shape, equally distinct, equally ghastly—a man's shape, a young man's. It was in the dress of the last century, or rather in a likeness of such dress; for both the male shape and the female, though defined, were evidently unsubstantial, impalpable—simulacre, fantasms; and there was something incongruous, grotesque, yet fearful, in the contrast between the elaborate finery, the courtly precision of that old-fashioned garb, with its ruffles and lace and buckles, and the corpse-like aspect and ghostlike stillness of the flitting wearer. Just as the male shape approached the female, the dark shadow darted from the wall, all three for a moment wrapped in darkness.

When the pale light returned, the two fantoms were as if in the grasp of the shadow that towered between them, and there was a bloodstain on the breast of the female; and the fantom male was leaning on its fantom sword, and blood seemed trickling fast from the ruffles, from the lace; and the darkness of the intermediate shadow swallowed them up—they were gone. And again the bubbles of light shot, and sailed, and undulated, growing thicker and thicker and more wildly confused in their movements.

The closet door to the right of the fire-place now opened, and from the aperture came the form of a woman, aged. In her hand she held letters—the very letters over which I had seen *the* hand close; and behind her I heard a footstep. She turned round as if to listen, and then she opened the letters and seemed to read: and over her shoulder I saw a livid face, the face as of a man long drowned—bloated, bleached, sea-weed tangled in its dripping hair; and at her feet lay a form as of a corpse, and beside the corpse cowered a child, a miserable squalid child, with famine in its cheeks and fear in its eyes. As I looked in the old woman's face, the wrinkles and lines vanished, and it became a face of youth—hard-eyed, stony, but still youth; and the shadow darted forth and darkened over these fantoms, as it had darkened over the last.

Nothing now was left but the shadow, and on that my eyes were intently fixed, till again eyes grew out of the shadow—malignant, serpent eyes. And the bubbles of light again rose and fell, and in their disordered, irregular, turbulent maze mingled with the wan moonlight. And now from these globules themselves, as from the shell of an egg, monstrous things burst out; the air grew filled with them; larvæ so bloodless and so hideous that I can in no way describe them except to remind the reader of the swarming life which the solar microscope brings before his eyes in a drop of water—things transparent, supple, agile, chasing each other, devouring each other —forms like naught ever beheld by the naked eye.

As the shapes were without symmetry, so their movements were without order. In their very vagrancies there was no sport; they came round me and round, thicker and faster and swifter, swarming over my head, crawling over my right arm, which was outstretched in involuntary command against all evil beings.

Sometimes I felt myself touched, but not by them; invisible hands touched me. Once I felt the clutch as of cold, soft fingers at my throat. I was still equally conscious that if I gave way to fear I should be in bodily peril, and I concentrated all my faculties in the single focus of resisting, stubborn will. And I turned my sight from the shadow, above all from those strange serpent eyes—eyes that had now become distinctly visible. For there, though in naught else around me, I was aware that there was a will, and a will of intense, creative, working evil, which might crush down my own.

The pale atmosphere in the room began now to redden as if in the air of some near conflagration. The larvæ grew lurid as things that live in fire. Again the room vibrated; again were heard the three measured knocks; and again all things were swallowed up in the darkness of the dark shadow, as if out of that darkness all had come, into that darkness all returned.

As the gloom receded, the shadow was wholly gone. Slowly as it had been withdrawn, the flame grew again into the candles on the table, again into the fuel in the grate. The whole room came once more calmly, healthfully into sight.

The two doors were still closed, the door communicating with the servant's room still locked. In the corner of the wall, into which he had convulsively niched himself, lay the dog. I called to him—no movement; I approached —the animal was dead; his eyes protruded, his tongue out of his mouth, the froth gathered round his jaws. I took him in my arms; I brought him to the fire; I felt acute grief for the loss of my poor favorite, acute self-reproach; I accused myself of his death; I imagined he had died of fright. But what was my surprise on finding that his neck was actually broken—actually twisted out of the vertebræ. Had this been done in the dark? Must it not have been done by a hand human as mine? Must there not have been a human agency all the while in that room? Good cause to suspect it. I cannot tell. I cannot do more than state the fact fairly; the reader may draw his own inference.

Another surprising circumstance—my watch was restored to the table from which it had been so mysteriously withdrawn; but it had stopped at the very moment it was so withdrawn; nor, despite all the skill of the watchmaker, has it ever gone since—that is, it will go in a strange, erratic way for a few hours, and then come to a dead stop; it is worthless.

Nothing more changed for the rest of the night; nor,

indeed, had I long to wait before the dawn broke. Not till it was broad daylight did I quit the haunted house. Before I did so I revisited the little blind room in which my servant and I had been for a time imprisoned.

I had a strong impression, for which I could not account, that from that room had originated the mechanism of the phenomena, if I may use the term, which had been experienced in my chamber; and though I entered it now in the clear day, with the sun peering through the filmy window, I still felt, as I stood on its floor, the creep of the horror which I had first experienced there the night before, and which had been so aggravated by what had passed in my own chamber.

I could not, indeed, bear to stay more than half a minute within those walls. I descended the stairs, and again I heard the footfall before me; and when I opened the street-door I thought I could distinguish a very low laugh. I gained my own home, expecting to find my run-away servant there. But he had not presented himself; nor did I hear more of him for three days, when I received a letter from him, dated from Liverpool, to this effect:

HONORED SIR—*I humbly entreat your pardon, though I can scarcely hope that you will think I deserve it, unless—which heaven forbid!—you saw what I did. I feel that it will be years before I can recover myself; and as to being fit for service, it is out of the question. I am therefore going to my brother-in-law at Melbourne. The ship sails tomorrow. Perhaps the long voyage may set me up. I do nothing now but start and tremble, and fancy it is behind me. I humbly beg you, honored sir, to order my clothes, and whatever wages are due to me, to be sent to my mother's, at Walworth: John knows her address.*

The letter ended with additional apologies, somewhat incoherent, and explanatory details as to effects that had been under the writer's charge.

This flight may perhaps warrant a suspicion that the man wished to go to Australia, and had been somehow or other fraudulently mixed up with the events of the night. I say nothing in refutation of that conjecture; rather, I suggest it as one that would seem to many persons the most probable solution of improbable occurrences.

My own theory remained unshaken. I returned in the evening to the house, to bring away in a hack cab the things I had left there, with my poor dog's body. In this task I was not disturbed, nor did any incident worth note befall me, except that still, on ascending and descending the stairs, I heard the same footfall in advance. On leaving the house, I went to Mr. J——'s. He was at home. I returned him the keys, told him that my curiosity was sufficiently gratified, and was about to relate quickly what had passed, when he stopped me and said, though with much politeness, that he had no longer any interest in a mystery which none had ever solved.

I determined at least to tell of the two letters I had read, as well as of the extraordinary manner in which they had disappeared; and I then inquired if he thought they had been addressed to the woman who had died in the house, and if there were anything in her early history which could possibly confirm the dark suspicions to which the letters gave rise.

Mr. J—— seemed startled, and after musing a few moments, answered:

"I know but little of the woman's earlier history, except as I before told you, that her family were known to mine. But you revive some vague reminiscences to her prejudice. I will make inquiries, and inform you of their result. Still, even if we could admit the popular superstition that a person who had been either the perpetrator or the victim of dark crimes in life could revisit, as a restless spirit, the scene in which those crimes had been committed, I should observe that the house was infested by strange sights and sounds before the old woman died. You smile; what would you say?"

"I would say this: that I am convinced, if we could get to the bottom of these mysteries, we should find a living, human agency."

"What! you believe it is all an imposture? For what object?"

"Not an imposture, in the ordinary sense of the word. If suddenly I were to sink into a deep sleep, from which you could not awake me, but in that deep sleep could answer questions with an accuracy which I could not pretend to when awake—tell you what money you had in your pocket, nay, describe your very thoughts—it is not necessarily an imposture, any more than it is necessarily supernatural. I should be, unconsciously to myself, under a mesmeric influence, conveyed to me from a distance by a human being who had acquired power over me by previous *rapport.*"

"Granting mesmerism, so far carried, to be a fact, you are right. And you would infer from this that a mesmerizer might produce the extraordinary effects you and others have witnessed over inanimate objects—fill the air with sights and sounds?"

"Or impress our senses with the belief in them, we never having been *en rapport* with the person acting on us? No. What is commonly called mesmerism could not do this; but there may be power akin to mesmerism and superior to it—the power that in the old days was called magic. That such a power may extend to all inanimate objects of matter, I do not say; but if so, it would not be against nature, only a rare power in nature, which might be given to constitutions with certain peculiarities, and cultivated by practice to an extraordinary degree.

"That such a power might extend over the dead—that

is, over certain thoughts and memories that the dead may still retain—and compel, not that which ought properly to be called the SOUL, and which is far beyond human reach, but rather a fantom of what has been most earth-stained on earth, to make itself apparent to our senses—is a very ancient though obsolete theory, upon which I will hazard no opinion. But I do not conceive the power would be supernatural.

"Let me illustrate what I mean, from an experiment which Paracelsus describes as not difficult, and which the author of the 'Curiosities of Literature' cites as credible: A flower perishes; you burn it. Whatever were the elements of that flower while it lived are gone, dispersed, you know not whither; you can never discover nor re-collect them. But you can, by chemistry, out of the burnt dust of that flower, raise a spectrum of that flower, just as it seemed in life.

"It may be the same with a human being. The soul has as much escaped you as the essence or elements of the flower. Still you may make a spectrum of it. And this fantom, though in the popular superstition it is held to be the soul of the departed, must not be confounded with the true soul; it is but the eidolon of the dead form.

"Hence, like the best-attested stories of ghosts or spirits, the thing that most strikes us is the absence of what we hold to be soul—that is, of superior, emancipated intelligence. They come for little or no object; they seldom speak, if they do come; they utter no ideas above those of an ordinary person on earth. These American spirit-seers have published volumes of communications in prose and verse, which they assert to be given in the names of the most illustrious dead—Shakespeare, Bacon, heaven knows whom.

"Those communications, taking the best, are certainly not of a whit higher order than would be communications from living persons of fair talent and education; they are wondrously inferior to what Bacon, Shakespeare, and

Plato said and wrote when on earth. Nor, what is more notable, do they ever contain an idea that was not on the earth before.

"Wonderful, therefore, as such phenomena may be (granting them to be truthful), I see much that philosophy may question, nothing that it is incumbent on philosophy to deny, namely, nothing supernatural. They are but ideas conveyed somehow or other (we have not yet discovered the means) from one mortal brain to another. Whether in so doing tables walk of their own accord, or fiend-like shapes appear in a magic circle, or bodiless hands rise and remove material objects, or a thing of darkness, such as presented itself to me, freeze our blood—still am I persuaded that these are but agencies conveyed, as by electric wires, to my own brain from the brain of another.

"In some constitutions there is a natural chemistry, and these may produce chemic wonders; in others a natural fluid, call it electricity, and these produce electric wonders. But they differ in this from normal science: they are alike objectless, purposeless, puerile, frivolous. They lead on to no grand results, and therefore the world does not heed, and true sages have not cultivated them. But sure I am, that of all I saw or heard, a man, human as myself, was the remote originator; and, I believe, unconsciously to himself as to the exact effects produced, for this reason: no two persons, you say, have ever told you that they experienced exactly the same thing; well, observe, no two persons ever experience exactly the same dream.

"If this were an ordinary imposture, the machinery would be arranged for results that would but little vary; if it were a supernatural agency permitted by the Almighty, it would surely be for some definite end. These phenomena belong to neither class. My persuasion is that they originate in some brain now far distant; that that brain had no distinct volition in anything that occurred; that what does occur reflects but its devious, motley, ever-shifting, half-formed thoughts; in short, that it has been but the dreams of such a brain put into action and invested with a semi-substance.

"That this brain is of immense power, that it can set matter into movement, that it is malignant and destructive, I believe. Some material force must have killed my dog; it might, for aught I know, have sufficed to kill myself, had I been as subjugated by terror as the dog—had my intellect or my spirit given me no countervailing resistance in my will."

"It killed your dog! That is fearful! Indeed, it is strange that no animal can be induced to stay in that house; not even a cat. Rats and mice are never found in it."

"The instincts of the brute creation detect influences deadly to their existence. Man's reason has a sense less subtle, because is has a resisting power more supreme. But enough; do you comprehend my theory?"

"Yes, though imperfectly; and I accept any crotchet (pardon the word), however odd, rather than embrace at once the notion of ghosts and hobgoblins we imbibed in our nurseries. Still, to my unfortunate house the evil is the same. What on earth can I do with the house?"

"I will tell you what I would do. I am convinced from my own internal feelings that the small unfurnished room, at right angles to the door of the bedroom which I occupied, forms a starting-point or receptacle for the influences which haunt the house; and I strongly advise you to have the walls opened, the floor removed, nay, the whole room pulled down. I observe that it is detached from the body of the house, built over the small backyard, and could be removed without injury to the rest of the building."

"And you think that if I did that——"

"You would cut off the telegraph-wires. Try it. I am so persuaded that I am right that I will pay half the expense if you will allow me to direct the operations."

"Nay, I am well able to afford the cost; for the rest, allow me to write to you."

About ten days afterwards I received a letter from Mr. J——, telling me that he had visited the house since I had seen him; that he had found the two letters I had described replaced in the drawer from which I had taken them; that he had read them with misgivings like my own; that he had instituted a cautious inquiry about the woman to whom I rightly conjectured they had been written.

It seemed that thirty-six years ago (a year before the date of the letters) she had married, against the wish of her relatives, an American of very suspicious character; in fact, he was generally believed to have been a pirate. She herself was the daughter of very respectable tradespeople, and had served in the capacity of nursery governess before her marriage. She had a brother, a widower, who was considered wealthy, and who had one child about six years old. A month after the marriage the body of this brother was found in the Thames, near London Bridge; there seemed some marks of violence about his throat, but they were not deemed sufficient to warrant the inquest in any other verdict than that of "found drowned."

The American and his wife took charge of the little boy, the deceased brother having by his will left his sister the guardian of his only child, and in the event the child's death the sister inherited. The child died about six months afterward; it was supposed to have been neglected and ill-treated. The neighbors deposed to have heard it shriek at night.

The surgeon who had examined it after death said that it was emaciated as if from want of nourishment, and the body was covered with livid bruises. It seemed that one winter night the child had sought to escape; had crept out into the back-yard, tried to scale the wall, fallen back exhausted, and had been found at morning on the stones in a dying state.

But though there was some evidence of cruelty, there was none of murder; and the aunt and her husband had

sought to palliate cruelty by alleging the exceeding stubbornness and perversity of the child, who was declared to
be half-witted. Be that as it may, at the orphan's death
the aunt inherited her brother's fortune.

Before the first wedded year was out, the American
quitted England abruptly, and never returned to it. He obtained a cruising vessel, which was lost in the Atlantic two
years afterward. The widow was left in affluence; but re-
verses of various kinds had befallen her; a bank broke, an
investment failed, she went into a small business and
became insolvent, then she entered into service, sinking
lower and lower, from housekeeper down to maid-of-all-
work, never long retaining a place though nothing peculiar
against her character was ever alleged.

She was considered sober, honest, and peculiarly quiet
in her ways; still nothing prospered with her. And so
she had dropped into the workhouse, from which Mr.
J—— had taken her, to be placed in charge of the very
house which she had rented as mistress in the first year
of her wedded life.

Mr. J—— added that he had passed an hour alone in
the unfurnished room which I had urged him to destroy,
and that his impressions of dread while there were so
great, though he had neither heard nor seen anything, that
he was eager to have the walls bared and the floors removed, as I had suggested. He had engaged persons for
the work, and would commence any day I would name.

The day was accordingly fixed. I repaired to the haunted
house; we went into the blind, dreary room, took up the
skirting and then the floors. Under the rafters, covered
with rubbish, was found a trap-door, quite large enough
to admit a man. It was closely nailed down with clamps
and rivets of iron. On removing these we descended into
a room below, the existence of which had never been
suspected.

In this room there had been a window and a flue,
but they had been bricked over, evidently for many years.

By the help of candles we examined this place; it still retained some moldering furniture—three chairs, an oak settee, a table—all of the fashion of about eighty years ago.

There was a chest of drawers against the wall, in which we found, half rotted away, old-fashioned articles of a man's dress, such as might have been worn eighty or a hundred years ago, by a gentleman of some rank; costly steel buckles and buttons, like those yet worn in court-dresses, a handsome court-sword; in a waistcoat which had once been rich with gold-lace, but which was now blackened and foul with damp, we found five guineas, a few silver coins, and an ivory ticket, probably for some place of entertainment long since passed away.

But our main discovery was in a kind of iron safe fixed to the wall, the lock of which it cost us much trouble to get picked.

In this safe were three shelves and two small drawers. Ranged on the shelves were several small bottles of crystal, hermetically stopped. They contained colorless volatile essences, of what nature I shall say no more than that they were not poisons; phosphor and ammonia entered into some of them. There were also some very curious glass tubes, and a small pointed rod of iron, with a large lump of rock crystal, and another of amber, also a lodestone of great power.

In one of the drawers we found a miniature portrait set in gold, and retaining the freshness of its colors most remarkably, considering the length of time it had probably been there. The portrait was that of a man who might be somewhat advanced in middle life, perhaps forty-seven or forty-eight.

It was a most peculiar face, a most impressive face. If you could fancy some mighty serpent transformed into man, preserving in the human lineaments the old serpent type, you would have a better idea of that countenance than long descriptions can convey; the width and flatness of frontal, the tapering elegance of contour, disguising the strength of the deadly jaw; the long, large, terrible eye, glittering and green as the emerald, and withal a certain ruthless calm, as if from the consciousness of an immense power.

The strange thing was this: the instant I saw the miniature I recognized a startling likeness to one of the rarest portraits in the world; the portrait of a man of rank only below that of royalty, who in his own day had made a considerable noise. History says little or nothing of him; but search the correspondence of his contemporaries, and you find reference to his wild daring, his bold profligacy, his restless spirit, his taste for the occult sciences.

While still in the meridian of life he died and was buried, so say the chronicles, in a foreign land. He died in time to escape the grasp of the law; for he was accused of crimes which would have given him to the headsman. After his death the portraits of him, which had been numerous, for he had been a munificent encourager of art, were bought up and destroyed, it was supposed by his heirs, who might have been glad could they have razed his name from their splendid line.

He had enjoyed vast wealth; a large portion of this was believed to have been embezzled by a favorite astrologer or soothsayer; at all events, it had unaccountably vanished at the time of his death. One portrait alone of him was supposed to have escaped the general destruction; I had seen it in the house of a collector some months before. It had made on me a wonderful impression, as it does on all who behold it—a face never to be forgotten; and there was that face in the miniature that lay within my hand. True that in the miniature the man was a few years older than in the portrait I had seen, or than the original was even at the time of his death. But a few years!—why, between the date in which flourished that direful noble and the date in which the miniature was evidently painted there was an interval of more than two centuries. While I was thus gazing, silent and wondering, Mr. J—— said:

"But is it possible? I have known this man."

"How? where?" cried I.

"In India. He was high in the confidence of the Rajah of ——, and well-nigh drew him into a revolt which would have lost the Rajah his dominions. The man was a Frenchman; his name De V——; clever, bold, lawless; we insisted on his dismissal and banishment. It must be the same man, no two faces like his, yet this miniature seems nearly a hundred years old."

Mechanically I turned round the miniature to examine the back of it, and on the back was engraved a pentacle; in the middle of the pentacle a ladder, and the third step of the ladder was formed by the date 1765. Examining still more minutely, I detected a spring; this, on being pressed, opened the back of the miniature as a lid.

Within-side the lid were engraved; "Mariana, to thee. Be faithful in life and in death to ——."

Here follows a name that I will not mention, but it was not unfamiliar to me. I had heard it spoken of by old men in my childhood as the name borne by a dazzling charlatan, who had made a great sensation in London for a year or so, and had fled the country on the charge of a double murder within his own house— that of his mistress and his rival. I said nothing of this to Mr. J——, to whom reluctantly I resigned the miniature.

We had found no difficulty in opening the first drawer within the iron safe; we found great difficulty in opening the second: it was not locked, but it resisted all efforts, till we inserted in the chinks the edge of a chisel. When we had thus drawn it forth we found a very singular apparatus, in the nicest order.

Upon a small, thin book, or rather tablet, was placed a saucer of crystal; this saucer was filled with a clear liquid; on that liquid floated a kind of compass, with a needle shifting rapidly round; but instead of the usual points of a compass, were seven strange characters, not very unlike those used by astrologers to denote the planets.

A very peculiar, but not strong nor displeasing odor came from this drawer, which was lined with a wood that we afterward discovered to be hazel. Whatever the cause of this odor, it produced a material effect on the nerves. We all felt it, even the two workmen who were in the room; a creeping, tingling sensation, from the tips of the fingers to the roots of the hair.

Impatient to examine the tablet, I removed the saucer. As I did so, the needle of the compass went round and round with exceeding swiftness, and I felt a shock that ran through my whole frame, so that I dropped the saucer on the floor. The liquid was spilt, the saucer was broken, the compass rolled to the end of the room, and at that instant the walls shook to and fro as if a giant had swayed and rocked them.

The two workmen were so frightened that they ran up the ladder by which we had descended from the trapdoor; but, seeing that nothing more happened, they were easily induced to return.

Meanwhile I had opened the tablet; it was bound in plain red leather, with a silver clasp; it contained but one sheet of thick vellum, and on that sheet were inscribed, within a double pentacle, words in old monkish Latin, which are literally to be translated thus:

On all that it can reach within these walls, sentient or inanimate, living or dead, as moves the needle, so works my will! Accursed be the house, and restless the dwellers therein.

We found no more. Mr. J—— burned the tablet and its anathema. He razed to the foundation the part of the building containing the secret room, with the chamber over it. He had then the courage to inhabit the house himself for a month, and a quieter, better conditioned house could not be found in all London. Subsequently he let it to advantage, and his tenant had made no complaints.

But my story is not yet done. A few days after Mr. J—— had removed into the house, I paid him a visit. We were standing by the open window and conversing. A van containing some articles of furniture which he was moving from his former house was at the door.

I had just urged on him my theory that all those phenomena regarded as supermundane had emanated from a human brain; adducing the charm, or rather curse we had found and destroyed, in support of my theory.

Mr. J—— was observing in reply, "that even if mesmerism, or whatever analogous power it might be called, could really thus work in the absence of the operator, and produce effects so extraordinary, still could those effects continue when the operator himself was dead? and if the spell had been wrought, and, indeed, the room walled up, more than seventy years ago, the probability was that the operator had long since departed this life"—Mr. J——, I say, was thus answering, when I caught hold of his arm and pointed to the street below.

A well-dressed man had crossed from the opposite side, and was accosting the carrier in charge of the van. His face, as he stood, was exactly fronting our window. It was the face of the miniature we had discovered; it was the face of the portrait of the noble three centuries ago.

"Good heavens!" cried Mr. J——, "that is the face of De V——, and scarcely a day older than when I saw it in the Rajah's court in my youth!"

Seized by the same thought, we both hastened downstairs; I was first in the street, but the man had already gone. I caught sight of him, however, not many yards in advance, and in another moment I was by his side.

I had resolved to speak to him, but when I looked into his face I felt as if it were impossible to do so. That eye —the eye of the serpent—fixed and held me spellbound.

And withal, about the man's whole person there was a dignity, an air of pride and station and superiority that would have made any one, habituated to the usages of the world, hesitate long before venturing upon a liberty or impertinence.

And what could I say? What was it I could ask?

Thus ashamed of my first impulse, I fell a few paces back, still, however, following the stranger, undecided what else to do. Meanwhile he turned the corner of the street; a plain carriage was in waiting with a servant out of livery, dressed like a *valet de place,* at the carriage door. In another moment he had stepped into the carriage, and it drove off. I returned to the house.

Mr. J—— was still at the street-door. He had asked the carrier what the stranger had said to him.

"Merely asked whom that house now belonged to."

The same evening I happened to go with a friend to a place in town called the Cosmopolitan Club, a place open to men of all countries, all opinions, all degrees. One orders one's coffee, smokes one's cigar. One is always sure to meet agreeable, sometimes remarkable persons.

I had not been two minutes in the room before I beheld at table, conversing with an acquaintance of mine, whom I will designate by the initial G——, the man, the original of the miniature. He was now without his hat, and the likeness was yet more startling, only I observed that while he was conversing there was less severity in the countenance; there was even a smile, though a very quiet and very cold one. The dignity of mien I had acknowledged in the street was also more striking; a dignity akin to that which invests some prince of the East, conveying the idea of supreme indifference and habitual, indisputable, indolent but resistless power.

G—— soon after left the stranger, who then took up a scientific journal, which seemed to absorb his attention.

I drew G—— aside.

"Who and what is that gentleman?"

"That? Oh, a very remarkable man indeed! I met him last year amid the caves of Petra, the Scriptural Edom. He is the best Oriental scholar I know. We joined company, had an adventure with robbers, in which he showed a coolness that saved our lives; afterward he invited me to spend a day with him in a house he had bought at Damascus, buried among almond-blossoms and roses—the most beautiful thing. He lived there for some time, quite as an Oriental, in grand style.

"I half suspect he is a renegade, immensely rich, very odd; by the by, a great mesmerizer. I have seen him with my own eyes produce an effect on inanimate things. If you take a letter from your pocket and throw it to the other end of the room, he will order it to come to his feet, and you will see the letter wriggle itself along the floor till it has obeyed his command. 'Pon my honor 'tis true; I have seen him affect even the weather, disperse or collect clouds by means of a glass tube or wand. But he does not like talking of these matters to strangers. He has only just arrived in England; says he has not been here for a great many years; let me introduce him to you."

"Certainly! He is English, then? What is his name?"

"Oh! a very homely one—Richards."

"And what is his birth—his family?"

"How do I know? What does it signify? No doubt some *parvenue;* but rich, so infernally rich!"

G—— drew me up to the stranger, and the introduction was effected. The manners of Mr. Richards were not those of an adventurous traveler. Travelers are in general gifted with high animal spirits; they are talkative, eager, imperious. Mr. Richards was calm and subdued in tone, with manners which were made distant by the loftiness of punctilious courtesy, the manners of a former age.

I observed that the English he spoke was not exactly of our day. I should even have said that the accent was slightly foreign. But then Mr. Richards remarked that he had been little in the habit for years of speaking in his native tongue.

The conversation fell upon the changes in the aspect of London since he had visited our metropolis. G—— then glanced off to the moral changes—literary, social, political—the great men who were removed from the stage within the last twenty years; the new great men who were coming on.

In all this Mr. Richards evinced no interest. He had evidently read none of our living authors, and seemed scarcely acquainted by name with our younger statesmen. Once, and only once, he laughed; it was when G—— asked him whether he had any thoughts of getting into Parliament; and the laugh was inward, sarcastic, sinister —a sneer raised into a laugh.

After a few minutes, G—— left us to talk to some other acquaintances who had just lounged into the room, and I then said, quietly:

"I have seen a miniature of you, Mr. Richards, in the house you once inhabited, and perhaps built—if not wholly, at least in part—in Oxford Street. You passed by that house this morning."

Not till I had finished did I raise my eyes to his, and then he fixed my gaze so steadfastly that I could not withdraw it—those fascinating serpent-eyes. But involuntarily, and as if the words that translated my thought were dragged from me, I added, in a low whisper, "I have been a student in the mysteries of life and nature; of those mysteries I have known the occult professors. I have the right to speak to you thus." And I uttered a certain password.

"Well, I concede the right. What would you ask?"

"To what extent human will in certain temperaments can extend?"

"To what extent can thought extend? Think, and before you draw breath you are in China!"

"True; but my thought has no power in China."

"Give it expression, and it may have. You may write down a thought which, sooner or later, may alter the whole condition of China. What is a law but a thought? Therefore thought is infinite. Therefore thought has power; not in proportion to its value—a bad thought may make a bad law as potent as a good thought can make a good one."

"Yes; what you say confirms my own theory. Through invisible currents one human brain may transmit its ideas to other human brains, with the same rapidity as a thought promulgated by visible means. And as thought is imperishable, as it leaves its stamp behind it in the natural world, even when the thinker has passed out of this world, so the thought of the living may have power to rouse up and revive the thoughts of the dead, such as those thoughts *were in life,* though the thought of the living cannot reach the thoughts which the dead *now* may entertain. Is it not so?"

"I decline to answer, if in my judgment thought has the limit you would fix to it. But proceed; you have a special question you wish to put."

"Intense malignity in an intense will, engendered in a peculiar temperament, and aided by natural means within the reach of science may produce effects like those ascribed of old to evil magic. It might thus haunt the walls of human habitation with spectral revivals of all guilty thoughts and guilty deeds once conceived and done within those walls; all, in short, with which the evil will claims *rapport* and affinity—imperfect, incoherent, fragmentary snatches at the old dramas acted therein years ago.

"Thoughts thus crossing each other haphazard, as in the nightmare of a vision, growing up into fantom sights and sounds, and all serving to create horror; not because those sights and sounds are really visitations from a world without, but that they are ghastly, monstrous renewals of what have been in this world itself, set into malignant play by a malignant mortal. And it is through the material agency of that human brain that these things would acquire even a human power; would strike as with the shock of electricity, and might kill, if the thought of the person assailed did not rise superior to the dignity of the original assailer; might kill the most powerful animal, if unnerved by fear, but not injure the feeblest man, if, while his flesh crept, his mind stood out fearless.

"Thus when in old stories we read of a magician rent to pieces by the fiends he had invoked, or still more, in Eastern legends, that one magician succeeds by arts in destroying another, there may be so far truth, that a material being has clothed, from his own evil propensities, certain elements and fluids, usually quiescent or harmless, with awful shapes and terrific force; just as the lightning, that had lain hidden and innocent in the cloud, becomes by natural law suddenly visible, takes a distinct shape to the eye, and can strike destruction on the object to which it is attracted."

"You are not without glimpses of a mighty secret," said Mr. Richards, composedly. "According to your view, could a mortal obtain the power you speak of, he would necessarily be a malignant and evil being."

"If the power were exercised, as I have said, most malignant and most evil; though I believe in the ancient traditions that he could not injure the good. His will could only injure those with whom it has established an affinity, or over whom it forces unresisted sway. I will now imagine an example that may be within the laws of nature, yet seem wild as the fables of a bewildered monk.

"You will remember that Albertus Magnus, after describing minutely the process by which the spirits may be invoked and commanded, adds emphatically that the process will instruct and avail only to the few; that *a man must be born a magician!*—that is, born with a peculiar physical temperament, as a man is born a poet.

"Rarely are men in whose constitutions lurks this occult power of the highest order of intellect; usually in the intellect there is some twist, perversity, or disease. But on the other hand, they must possess, to an astonishing degree, the faculty to concentrate thought on a single object—the energic faculty that we call WILL. Therefore, though their intellect be not sound, it is exceedingly forcible for the attainment of what it desires. I will imagine such a person, preeminently gifted with this constitution and its concomitant forces. I will place him in the loftier grades of society.

"I will suppose his desires emphatically those of the sensualist; he has, therefore, a strong love of life. He is an absolute egotist; his will is concentrated in himself; he has fierce passions; he knows no enduring, no holy affections, but he can covet eagerly what for the moment he desires; he can hate implacably what opposes itself to his objects; he can commit fearful crimes, yet feel small remorse; he resorts rather to curses upon others than to penitence for his misdeeds. Circumstances to which his constitution guides him, lead him to a rare knowledge of the natural secrets which may serve his egotism. He is a close observer where his passions encourage observation; he is a minute calculator, not from love of truth, but where love of self sharpens his faculties; therefore he can be a man of science.

"I suppose such a being, having by experience learned the power of his arts over others, trying what may be the power of will over his own frame, and studying all that in nautral philosophy may increase that power. He loves life, he dreads death; *he wills to live on.* He cannot restore himself to youth; he cannot entirely stay the progress of death; he cannot make himself immortal in the flesh and blood. But he may arrest, for a time so long as to appear incredible if I said it, that hardening of the parts which constitutes old age.

"A year may age him no more than an hour ages another. His intense will, scientifically trained into system, operates, in short, over the wear and tear of his own frame. He lives on. That he may not seem a portent and a miracle, he *dies*, from time to time, seemingly, to certain persons. Having schemed the transfer of a wealth that suffices to his wants, he disappears from one corner of the world, and contrives that his obsequies shall be celebrated.

"He reappears at another corner of the world, where he resides undetected, and does not visit the scenes of his former career till all who could remember his features are no more. He would be profoundly miserable if he had affections; he has none but for himself. No good man would accept his longevity; and to no man, good or bad, would he or could he communicate its true secret.

"Such a man might exist; such a man as I have described I see now before me—Duke of ——, in the court of ——, dividing time between lust and brawl, alchemists and wizards; again, in the last century, charlatan and criminal, with name less noble, domiciled in the house at which you gazed to-day, and flying from the law you had outraged, none knew whither; traveler once more revisiting London with the same earthy passion which filled your heart when races now no more walked through yonder streets; outlaw from the school of all the nobler and diviner mysteries. Execrable image of life in death and death in life, I warn you back from the cities and homes of healthful men! back to the ruins of departed empires! back to the desert of nature unredeemed!"

There answered me a whisper so musical, so potently musical, that it seemed to enter into my whole being and subdue me despite myself. Thus it said:

"I have sought one like you for the last hundred years. Now I have found you, we part not till I desire. The vision that sees through the past and cleaves through the veil of the future is in you at this hour—never before, never to come again. The vision of no puling, fantastic girl, of no sick-bed somnambule, but of a strong man with a vigorous brain. Soar, and look forth!"

As he spoke, I felt as if I rose out of myself upon eagle wings. All the weight seemed gone from air, roofless the room, roofless the dome of space. I was not in the body—where, I knew not; but aloft over time, over earth.

Again I heard the melodious whisper:

"You say right. I have mastered great secrets by the power of will. True, by will and by science I can retard the process of years, but death comes not by age alone. Can I frustrate the accidents which bring death upon the young?"

"No; every accident is a providence. Before a providence snaps every human will."

"Shall I die at last, ages and ages hence, by the slow though inevitable growth of time, or by the cause that I call accident?"

"By a cause you call accident."

"Is not the end still remote?" asked the whisper, with a slight tremor.

"Regarded as my life regards time, it is still remote."

"And shall I, before then, mix with the world of men as I did ere I learned these secrets; resume eager interest in their strife and their trouble; battle with ambition, and use the power of the sage to win the power that belongs to kings?"

"You will yet play a part on the earth that will fill earth with commotion and amaze. For wondrous designs have you, a wonder yourself, been permitted to live on through the centuries. All the secrets you have stored will then have their uses; all that now makes you a stranger amid the generations will contribute then to make you their lord. As the trees and the straws are drawn into a whirlpool, as they spin round, are sucked to the deep, and again tossed aloft by the eddies, so shall races and thrones be drawn into your vortex. Awful destroyer! but in destroying, made, against your own will, a constructor."

"And that date, too, is far off?"

"Far off; when it comes, think your end in this world is at hand!"

"How and what is the end? Look east, west, south, and north."

"In the north, where you never yet trod, toward the point whence your instincts have warned you, there a specter will seize you. 'Tis Death! I see a ship; it is haunted; 'tis chased! it sails on. Baffled navies sail after that ship. It enters the region of ice. It passes a sky red with meteors. Two moons stand on high, over ice-reefs. I see the ship locked between white defiles; they are ice-rocks. I see the dead strew the decks, stark and livid, green mold on their limbs. All are dead but one man—it is you! But years, though so slowly they come, have then scathed you. There is the coming of age on your brow, and the will is relaxed in the cells of the brain. Still that will, though enfeebled, exceeds all that man knew before you; through the will you live on, gnawed with famine. And nature no longer obeys you in that death-spreading region; the sky is a sky of iron, and the air has iron clamps, and the ice-rocks wedge in the ship. Hark how it cracks and groans! Ice will imbed it as amber imbeds a straw. And a man has gone forth, living yet, from the ship and its dead; and he has clambered up the spikes of an iceberg, and the two moons gaze down on his form. That man is yourself, and terror is on you— terror; and terror has swallowed up your will.

"And I see, swarming up the steep ice-rock, gray, grizzly things. The bears of the North have scented their quarry; they come nearer and nearer, shambling, and rolling their bulk. In that day every moment shall seem to you longer than the centuries through which you have passed. Heed this: after life, moments continued make the bliss or the hell of eternity."

"Hush!" said the whisper. "But the day, you assure me, is far off, very far! I go back to the almond and rose of Damascus! Sleep!"

The room swam before my eyes. I became insensible. When I recovered, I found G—— holding my hand and smiling. He said, "You, who have always declared yourself proof against mesmerism, have succumbed at last to my friend Richards."

"Where is Mr. Richards?"

"Gone, when you passed into a trance, saying quietly to me, 'Your friend will not wake for an hour.' "

I asked, as collectedly as I could, where Mr. Richards lodged.

"At the Trafalgar Hotel."

"Give me your arm," said I to G——. "Let us call on him; I have something to say."

When we arrived at the hotel we were told that Mr. Richards had returned twenty minutes before, paid his bill, left directions with his servant (a Greek) to pack his effects, and proceed to Malta by the steamer that should leave Southhampton the next day. Mr. Richards had merely said of his own movements that he had visits to pay in the neighborhood of London, and it was uncertain whether he should be able to reach Southhampton in time for that steamer; if not, he should follow in the next one.

The waiter asked me my name. On my informing him, he gave me a note that Mr. Richards had left for me in case I called.

The note was as follows:

I wished you to utter what was in your mind. You obeyed. I have therefore established power over you. For three months from this day you can communicate to no living man what has passed between us. You cannot even show this note to the friend by your side. During three months silence complete as to me and mine. Do you doubt my power to lay on you this command? Try to disobey me. At the end of the third month the spell is raised. For the rest, I spare you. I shall visit your grave a year and a day after it has received you.

So ends the strange story, which I ask no one to believe. I write it down exactly three months after the above note. I could not write it before, nor could I show to G——, in spite of his urgent request, the note which I read under the gas-lamp by his side.

The Fall of the House of Usher

by Edgar Allan Poe

> Son cœur est luth suspendu;
> Sitôt qu'on le touche il résonne.
> DE BERANGER.

During the whole of a dull, dark, and soundless day in the autumn of the year, when the clouds hung oppressively low in the heavens, I had been passing alone, on horseback, through a singularly dreary tract of country; and at length found myself, as the shades of the evening drew on, within a view of the melancholy House of Usher. I know not how it was—but, with the first glimpse of the building, a sense of insufferable gloom pervaded my spirit. I say insufferable; for the feeling was unrelieved by any of that half-pleasurable, because poetic, sentiment, with which the mind usually receives even the sternest natural images of the desolate or terrible. I looked upon the scene before me—upon the mere house, and the simple landscape features of the domain—upon the black walls—upon the vacant eye-like windows—upon a few rank sedges—and upon a few white trunks of decayed trees—with an utter depression of soul which I can compare to no earthly sensation more properly than to the after-dream of the reveler upon opium—the bitter lapse into everyday life—the hideous dropping off of the veil. There was an iciness, a sinking, a sickening of the heart —an unredeemed dreariness of thought which no goading of the imagination could torture into aught of the sublime. What was it—I paused to think—what was it that so unnerved me in the contemplation of the House of Usher? It was a mystery all insoluble; nor could I grapple with the shadowy fancies that crowded upon me as I pondered. I was forced to fall back upon the unsatisfactory conclusion, that while, beyond doubt, there *are* combinations of very simple natural objects which have the power of thus affecting us, still the analysis of this power lies among considerations beyond our depth. It was possible, I reflected, that a mere different arrangement of the particulars of the scene, of the details of the picture, would be sufficient to modify, or perhaps to annihilate its capacity for sorrowful impression; and, acting upon this idea, I reined my horse to the precipitous brink of a black and lurid tarn that lay in unruffled luster by the dwelling, and gazed down—but with a shudder even more thrilling than before—upon the remodeled and inverted images of the gray sedge, and the ghastly tree-stems, and the vacant and eye-like windows.

Nevertheless, in this mansion of gloom I now proposed to myself a sojourn of some weeks. Its proprietor, Roderick Usher, had been one of my boon companions in boyhood; but many years had elapsed since our last meeting. A letter, however, had lately reached me in a distant part of the country—a letter from him—which, in its wildly importunate nature, had admitted of no other than a personal reply. The MS. gave evidence of nervous agitation. The writer spoke of acute bodily illness —of a mental disorder which oppressed him—and of an earnest desire to see me, as his best, and indeed his only personal friend, with a view of attempting, by the cheerfulness of my society, some alleviation of his malady. It was the manner in which all this, and much more, was said—it was the apparent *heart* that went with his request —which allowed me no room for hesitation; and I accordingly obeyed forthwith what I still consider a very singular summons.

Although, as boys, we had been even intimate associates, yet I really knew little of my friend. His reserve had been always excessive and habitual. I was aware, however, that his very ancient family had been noted, time out of mind, for a peculiar sensibility of temperament, displaying itself, through long ages, in many works of exalted art, and manifested, of late, in repeated deeds of munificent yet unobtrusive charity, as well as in a passionate devotion to the intricacies, perhaps even more than to the orthodox and easily recognizable beauties, of musical science. I had learned, too, the very remarkable fact, that the stem of the Usher race, all time-honored as it was, had put forth, at no period, any enduring branch; in other words, that the entire family lay in the direct line of descent, and had always, with very trifling and very temporary variation, so lain. It was this deficiency, I considered, while running over in thought the perfect keeping of the character of the premises with the accredited character of the people, and while speculating upon the possible influence which the one, in the long lapse of centuries, might have exercised upon the other—it was this deficiency, perhaps, of collateral issue, and the consequent undeviating transmission, from sire to son, of the patrimony with the name, which had, at length, so identified the two as to merge the original title of the estate in the quaint and equivocal appellation of the "House of Usher"—an appellation which seemed to include, in the minds of the peasantry who used it, both the family and the family mansion.

I have said that the sole effect of my somewhat childish experiment—that of looking down within the tarn—had been to deepen the first singular impression. There can be no doubt that the consciousness of the rapid increase of my superstition—for why should I not so term it? —served mainly to accelerate the increase itself. Such, I have long known, is the paradoxical law of all sentiments having terror as a basis. And it might have been for this reason only, that, when I again uplifted my eyes to the house itself, from its image in the pool, there grew in my mind a strange fancy—a fancy so ridiculous, indeed, that I but mention it to show the vivid force of the sensations which oppressed me. I had so worked upon my imagination as really to believe that about the whole mansion and domain there hung an atmosphere peculiar to themselves and their immediate vicinity—an atmosphere which had no affinity with the air of heaven, but which had reeked up from the decayed trees, and the gray wall, and the silent tarn—a pestilent and mystic vapor, dull, sluggish, faintly discernible, and leaden-hued.

Shaking off from my spirit what *must* have been a dream, I scanned more narrowly the real aspect of the building. Its principal feature seemed to be that of an excessive antiquity. The discoloration of ages had been great. Minute *fungi* overspread the whole exterior, hanging in a fine tangled webwork from the eaves. Yet all this was apart from any extraordinary dilapidation. No portion of the masonry had fallen; and there appeared to be a wild inconsistency between its still perfect adaptation of parts, and the crumbling condition of the individual stones. In this there was much that reminded me of the specious totality of old woodwork which has rotted for long years in some neglected vault, with no disturbance from the breath of the external air. Beyond this indication of extensive decay, however, the fabric gave little token of instability. Perhaps the eye of a scrutinizing observer might have discovered a barely perceptible fissure, which, extending from the roof of the building in front, made its way down the wall in a zigzag direction, until it became lost in the sullen waters of the tarn.

Noticing these things, I rode over a short causeway to the house. A servant in waiting took my horse, and I entered the Gothic archway of the hall. A valet, of stealthy step, thence conducted me, in silence, through many dark and intricate passages in my progress to the *studio* of his master. Much that I encountered on the way contributed, I know not how, to heighten the vague sentiments of which I have already spoken. While the objects around me—while the carvings of the ceilings, the somber tapestries of the walls, the ebon blackness of the floors, and the phantasmagoric armorial trophies which rattled as I strode, were but matters to which, or to such as which, I had been accustomed from my infancy —while I hesitated not to acknowledge how familiar was all this—I still wondered to find how unfamiliar were the fancies which ordinary images were stirring up. On one of the staircases, I met the physician of the family. His countenance, I thought, wore a mingled expression of low cunning and perplexity. He accosted me with trepidation and passed on. The valet now threw open a door and ushered me into the presence of his master.

The room in which I found myself was very large and lofty. The windows were long, narrow, and pointed, and at so vast a distance from the black oaken floor as to be altogether inaccessible from within. Feeble gleams of encrimsoned light made their way through the trellised panes, and served to render sufficiently distinct the more prominent objects around; the eye however, struggled in vain to reach the remoter angles of the chamber, or the recesses of the vaulted and fretted ceiling. Dark draperies hung upon the walls. The general furniture was profuse, comfortless, antique, and tattered. Many books and musical instruments lay scattered about, but failed to give any vitality to the scene. I felt that I breathed an atmosphere of sorrow. An air of stern, deep, and irredeemable gloom hung over and pervaded all.

Upon my entrance, Usher arose from a sofa on which he had been lying at full length, and greeted me with a vivacious warmth which had much in it, I at first thought, of an overdone cordiality—of the constrained effort of the *ennuyé* man of the world. A glance, however, at his countenance, convinced me of his perfect sincerity. We sat down; and for some moments, while he spoke not, I gazed upon him with a feeling half of pity, half of awe. Surely, man had never before so terribly altered, in so brief a period, as had Roderick Usher! It was with difficulty that I could bring myself to admit the identity of the wan being before me with the companion of my early boyhood. Yet the character of his face had been at all times remarkable. A cadaverousness of complexion; an eye large, liquid, and luminous beyond comparison; lips somewhat thin and very pallid, but of a surpassingly beautiful curve; a nose of a delicate Hebrew model, but with a breadth of nostril unusual in similiar formations; a finely-moulded chin, speaking, in its want of prominence, of a want of moral energy; hair of a more than web-like softness and tenuity; these features, with an inordinate expansion above the regions of the temple, made up altogether a countenance not easily to be forgotten. And now in the mere exaggeration of the prevailing character of these features, and of the expression they were wont to convey, lay so much of change that I doubted to whom I spoke. The now ghastly pallor of the skin, and the now miraculous luster of the eye, above all things startled and even awed me. The silken hair, too, had been suffered to grow all unheeded, and as, in its wild gossamer texture, it floated rather than fell about the face, I could not, even with effort, connect its arabesque expression with any idea of simple humanity.

In the manner of my friend I was at once struck with an incoherence—an inconsistency; and I soon found this to arise from a series of feeble and futile struggles to overcome an habitual trepidancy—an excessive nervous agitation. For something of this nature I had indeed been prepared, no less by his letter, than by reminiscences of certain boyish traits, and by conclusions deduced from his peculiar physical conformation and temperament. His action was alternately vivacious and sullen. His voice varied rapidly from a tremulous indecision (when the animal spirits seemed utterly in abeyance) to that species of energetic concision—that abrupt, weighty, unhurried, and hollow-sounding enunciation—that leaden, self-balanced and perfectly modulated guttural utterance, which may be observed in the lost drunkard, or the irreclaimable eater of opium, during the periods of his most intense excitement.

It was thus that he spoke of the object of my visit, of his earnest desire to see me, and of the solace he expected me to afford him. He entered, at some length, into what he conceived to be the nature of his malady. It was, he said, a constitutional and a family evil, and one for which he despaired to find a remedy—a mere nervous affection, he immediately added, which would undoubtedly soon pass off. It displayed itself in a host of unnatural sensations. Some of these, as he detailed them, interested and bewildered me; although, perhaps, the terms, and the general manner of the narration had their weight. He suffered much from a morbid acuteness of the senses; the most insipid food was alone endurable; he could wear only garments of certain texture; the odors of all flowers were oppressive; his eyes were tortured by even a faint light; and there were but peculiar sounds, and these from stringed instruments, which did not inspire him with horror.

To an anomalous species of terror I found him a bounden slave. "I shall perish," said he, "I *must* perish in this deplorable folly. Thus, thus, and not otherwise, shall I be lost. I dread the events of the future, not in

themselves, but in their results. I shudder at the thought
of any, even the most trivial, incident, which may operate
upon this intolerable agitation of soul. I have, indeed, no
abhorrence of danger, except in its absolute effect—in
terror. In this unnerved—in this pitiable condition—I feel
that the period will sooner or later arrive when I must
abandon life and reason together, in some struggle with
the grim phantasm, FEAR."

I learned, moreover, at intervals, and through broken
and equivocal hints, another singular feature of his mental
condition. He was enchained by certain superstitious impressions in regard to the dwelling which he tenanted, and
whence, for many years, he had never ventured forth
—in regard to an influence whose supposititious force was
conveyed in terms too shadowy here to be re-stated—an
influence which some peculiarities in the mere form and
substance of his family mansion, had, by dint of long
sufferance, he said, obtained over his spirit—an effect
which the *physique* of the gray walls and turrets, and
of the dim tarn into which they all looked down, had, at
length, brought about upon the *morale* of his existence.

He admitted, however, although with hesitation, that
much of the peculiar gloom which thus afflicted him could
be traced to a more natural and far more palpable origin
—to the severe and long-continued illness—indeed to
the evidently approaching dissolution—of a tenderly beloved sister—his sole companion for long years—his
last and only relative on earth. "Her decease," he said,
with a bitterness which I can never forget, "would leave
him (him the hopeless and the frail) the last of the
ancient race of the Ushers." While he spoke, the Lady
Madeline (for so was she called) passed slowly through
a remote portion of the apartment, and, without having
noticed my presence, disappeared. I regarded her with
an utter astonishment not unmingled with dread—and
yet I found it impossible to account for such feelings. A
sensation of stupor oppressed me, as my eyes followed

her retreating steps. When a door, at length, closed upon her, my glance sought instinctively and eagerly the countenance of the brother—but he had buried his face in his hands, and I could only perceive that a far more than ordinary wanness had overspread the emaciated fingers through which trickled many passionate tears.

The disease of the Lady Madeline had long baffled the skill of her physicians. A settled apathy, a gradual wasting away of the person, and frequent although transient affections of a partially cataleptical character, were the unusual diagnosis. Hitherto she had steadily borne up against the pressure of her malady, and had not betaken herself finally to bed; but, on the closing in of the evening of my arrival at the house, she succumbed (as her brother told me at night with inexpressible agitation) to the prostrating power of the destroyer; and I learned that the glimpse I had obtained of her person would thus probably be the last I should obtain—that the lady, at least while living, would be seen by me no more.

For several days ensuing, her name was unmentioned by either Usher or myself: and during this period I was busied in earnest endeavors to alleviate the melancholy of my friend. We painted and read together; or I listened, as if in a dream, to the wild improvisations of his speaking guitar. And thus, as a closer and still closer intimacy admitted me more unreservedly into the recesses of his spirit, the more bitterly did I perceive the futility of all attempt at cheering a mind from which darkness, as if an inherent positive quality, poured forth upon all objects of the moral and physical universe, in one unceasing radiation of gloom.

I shall ever bear about me a memory of the many solemn hours I thus spent alone with the master of the House of Usher. Yet I should fail in any attempt to convey an idea of the exact character of the studies, or of the occupations, in which he involved me, or led me the way. An excited and highly distempered ideality threw a sulphureous luster over all. His long improvised dirges will ring forever in my ears. Among other things, I hold painfully in mind a certain singular perversion and amplification of the wild air of the last waltz of Von Weber. From the paintings over which his elaborate fancy brooded, and which grew, touch by touch, into vagueness at which I shuddered the more thrillingly, because I shuddered knowing not why;—from these paintings (vivid as their images now are before me) I would in vain endeavor to educe more than a small portion which should lie within the compass of merely written words. By the utter simplicity, by the nakedness of his designs, he arrested and overawed attention. If ever mortal painted an idea, that mortal was Roderick Usher. For me at least—in the circumstances then surrounding me—there arose out of the pure abstractions which the hypochondriac contrived to throw upon his canvas, an intensity of intolerable awe, no shadow of which felt I ever yet in the contemplation of the certainly glowing yet too concrete reveries of Fuseli.

One of the phantasmagoric conceptions of my friend, partaking not so rigidly of the spirit of abstraction, may be shadowed forth, although feebly, in words. A small picture presented the interior on an immensely long and rectangular vault or tunnel, with low walls, smooth, white, and without interruption or device. Certain accessory points of the design served well to convey the idea that this excavation lay at an exceeding depth below the surface of the earth. No outlet was observed in any portion of its vast extent, and no torch, or other artificial source of light was discernible; yet a flood of intense rays rolled throughout, and bathed the whole in a ghastly and inappropriate splendor.

I have just spoken of that morbid condition of the auditory nerve which rendered all music intolerable to the sufferer, with the exception of certain effects of stringed instruments. It was, perhaps, the narrow limits to which he thus confined himself upon the guitar, which gave birth, in great measure, to the fantastic character of his performances. But the fervid *facility* of his *impromptus* could not be so accounted for. They must have been, and were, in the notes, as well as in the words of his wild fantasias (for he not unfrequently accompanied himself with rhymed verbal improvisations), the result of that intense mental collectedness and concentration to which I have previously alluded as observable only in particular moments of the highest artificial excitement. The words of one of these rhapsodies I have easily remembered. I was, perhaps, the more forcibly impressed with it, as he gave it, because, in the under or mystic current of its meaning, I fancied that I perceived, and for the first time, a full consciousness on the part of Usher, of the tottering of his lofty reason upon her throne. The verses, which were entitled "The Haunted Palace," ran very nearly, if not accurately, thus:

I.

In the greenest of our valleys,
  By good angels tenanted,
Once a fair and stately palace—
  Radiant palace—reared its head.
In the monarch Thought's dominion—
  It stood there!
Never seraph spread a pinion
  Over fabric half so fair.

II.

Banners yellow, glorious, golden,
  On its roof did float and flow;
(This—all this—was in the olden
  Time long ago)
And every gentle air that dallied,
  In that sweet day,
Along the ramparts plumed and pallid,
  A winged odor went away.

III.

Wanderers in that happy valley
　　Through two luminous windows saw
Spirits moving musically
　　To a lute's well tunèd law,
Round about a throne, where sitting
　　(Porphyrogene!)
In state his glory well befitting,
　　The ruler of the realm was seen.

IV.

And all with pearl and ruby glowing
　　Was the fair palace door,
Through which came flowing, flowing, flowing
　　And sparkling evermore,
A troop of Echoes whose sweet duty
　　Was but to sing,
In voices of surpassing beauty,
　　The wit and wisdom of their king.

V.

But evil things, in robes of sorrow,
　　Assailed the monarch's high estate;
(Ah, let us mourn, for never morrow
　　Shall dawn upon him, desolate!)
And, round about his home, the glory
　　That blushed and bloomed
Is but a dim-remembered story
　　Of the old time entombed.

VI.

And travelers now within that valley,
　　Through the red-litten windows, see
Vast forms that move fantastically
　　To a discordant melody;
While, like a rapid ghastly river,
　　Through the pale door,
A hideous throng rush out forever,
　　And laugh—but smile no more.

I well remember that suggestions arising from this
ballad, led us into a train of thought wherein there be-

came manifest an opinion of Usher's which I mention not so much on account of its novelty (for other men have thought thus), as on account of the pertinacity with which he maintained it. This opinion, in its general form, was that of the sentience of all vegetable things. But, in his disordered fancy, the idea had assumed a more daring character, and trespassed, under certain conditions, upon the kingdom of inorganization. I lack words to express the full extent, or the earnest *abandon* of his persuasion. The belief, however, was connected (as I have previously hinted) with the gray stones of the home of his forefathers. The conditions of the sentience had been here, he imagined, fulfilled in the method of collocation of these stones—in the order of their arrangement, as well as in that of the many *fungi* which overspread them, and of the decayed trees which stood around —above all, in the long undisturbed endurance of this arrangement, and in its reduplication in the still waters of the tarn. Its evidence—the evidence of the sentience— was to be seen, he said, (and I here started as he spoke) in the gradual yet certain condensation of an atmosphere of their own about the waters and the walls. The result was discoverable, he added, in that silent, yet importunate and terrible influence which for centuries had moulded the destinies of his family, and which made *him* what I now saw him—what he was. Such opinions need no comment, and I will make none.

Our books—the books which, for years, had formed no small portion of the mental existence of the invalid —were, as might be supposed, in strict keeping with this character of phantasm. We pored together over such works as the *Ververt et Chartreuse* of Gresset; the *Belphegor* of Machiavelli; the *Heaven and Hell* of Swedenborg; the *Subterranean Voyage of Nicholas Klimm* by Holberg; the *Chiromancy* of Robert Flud, of Jean D'Indaginé, and of De la Chambre; the *Journey into the Blue Distance* of

Tieck; and the *City of the Sun* of Campanella. One favorite volume was a small octavo edition of the *Directorium Inquisitorum,* by the Dominican Eymeric de Gironne; and there were passages in *Pomponius Mela,* about the old African Satyrs and Ægipans, over which Usher would sit dreaming for hours. His chief delight, however, was found in the perusal of an exceedingly rare and curious book in quarto Gothic—the manual of a forgotten church—the *Vigiliæ Mortuorum Chorum Ecclesiæ Maguntinæ.*

I could not help thinking of the wild ritual of this work, and of its probable influence upon the hypochondriac, when, one evening, having informed me abruptly that the Lady Madeline was no more, he stated his intention of preserving her corpse for a fortnight (previously to its final interment), in one of the numerous vaults within the main walls of the building. The worldly reason, however, assigned for this singular proceeding, was one which I did not feel at liberty to dispute. The brother had been led to his resolution (so he told me) by consideration of the unusual character of the malady of the deceased, of certain obtrusive and eager inquiries on the part of her medical men, and of the remote and exposed situation of the burial-ground of the family. I will not deny that when I called to mind the sinister countenance of the person whom I met upon the staircase, on the day of my arrival at the house, I had no desire to oppose what I regarded as at best but a harmless, and by no means an unnatural, precaution.

At the request of Usher, I personally aided him in the arrangements for the temporary entombment. The body having been encoffined, we two alone bore it to its rest. The vault in which we placed it (and which had been so long unopened that our torches, half smothered in its oppressive atmosphere, gave us little opportunity for investigation) was small, damp, and entirely without means of admission for light; lying, at great depth, immediately beneath that portion of the building in which was my own sleeping apartment. It had been used, apparently, in remote feudal times, for the worst purpose of a donjon-keep, and, in later days, as a place of deposit for powder, or some other highly combustible substance, as a portion of its floor, and the whole interior of a long archway through which we reached it, were carefully sheathed with copper. The door, of massive iron, had been, also, similarly protected. Its immense weight caused an unusually sharp grating sound, as it moved upon its hinges.

Having deposited our mournful burden upon trestles within this region of horror, we partially turned aside the yet unscrewed lid of the coffin, and looked upon the face of the tenant. A striking similitude between the brother and sister now first arrested my attention; and Usher, divining, perhaps, my thoughts, murmured out some few words from which I learned that the deceased and himself had been twins, and that sympathies of a scarcely intelligible nature had always existed between them. Our glances, however, rested not long upon the dead—for we could not regard her unawed. The disease which had thus entombed the lady in the maturity of youth, had left, as usual in all maladies of a strictly cataleptical character, the mockery of a faint blush upon the bosom and the face, and that suspiciously lingering smile upon the lip which is so terrible in death. We replaced and screwed down the lid, and, having secured the door of iron, made our way, with toil, into the scarcely less gloomy apartments of the upper portion of the house.

And now, some days of bitter grief having elapsed, an observable change came over the features of the mental disorder of my friend. His ordinary manner had vanished. His ordinary occupations were neglected or forgotten. He roamed from chamber to chamber with hurried, unequal, and objectless step. The pallor of his countenance had assumed, if possible, a more ghastly hue—but the luminousness of his eye had utterly gone out. The once occasional huskiness of his tone was heard no more; and a tremulous quaver, as if of extreme terror, habitually characterized his utterance. There were times, indeed, when I thought his unceasingly agitated mind was laboring with some oppressive secret, to divulge which he struggled for the necessary courage. At times, again, I was obliged to resolve all into the mere inexplicable vagaries of madness, for I beheld him gazing upon vacancy for long hours, in an attitude of the profoundest attention, as if listening to some imaginary sound. It was no wonder that his condition terrified—that it infected me. I felt creeping upon me, by slow yet certain degrees, the wild influences of his own fantastic yet impressive superstitions.

It was, especially, upon retiring to bed late in the night of the seventh or eighth day after the placing of the Lady Madeline within the donjon, that I experienced the full power of such feelings. Sleep came not near my couch—while the hours waned and waned away. I struggled to reason off the nervousness which had dominion over me. I endeavored to believe that much, if not all of what I felt, was due to the bewildering influence of the gloomy furniture of the room—of the dark and tattered draperies, which, tortured into motion by the breath of a rising tempest, swayed fitfully to and fro upon the walls, and rustled uneasily about the decorations of the bed. But my efforts were fruitless. An irrepressible tremor gradually pervaded my frame; and, at length, there sat upon my very heart an incubus of utterly causeless alarm. Shaking this off with a gasp and a struggle, I uplifted myself upon the pillows, and, peering earnestly within the intense darkness of the chamber, hearkened—I know not why, except than an instinctive spirit prompted me—

to certain low and indefinite sounds which came, through the pauses of the storm, at long intervals, I knew not whence. Overpowered by an intense sentiment of horror, unaccountable yet unendurable, I threw on my clothes with haste (for I felt that I should sleep no more during the night), and endeavored to arouse myself from the pitiable condition into which I had fallen, by pacing rapidly to and fro through the apartment.

I had taken but few turns in this manner, when a light step on an adjoining staircase arrested my attention. I presently recognized it as that of Usher. In an instant afterward he rapped, with a gentle touch, at my door, and entered, bearing a lamp. His countenance was, as usual, cadaverously wan—but, moreover, there was a species of mad hilarity in his eyes—an evidently restrained *hysteria* in his whole demeanor. His air appalled me—but anything was preferable to the solitude which I had long endured, and I even welcomed his presence as a relief.

"And you have not seen it?" he said abruptly, after having stared about him for some moments in silence— "you have not then seen it?—but, stay! you shall." Thus speaking, and having carefully shaded his lamp, he hurried to one of the casements, and threw it freely open to the storm.

The impetuous fury of the entering gust nearly lifted us from our feet. It was, indeed, a tempestuous yet sternly beautiful night, and one wildly singular in its terror and its beauty. A whirlwind had apparently collected its force in our vicinity; for there were frequent and violent alterations in the direction of the wind; and the exceeding density of the clouds (which hung so low as to press upon the turrets of the house) did not prevent our perceiving the lifelike velocity with which they flew careering from all points against each other, without passing away into the distance. I say that even their exceeding density did not prevent our perceiving this—yet we had no glimpse of the moon or stars—nor was there any flashing forth of the lightning. But the under surfaces of the huge masses of agitated vapor, as well as all terrestrial objects immediately around us, were glowing in the unnatural light of a faintly luminous and distinctly visible gaseous exhalation which hung about and enshrouded the mansion.

"You must not—you shall not behold this!" said I, shudderingly, to Usher, as I led him, with a gentle violence, from the window to a seat. "These appearances, which bewilder you, are merely electrical phenomena not uncommon—or it may be that they have their ghastly origin in the rank miasma of the tarn. Let us close this casement;—the air is chilling and dangerous to your frame. Here is one of your favorite romances. I will read, and you shall listen;—and so we will pass this terrible night together."

The antique volume which I had taken up was the *Mad Trist* of Sir Launcelot Canning; but I had called it a favorite of Usher's more in sad jest than in earnest; for, in truth, there is little in its uncouth and unimaginative prolixity which could have had interest for the lofty and spiritual ideality of my friend. It was, however, the only book immediately at hand; and I indulged a vague hope that the excitement which now agitated the hypochondriac, might find relief (for the history of mental disorder is full of similar anomalies) even in the extremeness of the folly which I should read. Could I have judged, indeed, by the wild overstrained air of vivacity with which he hearkened, or apparently hearkened, to the words of the tale, I might well have congratulated myself upon the success of my design.

I had arrived at that well-known portion of the story where Ethelred, the hero of the Trist, having sought in vain for peaceable admission into the dwelling of the hermit, proceeds to make good an entrance by force. Here, it will be remembered, the words of the narrative run thus:

"And Ethelred, who was by nature of a doughty heart, and who was now mighty withal, on account of the power-fulness of the wine which he had drunken, waited no longer to hold parley with the hermit, who, in sooth, was of an obstinate and maliceful turn, but, feeling the rain upon his shoulders, and fearing the rising of the tempest, uplifted his mace outright, and, with blows, made quickly room in the plankings of the door for his gauntleted hand; and now pulling therewith sturdily, he so cracked, and ripped, and tore all asunder, that the noise of the dry and hollow sounding wood alarmed and reverberated throughout the forest."

At the termination of this sentence I started, and for a moment, paused; for it appeared to me (although I at once concluded that my excited fancy had deceived me) —it appeared to me that, from some very remote portion of the mansion, there came, indistinctly, to my ears, what might have been, in its exact similarity of character, the echo (but a stifled and dull one certainly) of the very cracking and ripping sound which Sir Launcelot had so particularly described. It was, beyond doubt, the coinci-dence alone which had arrested my attention; for, amid the rattling of the sashes of the casements, and the ordinary commingled noises of the still increasing storm, the sound, in itself, had nothing, surely, which should have interested or disturbed me. I continued the story.

"But the good champion Ethelred, now entering within the door, was sore enraged and amazed to perceive no signal of the maliceful hermit; but, in the stead thereof, a dragon of a scaly and prodigious demeanor, and of a fiery tongue, which sate in guard before a palace of gold, with a floor of silver; and upon the wall there hung a shield of shining brass with this legend enwritten—

Who entereth herein, a conqueror hath bin;
Who slayeth the dragon, the shield he shall win;

and Ethelred uplifted his mace, and struck upon the head of the dragon, which fell before him, and gave up his pesty breath, with a shriek so horrid and harsh, and withal so piercing, that Ethelred had fain to close his ears with his hands against the dreadful noise of it, the like whereof was never before heard."

Here again I paused abruptly, and now with a feeling of wild amazement—for there could be no doubt whatever that, in this instance, I did actually hear (although from what direction it proceeded I found it impossible to say) a low and apparent distant, but harsh, protracted, and most unusual screaming or grating sound—the exact counterpart of what my fancy had already conjured up for the dragon's unnatural shriek as described by the romancer.

Oppressed, as I certainly was, upon the occurrence of the second and most extraordinary coincidence, by a thousand conflicting sensations, in which wonder and extreme terror were predominant, I still retained sufficient presence of mind to avoid exciting, by any observation, the sensitive nervousness of my companion. I was by no means certain that he had noticed the sounds in question; although, assuredly, a strange alteration had, during the last few minutes, taken place in his demeanor. From a position fronting my own, he had gradually brought round his chair, so as to sit with his face to the door of the chamber; and thus I could but partially perceive his features, although I saw that his lips trembled as if he were murmuring inaudibly. His head had dropped upon his breast—yet I knew that he was not asleep, from the wide and rigid opening of the eye as I caught a glance of it in profile. The motion of his body, too, was at variance with this idea—for he rocked from side to side with a gentle yet constant and uniform sway. Having rapidly taken notice of all this, I resumed the narrative of Sir Launcelot, which thus proceeded:

"And now, the champion, having escaped from the terrible fury of the dragon, bethinking himself of the brazen shield, and of the breaking up of the enchantment which was upon it, removed the carcass from out of the way before him, and approached valorously over the silver pavement of the castle to where the shield was upon the wall; which in sooth tarried not for his full coming, but fell down at his feet upon the silver floor, with a mighty great and terrible ringing sound."

No sooner had these syllables passed my lips, than —as if a shield of brass had indeed, at the moment, fallen heavily upon a floor of silver—I became aware of a distinct, hollow, metallic, and clangorous, yet apparently muffled reverberation. Completely unnerved, I leaped to my feet; but the measured rocking movement of Usher was undisturbed. I rushed to the chair in which he sat. His eyes were bent fixedly before him, and throughout his whole countenance there reigned a stony rigidity. But, as I placed my hand upon his shoulder, there came a strong shudder over his whole person; a sickly smile quivered about his lips; and I saw that he spoke in a low, hurried, and gibbering murmur, as if unconscious of my presence. Bending closely over him, I at length drank in the hideous import of his words.

"Not hear it?—yes, I hear it, and *have* heard it. Long —long—long—many minutes, many hours, many days, have I heard it—yet I dared not—oh, pity me, miserable wretch that I am!—I dared not—*I dared* not speak! *We have put her living in the tomb!* Said I not that my senses were acute? I *now* tell you that I heard her first feeble movements in the hollow coffin. I heard them—many, many days ago—yet I dared not—*I dared not speak!* And now—to-night—Ethelred—ha! ha!—the breaking of the hermit's door, and the death-cry of the dragon, and the clangor of the shield!—say, rather, the rending of her coffin, and the grating of the iron hinges of her prison, and her struggles within the coppered archway of the vault! Oh whither shall I fly? Will she not be here anon? Is she not hurrying to upbraid me for my haste? Have I not heard her footsteps on the stair? Do I not distinguish that heavy and horrible beating of her heart? MADMAN!"—here he sprang furiously to his feet, and shrieked out his syllables, as if in the effort he were giving up his soul—"MADMAN! I TELL YOU THAT SHE STANDS WITHOUT THE DOOR!"

As if in the superhuman energy of his utterance there had been found the potency of a spell—the huge antique panels to which the speaker pointed, threw slowly back, upon the instant, their ponderous and ebony jaws. It was the work of the rushing gust—but then without those doors there DID stand the lofty and enshrouded figure of the Lady Madeline of Usher. There was blood upon her white robes, and the evidence of some bitter struggle upon every portion of her emaciated frame. For a moment she remained trembling and reeling to and fro upon the threshold, then, with a low moaning cry, fell heavily inward upon the person of her brother, and in her violent and now final death-agonies, bore him to the floor a corpse, and a victim to the terrors he had anticipated.

From that chamber, and from that mansion, I fled aghast. The storm was still abroad in all its wrath as I found myself crossing the old causeway. Suddenly there shot along the path a wild light, and I turned to see whence a gleam so unusual could have issued; for the vast house and its shadows were alone behind me. The radiance was that of the full, setting, and blood-red moon which now shone vividly through that once barely-discernible fissure of which I have before spoken as extending from the roof of the building, in a zigzag direction, to the base. While I gazed, this fissure rapidly widened—there came a fierce breath of the whirlwind—the entire orb of the satellite burst at once upon my sight—my brain reeled as I saw the mighty walls rushing asunder—there was a long tumultuous shouting sound like the voice of a thousand waters—and the deep and dank tarn at my feet closed sullenly and silently over the fragments of the "HOUSE OF USHER."

from

The House of the Seven Gables

by Nathaniel Hawthorne

CHAPTER I.

THE OLD PYNCHEON FAMILY

The House of the Seven Gables, antique as it now looks, was not the first habitation erected by civilized man, on precisely the same spot of ground. Pyncheon-street formerly bore the humbler appellation of Maule's Lane, from the name of the original occupant of the soil, before whose cottage-door it was a cow-path. A natural spring of soft and pleasant water—a rare treasure on the sea-girt peninsula, where the Puritan settlement was made—had early induced Matthew Maule to build a hut, shaggy with thatch, at this point, although somewhat too remote from what was then the centre of the village. In the growth of the town, however, after some thirty or forty years, the site covered by this rude hovel had become exceedingly desirable in the eyes of a prominent and powerful personage, who asserted plausible claims to the proprietorship of this, and a large adjacent tract of land, on the strength of a grant from the legislature. Colonel Pyncheon, the claimant, as we gather from whatever traits of him are preserved, was characterized by an iron energy of purpose. Matthew Maule, on the other hand, though an obscure man, was stubborn in the defence of what he considered his right; and, for several years, he succeeded in protecting the acre or two of earth which, with his own toil, he had hewn out of the primeval forest, to be his garden-ground and homestead. No written record of this dispute is known to be in existence. Our acquaintance with the whole subject is derived chiefly from tradition. It would be bold, therefore, and possibly unjust, to venture a decisive opinion as to its merits; although it appears to have been at least a matter of doubt, whether Colonel Pyncheon's claim were not unduly stretched, in order to make it cover the small metes and bounds of Matthew Maule. What greatly strengthens such a suspicion is the fact, that this controversy between two ill-matched antagonists—at a period, moreover, laud it as we may, when personal influence had far more weight than now—remained for years undecided, and came to a close only with the death of the party occupying the disputed soil. The mode of his death, too, affects the mind differently, in our day, from what it did a century and a half ago. It was a death that blasted with strange horror the humble name of the dweller in the cottage, and made it seem almost a religious act to drive the plough over the little area of his habitation, and obliterate his place and memory from among men.

Old Matthew Maule, in a word, was executed for the crime of witchcraft. He was one of the martyrs to that terrible delusion which should teach us, among its other morals, that the influential classes, and those who take upon themselves to be leaders of the people, are fully liable to all the passionate error that has ever characterized the maddest mob. Clergymen, judges, statesmen—the wisest, calmest, holiest persons of their day—stood in the inner circle roundabout the gallows, loudest to applaud the work of blood, latest to confess themselves miserably deceived. If any one part of their proceedings can be said to deserve less blame than another, it was the singular indiscrimination with which they persecuted, not merely the poor and aged, as in former judicial massacres, but people of all ranks; their own equals, brethren, and wives. Amid the disorder of such various ruin, it is not strange that a man of inconsiderable note, like Maule, should have trodden the martyr's path to the hill of execution, almost unremarked in the throng of his fellow-sufferers. But, in after days, when the frenzy of that hideous epoch had subsided, it was remembered how loudly Colonel Pyncheon had joined in the general cry, to purge the land from witchcraft; nor did it fail to be whispered, that there was an invidious acrimony in the zeal with which he had sought the condemnation of Matthew Maule. It was well known, that the victim had recognized the bitterness of personal enmity in his persecutor's conduct towards him, and that he declared himself hunted to death for his spoil. At the moment of execution—with the halter about his neck, and while Colonel Pyncheon sat on horseback, grimly gazing at the scene—Maule had addressed him from the scaffold, and uttered a prophecy, of which history, as well as fireside tradition, has preserved the very words.—"God," said the dying man, pointing his finger with a ghastly look at the undismayed countenance of his enemy, "God will give him blood to drink!"

After the reputed wizard's death, his humble homestead had fallen an easy spoil into Colonel Pyncheon's grasp. When it was understood, however, that the Colonel intended to erect a family mansion—spacious, ponderously framed of oaken timber, and calculated to endure for many generations of his posterity—over the spot first covered by the log-built hut of Matthew Maule, there was much shaking of the head among the village-gossips. Without absolutely expressing a doubt whether the stalwart Puritan had acted as a man of conscience and integrity, throughout the proceedings which have been sketched, they nevertheless hinted that he was about to build his house over an unquiet grave. His home would include the home of the dead and buried wizard, and would thus afford the ghost of the latter a kind of privilege to haunt its new apartments, and the chambers into which future bridegrooms were to lead their brides, and where children of the Pyncheon blood were to be born. The terror and ugliness of Maule's crime, and the wretchedness of his punishment, would darken the freshly plastered walls, and infect them early with the scent of an old and melancholy house. Why, then—while so much of the soil around him was bestrewn with the virgin forest-leaves—why should Colonel Pyncheon prefer a site that had already been accurst?

But the Puritan soldier and magistrate was not a man to be turned aside from his well-considered scheme, either by dread of the wizard's ghost, or by the flimsy sentimentalities of any kind, however specious. Had he been told of a bad air, it might have moved him somewhat; but he was ready to encounter an evil spirit, on his own ground. Endowed with common-sense, as massive and hard as blocks of grantite, fastened together by stern rigidity of purpose, as with iron clamps, he followed out his original design, probably without so much as imagining an objection to it. On the score of delicacy, or any scrupulousness which a finer sensibility might have taught him, the Colonel, like most of his breed and generation, was impenetrable. He therefore dug his cellar, and laid the deep foundations of his mansion, on the square of earth whence Matthew Maule, forty years before, had first swept away the fallen leaves. It was curious, and, as some people thought, an ominous fact, that, very soon after the workmen began their operations, the spring of water, above-mentioned, entirely lost the deliciousness of its pristine quality. Whether its scources were disturbed by the depth of the new cellar, or whatever subtler cause might lurk at the bottom, it is certain that the water of Maule's Well, as it continued to be called, grew hard and brackish. Even such we find it now; and any old woman of the neighborhood will certify, that it is productive of intestinal mischief to those who quench their thirst there.

The reader may deem it singular, that the head-carpenter of the new edifice was no other than the son of the very man, from whose dead gripe the property of the soil had been wrested. Not improbably, he was the best workman of his time; or, perhaps, the Colonel thought it expedient, or was impelled by some better feeling, thus openly to cast aside all animosity against the race of his fallen antagonist. Nor was it out of keeping with the general coarseness and matter-of-fact character of the age, that the son should be willing to earn an honest penny —or rather, a weighty amount of sterling pounds—from the purse of his father's deadly enemy. At all events, Thomas Maule became the architect of the House of the Seven Gables, and performed his duty so faithfully, that the timber frame-work, fastened by his hands, still holds together.

Thus the great house was built. Familiar as it stands in the writer's recollection—for it has been an object of curiosity with him from boyhood, both as a specimen of the best and stateliest architecture of a long-past epoch, and as the scene of events more full of human interest, perhaps, that those of a gray, feudal castle—familiar as it stands, in its rusty old-age, it is therefore only the more difficult to imagine the bright novelty with which it first caught the sunshine. The impression of its actual state, at this distance of a hundred and sixty years, darkens inevitably through the picture which we would fain give of its appearance, on the morning when the Puritan magnate bade all the town to be his guests. A ceremony of consecration, festive, as well as religious, was now to be performed. A prayer and discourse from the Reverend Mr. Higginson, and the outpouring of a psalm from the general throat of the community, was to be made acceptable to the grosser scene by ale, cider, wine, and brandy, in copious effusion, and, as some authorities aver, by an ox roasted whole, or, at least, by the weight and substance of an ox, in more manageable joints and sirloins. The carcass of a deer, shot within twenty miles, had supplied material for the vast circumference of a pasty. A cod-fish of sixty pounds, caught in the bay, had been dissolved into the rich liquid of a chowder. The chimney of the new house, in short, belching forth its kitchen-smoke, impregnated the whole air with the scent of meats, fowls, and fishes, spicily concocted with odoriferous herbs, and onions in abundance. The mere smell of such festivity, making its way to everybody's nostrils, was at once an invitation and an appetite.

Maule's Lane—or Pyncheon-street, as it were now more decorous to call it—was thronged, at the appointed hour, as with a congregation on its way to church. All, as they approached, looked upward at the imposing edifice, which was henceforth to assume its rank among the habitations of mankind. There it rose, a little withdrawn from the line of the street, but in pride, not modesty. Its whole visible exterior was ornamented with quaint figures, conceived in the grotesqueness of a Gothic fancy, and drawn or stamped in the glittering plaster, composed of lime, pebbles, and bits of glass, with which the wood-work of the walls was overspread. On every side, the seven gables pointed sharply towards the sky, and presented the aspect of a whole sisterhood of edifices, breathing through the spiracles of one great chimney. The many lattices, with their small, diamond-shaped panes, admitted the sunlight into hall and chamber; while, nevertheless, the second story, projecting far over the base, and itself retiring beneath the third, threw a shadow and thoughtful gloom into the lower rooms. Carved globes of wood were affixed under the jutting stories. Little, spiral rods of iron beautified each of the seven peaks. On the triangular portion of the gable that fronted next the street, was a dial, put up that very morning, and on which the sun was still marking the passage of the first bright hour in a history, that was not destined to be all so bright. All around were scattered shavings, chips, shingles, and broken halves of bricks; these—together with the lately turned earth, on which the grass had not begun to grow—contributed to the impression of strangeness and novelty, proper to a house that had yet its place to make among men's daily interests.

The principal entrance, which had almost the breadth of a church-door, was in the angle between the two front gables, and was covered by an open porch, with benches beneath its shelter. Under this arched door-way, scraping their feet on the unworn threshold, now trod the clergymen, the elders, the magistrates, the deacons, and whatever of aristocracy there was in town or country. Thither, too, thronged the plebeian classes, as freely as their betters, and in larger numbers. Just within the entrance, however, stood two serving-men, pointing some of the guests to the neighborhood of the kitchen, and ushering others into the statelier rooms; hospitable alike to all, but still with a scrutinizing regard to the high or low degree of each. Velvet garments, sombre, but rich, stiffly plaited ruffs and bands, embroidered gloves, venerable beards, the mein and countenance of authority, made it easy to distinguish the gentleman of worship, at that period, from the tradesman, with his plodding air, or the laborer in his leathern jerkin, stealing awe-stricken into the house which he had perhaps helped to build.

One inauspicious circumstance there was, which awakened a hardly concealed displeasure in the breasts of a few of the more punctilious visitors. The founder of this stately mansion—a gentleman noted for the square and ponderous courtesy of his demeanor—ought surely to have stood in his own hall, and to have offered the first welcome to so many eminent personages as here presented themselves, in honor of his solemn festival. He was as yet invisible; the most favored of the guests had not beheld him. This sluggishness on Colonel Pyncheon's part became still more unaccountable, when the second dignitary of the province made his appearance, and found no more ceremonious a reception. The Lieutenant Governor, although his visit was one of the anticipated glories of the day, had alighted from his horse, and assisted his lady from her side-saddle, and crossed the Colonel's threshold, without other greeting than that of the principal domestic.

This person—a gray-headed man of quiet and most respectful deportment—found it necessary to explain that his master still remained in his study, or private apartment; on entering which, an hour before, he had expressed a wish on no account to be disturbed.

"Do not you see, fellow," said the high-sheriff of the county, taking the servant aside, "that this is no less a man than the Lieutenant Governor? Summon Colonel Pyncheon at once! I know that he received letters from England, this morning; and, in the perusal and consideration of them, an hour may have passed away, without his noticing it. But he will be ill-pleased, I judge, if you suffer him to neglect the courtesy due to one of our chief rulers, and who may be said to represent King William, in the absence of the Governor himself. Call your master instantly!"

"Nay, please your worship," answered the man, in much perplexity, but with a backwardness that strikingly indicated the hard and severe character of Colonel Pyncheon's domestic rule, "my master's orders were exceedingly strict; and, as your worship knows, he permits of no discretion in the obedience of those who owe him service. Let who list open yonder door! I dare not, though the Governor's own voice should bid me do it!"

"Pooh, pooh, Master High Sheriff!" cried the Lieutenant Governor, who had overheard the foregoing discussion, and felt himself high enough in station to play a little with his dignity.—"I will take the matter into my own hands. It is time that the good Colonel came forth to greet his friends; else we shall be apt to suspect that he has taken a sip too much of his Canary wine, in his extreme deliberation which cask it were best to broach, in honor of the day! But since he is so much behindhand, I will give him a remembrancer myself!"

Accordingly—with such a tramp of his ponderous ridingboots as might of itself have been audible in the remotest of the seven gables—he advanced to the door, which the servant pointed out, and made its new panels re-echo with a loud, free knock. Then, looking round with a smile to the spectators, he awaited a response. As none came, however, he knocked again, but with the same unsatisfactory result as at first. And, now, being a trifle choleric in his temperament, the Lieutenant Governor uplifted the heavy-hilt of his sword, wherewith he so beat and banged upon the door, that, as some of the bystanders whispered, the racket might have disturbed the dead. Be that as it might, it seemed to produce no awakening effect on Colonel Pyncheon. When the sound subsided, the silence through the house was deep, dreary, and oppressive; notwithstanding that the tongues of many of the guests had already been loosened by a surreptitious cup or two of wine or spirits.

"Strange, forsooth! very strange!" cried the Lieutenant Governor, whose smile was changed to a frown. "But, seeing that our host sets us the good example of forgetting ceremony, I shall likewise throw it aside, and make free to intrude on his privacy!"

He tried the door which yielded to his hand, and was flung wide open by a sudden gust of wind that passed, as with a loud sigh, from the outermost portal through all the passages and apartments of the new house. It rustled the silken garments of the ladies, and waved the long curls of the gentlemen's wigs, and shook the window-hangings and the curtains of the bed-chambers; causing everywhere a singular stir, which yet was more like a hush. A shadow of awe and half-fearful anticipation—nobody knew wherefore, nor of what—had all at once fallen over the company.

They thronged, however, to the now open door, pressing the Lieutenant Governor, in the eagerness of their curiosity, into the room in advance of them. At the first glimpse, they beheld nothing extraordinary, a handsomely furnished room of moderate size, somewhat darkened by curtains; books arranged on shelves; a large map on the wall, and likewise a portrait of Colonel Pyncheon, beneath which sat the original Colonel himself, in an oaken elbow-chair, with a pen in his hand. Letters, parchments, and blank sheets of paper were on the table before him. He appeared to gaze at the curious crowd, in front of which stood the Lieutenant Governor; and there was a frown on his dark and massive countenance, as if sternly resentful of the boldness that had impelled them into his private retirement.

A little boy—the Colonel's grandchild, and the only human being that ever dared to be familiar with him—now made his way among the guests and ran towards the seated figure; then pausing half-way, he began to shriek with terror. The company—tremulous as the leaves of a tree, when all are shaking together—drew nearer, and perceived that there was an unnatural distortion in the fixedness of Colonel Pyncheon's stare; that there was blood on his ruff, and that his hoary beard was saturated with it. It was too late to give assistance. The iron-hearted Puritan—the relentless persecutor—the grasping and strong-willed man—was dead! Dead, in his new house! There is a tradition—only worth alluding to, as lending a tinge of superstitious awe to a scene, perhaps gloomy enough without it—that a voice spoke loudly among the guests, the tones of which were like those of old Matthew

Maule, the executed wizard:—"God hath given him blood to drink!"

Thus early had that one guest—the only guest who is certain, at one time or another, to find his way into every human dwelling—thus early had Death stept across the threshold of the House of the Seven Gables!

* * * * * * * * * * * * * * * *

We have already hinted, that it is not our purpose to trace down the history of the Pyncheon family, in its unbroken connection with the House of the Seven Gables; nor to show, as in a magic picture, how the rustiness and infirmity of age gathered over the venerable house itself. As regards its interior life, a large, dim looking-glass used to hang in one of the rooms, and was fabled to contain within its depths all the shapes that had ever been reflected there; the old Colonel himself, and his many descendants, some in the garb of antique babyhood, and others in the bloom of feminine beauty, or manly prime, or saddened with the wrinkles of frosty age. Had we the secret of that mirror, we would gladly sit down before it, and transfer its revelations to our page. But there was a story, for which it is difficult to conceive any foundation, that the posterity of Matthew Maule had some connection with the mystery of the looking-glass, and that—by what appears to have been a sort of mesmeric process—they could make its inner region all alive with the departed Pyncheons; not as they had shown themselves to the world, nor in their better and happier hours, but as doing over again some deed of sin, or in the crisis of life's bitterest sorrow. The popular imagination, indeed, long kept itself busy with the affair of the old Puritan Pyncheon and the wizard Maule; the curse, which the latter flung from his scaffold, was remembered, with the very important addition, that it had become a part of the Pyncheon inheritance. If one of the family did but gurgle in his throat, a bystander would be likely enough to whisper, between jest and earnest—"He has Maule's blood to drink!"—The sudden death of Pyncheon, about a hundred years ago, with circumstances very similar to what have been related of the Colonel's exit, was held as giving additional probability to the received opinion on this topic. It was considered, moreover, an ugly and ominous circumstance, that Colonel Pyncheon's picture —in obedience, it was said, to a provision of his will— remained affixed to the wall of the room in which he died. Those stern, immitigable features seemed to symbolize an evil influence, and so darkly to mingle the shadow of their presence with the sunshine of the passing hour, that no good thoughts or purposes could ever spring up and blossom there. To the thoughtful mind, there will be no tinge of superstition in what we figuratively express, by affirming that the ghost of a dead progenitor —perhaps as a portion of his own punishment—is often doomed to become the Evil Genius of his family.

The Signal-Man

by Charles Dickens

"Halloa! Below there!"

When he heard a voice thus calling to him, he was standing at the door of his box, with a flag in his hand, furled round its short pole. One would have thought, considering the nature of the ground, that he could not have doubted from what quarter the voice came; but, instead of looking up to where I stood on the top of the steep cutting nearly over his head, he turned himself about and looked down the Line. There was something remarkable in his manner of doing so, though I could not have said, for my life, what. But I know it was remarkable enough to attract my notice, even though his figure was foreshortened and shadowed, down in the deep trench, and mine was high above him, and so steeped in the glow of an angry sunset that I had shaded my eyes with my hand before I saw him at all.

"Halloa! Below!"

From looking down the Line, he turned himself about again, and, raising his eyes, saw my figure high above him.

"Is there any path by which I can come down and speak to you?"

He looked up at me without replying, and I looked down at him without pressing him too soon with a repetition of my idle question. Just then there came a vague vibration in the earth and air, quickly changing into a violent pulsation, and an oncoming rush that caused me to start back, as though it had force to draw me down. When such vapor as rose to my height from this rapid train had passed me and was skimming away over the landscape, I looked down again, and saw him refurling the flag he had shown while the train went by.

I repeated my inquiry. After a pause, during which he seemed to regard me with fixed attention, he motioned with his rolled-up flag towards a point on my level, some two or three hundred yards distant. I called down to him, "All right!" and made for that point. There, by dint of looking closely about me, I found a rough zigzag descending path notched out; which I followed.

The cutting was extremely deep, and unusually precipitate. It was made through a clammy stone that became oozier and wetter as I went down. For these reasons, I found the way long enough to give me time to recall a singular air of reluctance or compulsion with which he had pointed out the path.

When I came down low enough upon the zigzag descent, to see him again, I saw that he was standing between the rails on the way by which the train had lately passed, in an attitude as if he were waiting for me to appear. He had his left hand at his chin, and that left elbow rested on his right hand crossed over his breast. His attitude was one of such expectation and watchfulness, that I stopped a moment, wondering at it.

I resumed my downward way, and, stepping out upon the level of the railroad and drawing nearer to him, saw that he was a dark, sallow man, with a dark beard and rather heavy eyebrows. His post was in as solitary and dismal a place as ever I saw. On either side, a dripping-wet wall of jagged stone, excluding all view but a strip of sky: the perspective one way, only a crooked prolongation of this great dungeon; the shorter perspective in the other direction, terminating in a gloomy red light, and the gloomier entrance to a black tunnel, in whose massive architecture there was a barbarous, depressing, and forbidding air. So little sunlight ever found its way to this spot, and it had an earthy deadly smell; and so much cold wind rushed through it, that it struck chill to me, as if I had left the natural world.

Before he stirred, I was near enough to him to have touched him. Not even then removing his eyes from mine, he stepped back one step, and lifted his hand.

This was a lonesome post to occupy (I said), and it had riveted my attention when I looked down from up yonder. A visitor was a rarity, I should suppose; not an unwelcome rarity, I hoped? In me, he merely saw a man who had been shut up within narrow limits all his life, and who, being at last set free, had a newly awakened interest in these great works. To such purpose I spoke to him; but I am far from sure of the terms I used, for, besides that I am not happy in opening any conversation, there was something in the man that daunted me.

He directed a most curious look towards the red light near the tunnel's mouth, and looked all about it, as if something were missing from it, then looked at me.

That light was part of his charge? Was it not?

He answered in a low voice, "Don't you know it is?"

The monstrous thought came into my mind, as I perused the fixed eyes and the saturnine face, that this was a spirit, not a man. I have speculated since whether there may have been infection in his mind.

In my turn, I stepped back. But in making the action, I detected in his eyes some latent fear of me. This put the monstrous thought to flight.

"You look at me," I said, forcing a smile, "as if you had a dread of me."

"I was doubtful," he returned, "whether I had seen you before."

"Where?"

He pointed to the red light he had looked at.

"There?" I said.

Intently watchful of me, he replied (but without sound), "Yes."

"My good fellow, what should I do there? However, be that as it may, I never was there, you may swear."

"I think I may," he rejoined. "Yes, I am sure I may."

His manner cleared, like my own. He replied to my remarks with readiness, and in well-chosen words. Had he much to do there? Yes; that was to say, he had enough responsibility to bear; but exactness and watchfulness were what was required of him, and of actual work—manual labor—he had next to none. To change that signal, to trim those lights, and to turn this iron handle now and then, was all he had to do under that head. Regarding those many long and lonely hours of which I seemed to make so much, he could only say that the routine of his life had shaped itself into that form, and he had grown used to it. He had taught himself a language down here,—if only to know it by sight, and to have formed his own crude ideas of its pronunciation, could be called learning it. He had also worked at fractions and decimals, and tried a little algebra; but he was, and had been as a boy, a poor hand at figures. Was it necessary for him, when on duty, always to remain in that channel of damp air, and could he never rise into the sunshine from between those high stone walls? Why, that depended upon times and circumstances. Under some conditions there would be less upon the Line than under others, and the same held good as to certain hours of the day and night. In bright weather, he did choose occasions for getting a little above these lower shadows; but, being at all times liable to be called by his electric bell, and at such times listening for it with redoubled anxiety, the relief was less than I would suppose.

He took me into his box, where there was a fire, a desk for an official book in which he had to make certain entries, a telegraphic instrument with its dial face and needles, and the little bell of which he had spoken. On my trusting that he would excuse the remark that he had been well educated, and (I hoped I might say without offence) perhaps educated above that station, he observed that instances of slight incongruity in such-wise would rarely be found wanting among large bodies of men; that he had heard it was so in workhouses, in the police force, even in that last desperate resource, the army; and that he knew it was so, more or less, in any great railway staff. He had been, when young (if I could believe it, sitting in that hut; he scarcely could), a student of natural philosophy, and had attended lectures; but he had run wild, misused his opportunities, gone down, and never risen again. He had no complaint to offer about that. He had made his bed, and he lay upon it. It was far too late to make another.

All that I have here condensed he said in a quiet manner, with his grave dark regards divided between me and the fire. He threw in the word "Sir" from time to time, and especially when he referred to his youth, as though to request me to understand that he claimed to be nothing but what I found him. He was several times interrupted by the little bell, and had to read off messages, and send replies. Once he had to stand without the door and display a flag as a train passed, and make some verbal communication to the driver. In the discharge of his duties I observed him to be remarkably exact and vigilant, breaking off his discourse at a syllable, and remaining silent until what he had to do was done.

In a word, I should have set this man down as one of the safest of men to be employed in that capacity, but for the circumstance that while he was speaking to me he twice broke off with a fallen color, turned his face towards the little bell when it did NOT ring, opened the door of the hut (which was kept shut to exclude the unhealthy damp), and looked out towards the red light near the mouth of the tunnel. On both of those occasions he came back to the fire with the inexplicable air upon him which I had remarked, without being able to define, when we were so far asunder.

Said I, when I rose to leave him, "You almost make me think that I have met with a contented man."

(I am afraid I must acknowledge that I said it to lead him on.)

"I believe I used to be so," he rejoined, in the low voice in which he had first spoken; "but I am troubled, sir, I am troubled."

He would have recalled the words if he could. He had said them, however, and I took them up quickly.

"With what? What is your trouble?"

"It is very difficult to impart, sir. It is very, very difficult to speak of. If ever you make me another visit, I will try to tell you."

"But I expressly intend to make you another visit. Say, when shall it be?"

"I go off early in the morning, and I shall be on again at ten to-morrow night, sir."

"I will come at eleven."

He thanked me, and went out at the door with me. "I'll show my white light, sir," he said, in his peculiar low voice, "till you have found the way up. When you have found it, don't call out! And when you are at the top, don't call out!"

His manner seemed to make the place strike colder to me, but I said no more than, "Very well."

"And when you come down to-morrow night, don't call out! Let me ask you a parting question. What made you cry, 'Halloa! Below there!' to-night?"

"Heaven knows," said I. "I cried something to that effect—"

"Not to that effect, sir. Those were the very words. I know them well."

"Admit those were the very words. I said them, no doubt, because I saw you below."

"For no other reason?"

"What other reason could I possibly have?"

"You had no feeling that they were conveyed to you in any supernatural way?"

"No."

He wished me good night, and held up his light. I walked by the side of the down Line of rails (with a very disagreeable sensation of a train coming behind me), until I found the path. It was easier to mount than to descend, and I got back to my inn without any adventure.

Punctual to my appointment, I placed my foot on the first notch of the zigzag next night, as the distant clocks were striking eleven. He was waiting for me at the bottom, with his white light on.

"I have not called out," I said, when we came close together; "may I speak now?"

"By all means, sir."

"Good night, then, and here's my hand."

"Good night, sir, and here's mine."

With that, we walked side by side to his box, entered it, closed the door, and sat down by the fire.

"I have made up my mind, sir," he began, bending forward as soon as we were seated, and speaking in a tone but a little above a whisper, "that you shall not have to ask me twice what troubles me. I took you for some one else yesterday evening. That troubles me."

"That mistake?"

"No. That some one else."

"Who is it?"

"I don't know."

"Like me?"

"I don't know. I never saw the face. The left arm is across the face, and the right arm is waved. Violently waved. This way."

I followed his action with my eyes, and it was the action of an arm gesticulating with the utmost passion and vehemence: "For God's sake clear the way!"

"One moonlight night," said the man, "I was sitting here, when I heard a voice cry, 'Halloa! Below there!' I started up, looked from that door, and saw this some one else standing by the red light near the tunnel, waving as I just now showed you. The voice seemed hoarse with shouting, and it cried, 'Look out! Look out!' And then again, 'Halloa! Below there! Look out!' I caught up my lamp, turned it on red, and ran towards the figure, calling, 'What's wrong? What has happened? Where?' It stood just outside the blackness of the tunnel. I advanced so close upon it that I wondered at its keeping the sleeve across its eyes. I ran right up at it, and had my hand stretched out to pull the sleeve away, when it was gone."

"Into the tunnel?" said I.

"No. I ran on into the tunnel, five hundred yards. I stopped and held my lamp above my head, and saw the figures of the measured distance, and saw the wet stains stealing down the walls and trickling through the arch. I ran out again, faster than I had run in (for I had a mortal abhorrence of the place upon me), and I looked all round the red light with my own red light, and I went up the iron ladder to the gallery atop of it, and I came down again, and ran back here. I telegraphed both

ways, 'An alarm has been given. Is anything wrong?'
The answer came back, both ways, 'All well.' "

Resisting the slow touch of a frozen finger tracing out
my spine, I showed him how that this figure must be a
deception of his sense of sight, and how that figures,
originating in disease of the delicate nerves that minister
to the functions of the eye, were known to have often
troubled patients, some of whom had become conscious
of the nature of their affliction, and had even proved it
by experiments upon themselves. "As to an imaginary
cry," said I, "do but listen for a moment to the wind in
this unnatural valley while we speak so low, and to the
wild harp it makes of the telegraph wires!"

That was all very well, he returned, after we had sat
listening for a while, and he ought to know something of
the wind and the wires, he who so often passed long
winter nights there, alone and watching. But he would
beg to remark that he had not finished.

I asked his pardon, and he slowly added these words,
touching my arm:—

"Within six hours after the Appearance, the memorable accident on this Line happened, and within ten hours
the dead and wounded were brought along through the
tunnel over the spot where the figure had stood."

A disagreeable shudder crept over me, but I did my
best against it. It was not to be denied, I rejoined, that
this was a remarkable coincidence, calculated deeply to
impress the mind. But it was unquestionable that remarkable coincidences did continually occur, and they
must be taken into account in dealing with such a subject. Though to be sure I must admit, I added (for I
thought I saw that he was going to bring the objection
to bear upon me), men of common-sense did not allow
much for coincidences in making the ordinary calculations of life.

He again begged to remark that he had not finished.

I again begged his pardon for being betrayed into interruptions.

"This," he said, again laying his hand upon my arm, and glancing over his shoulder with hollow eyes, "was just a year ago. Six or seven months passed, and I had recovered from the surprise and shock, when one morning, as the day was breaking, I, standing at that door, looked towards the red light, and saw the spectre again." He stopped, with a fixed look at me.

"Did it cry out?"

"No. It was silent."

"Did it wave its arm?"

"No. It leaned against the shaft of the light, with both hands before the face. Like this."

Once more, I followed his action with my eyes. It was an action of mourning. I have seen such an attitude in stone figures on tombs.

"Did you go up to it?"

"I came in and sat down, partly to collect my thoughts, partly because it had turned me faint. When I went to the door again, daylight was above me, and the ghost was gone."

"But nothing followed? Nothing came of this?"

He touched me on the arm with his forefinger twice or thrice, giving a ghastly nod each time.

"That very day, as a train came out of the tunnel, I noticed, at a carriage window on my side, what looked like a confusion of hands and heads, and something waved. I saw it just in time to signal the driver, Stop! He shut off, and put his brake on, but the train drifted past here a hundred and fifty yards or more. I ran after it, and as I went along heard terrible screams and cries. A beautiful young lady had died instantaneously in one of the compartments, and was brought in here, and laid down on this floor between us."

Involuntarily I pushed my chair back, as I looked from the boards at which he pointed, to himself.

"True, sir. True. Precisely as it happened, so I tell it you."

I could think of nothing to say, to any purpose, and my mouth was very dry. The wind and the wires took up the story with a long lamenting wail.

He resumed. "Now, sir, mark this, and judge how my mind is troubled. The spectre came back, a week ago. Ever since, it has been there, now and again, by fits and starts."

"At the light?"

"At the Danger-light."

"What does it seem to do?"

He repeated, if possible with increased passion and vehemence, that former gesticulation of "For God's sake clear the way!"

Then he went on. "I have no peace or rest for it. It calls to me, for many minutes together, in an agonized manner, 'Below there! Look out! Look out!' It stands waving to me. It rings my little bell—"

I caught at that. "Did it ring your bell yesterday evening when I was here, and you went to the door?"

"Twice."

"Why, see," said I, "how your imagination misleads you. My eyes were on the bell, and my ears were open to the bell, and, if I am a living man, it did NOT ring at those times. No, nor at any other time, except when it was rung in the natural course of physical things by the station communicating with you."

He shook his head. "I have never made a mistake as to that, yet, sir. I have never confused the spectre's ring with the man's. The ghost's ring is a strange vibration in the bell that it derives from nothing else, and I have not asserted that the bell stirs to the eye. I don't wonder that you failed to hear it. But *I* heard it."

"And did the spectre seem to be there, when you looked out?"

"It WAS there."

"Both times?"

He repeated firmly: "Both times."

"Will you come to the door with me, and look for it now?"

He bit his under-lip as though he were somewhat unwilling, but arose. I opened the door, and stood on the step, while he stood in the doorway. There was the Danger-light. There was the dismal mouth of the tunnel. There were the high wet stone walls of the cutting. There were the stairs above them.

"Do you see it?" I asked him, taking particular note of his face. His eyes were prominent and strained; but not very much more so, perhaps, than my own had been when I had directed them earnestly towards the same point.

"No," he answered. "It is not there."

"Agreed," said I.

We went in again, shut the door, and resumed our seats. I was thinking how best to improve this advantage, if it might be called one, when he took up the conversation in such a matter-of-course way, so assuming that there could be no serious question of fact between us, that I felt myself placed in the weakest of positions.

"By this time you will fully understand, sir," he said, "that what troubles me so dreadfully is the question, What does the spectre mean?"

I was not sure, I told him, that I did fully understand.

"What is its warning against?" he said, ruminating, with his eyes on the fire, and only by times turning them on me. "What is the danger? Where is the danger? There is danger overhanging, somewhere on the Line. Some dreadful calamity will happen. It is not to be doubted this third time, after what has gone before. But surely this is a cruel haunting of *me*. What can *I* do?"

He pulled out his handkerchief, and wiped the drops from his heated forehead.

"If I telegraph Danger on either side of me, or on both, I can give no reason for it," he went on, wiping the palms of his hands. "I should get into trouble, and do no good. They would think I was mad. This is the way it would work:—Message: 'Danger! Take care!' Answer: 'What Danger? Where?' Message: 'Don't know. But for God's sake take care!' They would displace me. What else could they do?"

His pain of mind was most pitiable to see. It was the mental torture of a conscientious man, oppressed beyond endurance by an unintelligible responsibility involving life.

"When it first stood under the Danger-light," he went on, putting his dark hair back from his head, and drawing his hands outward across and across his temples in an extremity of feverish distress, "why not tell me where that accident was to happen,—if it must happen? Why not tell me how it could be averted,—if it could have been averted? When on its second coming it hid its face, why not tell me instead: 'She is going to die. Let them keep her at home'? If it came, on those two occasions, only to show me that its warnings were true, and so to prepare me for the third, why not warn me plainly now? And I, Lord help me! A mere poor signal-man on this solitary station! Why not go to somebody with credit to be believed, and power to act?"

When I saw him in this state, I saw that for the poor man's sake, as well as for the public safety, what I had to do for the time was to compose his mind. Therefore, setting aside all question of reality or unreality between us, I represented to him that whoever thoroughly discharged his duty must do well, and that at least it was his comfort that he understood his duty, though he did not understand these confounding Appearances. In this effort I succeeded far better than in the attempt to reason him out of his conviction. He became calm; the occupation incidental to his post, as the night advanced, began to make larger demands on his attention; and I left him at two in the morning. I had offered to stay through the night, but he would not hear of it.

That I more than once looked back at the red light as I ascended the pathway, that I did not like the red light, and that I should have slept but poorly if my bed had been under it, I see no reason to conceal. Nor did I like the two sequences of the accident and the dead girl. I see no reason to conceal that, either.

But what ran most in my thoughts was the consideration, how ought I to act, having become the recipient of this disclosure? I had proved the man to be intelligent, vigilant, painstaking, and exact; but how long might be remain so, in his state of mind? Though in a subordinate position, still he held a most important trust, and would I (for instance) like to stake my own life on the chances of his continuing to execute it with precision?

Unable to overcome a feeling that there would be something treacherous in my communicating what he had told me to his superiors in the Company, without first being plain with himself and proposing a middle course to him, I ultimately resolved to offer to accompany him (otherwise keeping his secret for the present) to the wisest medical practitioner we could hear of in those parts, and to take his opinion. A change in his time of duty would come round next night, he had apprised me, and he would be off an hour or two after sunrise, and on again soon after sunset. I had appointed to return accordingly.

Next evening was a lovely evening, and I walked out early to enjoy it. The sun was not yet quite down when I traversed the field-path near the top of the deep cutting. I would extend my walk for an hour, I said to myself, half an hour on and half an hour back, and it would then be time to go to my signal-man's box.

Before pursuing my stroll I stepped to the brink, and mechanically looked down, from the point from which I had first seen him. I cannot describe the thrill that seized upon me, when, close at the mouth of the tunnel, I saw the appearance of a man, with his left sleeve across his eyes, passionately waving his right arm.

The nameless horror that oppressed me passed in a moment, for in a moment I saw that this appearance of a man was a man indeed, and that there was a little group of other men standing at a short distance, to whom he seemed to be rehearsing the gesture he made. The Danger-light was not yet lighted. Against its shaft, a little low hut, entirely new to me, had been made of some wooden supports and tarpaulin. It looked no bigger than a bed.

With an irresistible sense that something was wrong, with a flashing self-reproachful fear that fatal mischief had come of my leaving the man there, and causing no one to be sent to overlook or correct what he did,—I descended the notched path with all the speed I could make.

"What is the matter?" I asked the men.

"Signal-man killed this morning, sir."

"Not the man belonging to that box?"

"Yes, sir."

"Not the man I know?"

"You will recognize him, sir, if you knew him," said the man who spoke for the others, solemnly uncovering his own head and raising an end of the tarpaulin, "for his face is quite composed."

"O, how did this happen, how did this happen?" I asked, turning from one to another as the hut closed in again.

"He was cut down by an engine, sir. No man in England knew his work better. But somehow he was not clear of the outer rail. It was just at broad day.

He had struck the light, and had the lamp in his hand. As the engine came out of the tunnel, his back was towards her, and she cut him down. That man drove her, and was showing how it happened. Show the gentleman, Tom."

The man, who wore a rough dark dress, stepped back to his former place at the mouth of the tunnel.

"Coming round the curve in the tunnel, sir," he said, "I saw him at the end, like as if I saw him down a perspective-glass. There was no time to check speed, and I knew him to be very careful. As he didn't seem to take heed of the whistle, I shut it off when we were running down upon him, and called to him as loud as I could call."

"What did you say?"

"I said, Below there! Look out! Look out! For God's sake, clear the way!"

I started.

"Ah! it was a dreadful time, sir. I never left off calling to him. I put this arm before my eyes, not to see, and I waved this arm to the last; but it was no use."

Without prolonging the narrative to dwell on any one of its curious circumstances more than on any other, I may, in closing it, point out the coincidence that the warning of the Engine-Driver included, not only the words that the unfortunate signal-man had repeated to me as haunting him, but also the words which I myself—not he—had attached, and that only in my own mind, to the gesticulation he had imitated.

Part Four

Human Monsters

The effectiveness of human monsters as agents of terror is rooted in man's instinctive association of the ugly and the alien with the threatening or evil. In general, Gothic writers have preferred to accentuate physical deformities as a way of designating monsters, but there are many exceptions. Melmoth, whose abnormality, like that of Faust, is an unusual longevity, is depicted as a man whose handsome appearance is marred only by the intensity of his red eyes—so brilliant that he must shield them from his intended victims. Dr. Jekyll and Wagner are both very presentable young men until they undergo transformation. Frankenstein's monster, on the other hand, is physically repugnant in appearance and frightening in his preternatural actions.

Much of the terror inspired by such creatures can be attributed to the resistance of man to accept anything different from the usual, from anything which threatens predictability, as such a difference poses a threat to the conventional way of life. The most obvious and drastic reaction to such monsters is either to flee from them or to annihilate them, both of which are exemplified in the selections in this chapter. But the Gothic message reflects more than man's fear of the ugly, the strange, and the unpredictable. It suggests the futility of probing into those realms of darkness which are forbidden to man and it indicates punishments which may follow if man allows his pride to take him further than it should. Thus man, like the monsters he creates, may himself become a a victim of forces beyond his control, may become an increasingly inhuman monster.

The ugliness or deformities of the monsters, infinitely variable, must always have a physical basis. One cannot, despite the common usage of the term, consider Ambrosio in *The Monk* as "monstrous" in the same sense that Frankenstein's creation is monstrous or that Wagner or Hyde are monstrous. And while psychological changes may or may not accompany physical transformations, it is only with some type of physical abnormality that this section is concerned, from the unnatural longevity of Melmoth to the hideously disfigured monster of Dr. Frankenstein and the almost eternal existence of Count Dracula. Nor does this category include those weird creatures, whether or not from outer space, whose origins are unknown.

Some of the monster tales are, of course, allegorical. *Melmoth* is a variation of the Faust theme, and, since Maturin was a preacher, the theme of regret and despair over trading one's soul to the devil for extended life would have an obvious allegorical message. Reynolds's *Wagner, the Wehr-Wolf* is similar to *Melmoth* in that both involve a pact with Satan, but in the former, the trade is to regain youth rather than to acquire longevity, and it also contains the additional element of transformation between human and wolf forms. The theme of transformation is also basic to *Dr. Jekyll and Mr. Hyde,* which may be taken to illustrate the Gothic theme that man is composed of both good and evil. At least that is the way Mrs. Stevenson interpreted her husband's novel, and she even suggested that the author eliminate the mysterious drug which causes the transformation, as its presence spoils the allegory. Mary Shelley's *Frankenstein* is most obviously allegorical, and she goes so far as to subtitle it "The Modern Prometheus," lest its allegorical implications be overlooked. Certainly one of the themes underlying the allegory is that man, like Prometheus, must bear the responsibility for what he creates, and so he must weigh carefully the possible consequences of his actions. But it should not be forgotten that both Dr. Frankenstein and the monster begin with good intentions.

Frankenstein has no desire to create horror and evil—he only wishes to find the secret of life. The monster has no malice at all in the beginning, only the desire to be accepted and loved. But Frankenstein cannot accept his creation's ugliness, nor can the monster live happily without love. Both are, in the end, victims of their own needs and desires.

In fact, the human-monster agency often develops into a somewhat sympathetic character as a result of this ambiguity between oppressor and victim. In Count Dracula's case, in which he remains an evil character from beginning to end, this is not so. But in the cases of Melmoth, Dr. Jekyll, and Frankenstein's monster, there is enough instance of the oppressor becoming in turn a victim—of himself or of others—to elicit some degree of sympathy from the reader. But no matter how much sympathy the monster may evoke, his destruction is, in balance, a good and necessary event. In sum, the use of human monsters as agents of terror serves to make man more aware of his own frailties and of the potential for evil which is within himself and others. Perhaps this awareness of how close each man is to the abyss is responsible for much of the terror these tales produce.

from

𝔇𝔯𝔞𝔠𝔲𝔩𝔞

𝔟𝔶 𝔅𝔯𝔞𝔪 𝔖𝔱𝔬𝔨𝔢𝔯

[*Jonathan Harker, agent for a London real estate firm, has traveled to a remote region of Transylvania to conclude a real estate deal with Count Dracula. Once he has arrived at Castle Dracula, Harker discovers he is virtually a prisoner of the strange count.*]

CHAPTER III.

JONATHAN HARKER'S JOURNAL, *continued*

When I found that I was a prisoner a sort of wild feeling came over me. I rushed up and down the stairs, trying every door and peering out of every window I could find; but after a little the conviction of my helplessness overpowered all other feelings. When I look back after a few hours I think I must have been mad for the time, for I behaved much as a rat does in a trap. When, however, the conviction had come to me that I was helpless I sat down quietly—as quietly as I have ever done anything in my life and began to think over what was best to be done. I am thinking still, and as yet have come to no definite conclusion. Of one thing only am I certain; that it is no use making my ideas known to the Count. He knows well that I am imprisoned; and as he has done it himself, and has doubtless his own motives for it, he would only deceive me if I trusted him fully with the facts. So far as I can see, my only plan will be to keep my knowledge and my fears to myself, and my eyes open. I am, I know, either being deceived, like a baby, by my own fears, or else I am in desperate straits; and if the latter be so, I need, and shall need, all my brains to get through.

I had hardly come to this conclusion when I heard the great door below shut, and knew that the Count had returned. He did not come at once into the library, so I went cautiously to my own room and found him making the bed. This was odd, but only confirmed what I had all along thought—that there were no servants in the house. When later I saw him through the chink of the hinges of the door laying the table in the dining-room, I was assured of it; for if he does himself all these menial offices, surely it is proof that there is no one else to do them. This gave me a fright, for if there is no one else in the castle, it must have been the Count himself who was the driver of the coach that brought me here. This is a terrible thought; for if so, what does it mean that he could control the wolves, as he did, by only holding up his hand in silence. How was it that all the people at Bistritz and on the coach had some terrible fear for me? What meant the giving of the crucifix, of the garlic, of the wild rose, of the mountain ash? Bless that good, good woman who hung the crucifix round my neck! for it is a comfort and a strength to me whenever I touch it. It is odd that a thing which I have been taught to regard with disfavour and as idolatrous should in a time of loneliness and trouble be of help. Is it that there is something in the essence of the thing itself, or that it is a medium, a tangible help, in conveying memories of sympathy and comfort? Some time, if it may be, I must examine this matter and try to make up my mind about it. In the meantime I must find out all I can about Count Dracula, as it may help me to understand. To-night he may talk of himself, if I turn the conversation that way. I must be very careful, however, not to awake his suspicion.

Midnight.—I have had a long talk with the Count. I asked him a few questions on Transylvania history, and he warmed up to the subject wonderfully. In his speaking of things and people, and especially of battles, he spoke as if he had been present at them all. This he afterwards explained by saying that to a *boyar* the pride of his house and name is his own pride, that their glory is his glory, that their fate is his fate. Whenever he spoke of his house he always said "we," and spoke almost in the plural, like a king speaking. I wish I could put down all he said exactly as he said it, for to me it was most fascinating. It seemed to have in it a whole history of the country. He grew excited as he spoke, and walked about the room pulling his great white moustache and grasping anything on which he laid his hands as though he would crush it by main strength. One thing he said which I shall put down as nearly as I can; for it tells in its way the story of his race:—

"We Szekelys have a right to be proud, for in our veins flows the blood of many brave races who fought as the lion fights, for lordship. Here, in the whirlpool of European races, the Ugric tribe bore down from Iceland the fighting spirit which Thor and Wodin gave them, which their Berserkers displayed to such fell intent on the seaboards of Europe, ay, and of Asia and Africa too, till the peoples thought that the were wolves themselves had come. Here, too, when they came, they found the Huns, whose warlike fury had swept the earth like a living flame, till the dying peoples held that in their veins ran the blood of those old witches, who, expelled from Scythia had mated with the devils in the desert. Fools, fools! What devil or what witch was ever so great as Attila, whose blood is in these veins?" He held up his arms. "Is it a wonder that we were a conquering race; that we were proud; that when the Magyar, the Lombard, the Avar, the Bulgar, or the Turk poured his thousands on our frontiers, we drove them back? Is it strange that when Arpad and his legions swept through the Hungarian fatherland he found us here when he reached the frontier; that the Honfoglalas was completed there? And when the Hungarian flood swept eastward, the Szekelys were claimed as kindred by the victorious Magyars, and to us for centuries was trusted the guarding of the frontier of Turkey-land; ay, and more than that, endless duty of the frontier guard, for, as the Turks say, 'water sleeps, and enemy is sleepless.' Who more gladly than we throughout the Four Nations received the 'bloody sword,' or at its warlike call flocked quicker to the standard of the King? When was redeemed that great shame of my nation, the shame of Cassova when the flags of the Wallach and the Magyar went down beneath the Crescent? Who was it but one of my own race who as Voivode crossed the Danube and beat the Turk on his own ground? This was a Dracula indeed! Woe was it that his own unworthy brother, when he had fallen, sold his people to the Turk and brought the shame of slavery on them! Was it not this Dracula, indeed, who inspired that other of his race who in a later age again and again brought his forces over the great river into Turkey-land; who, when he was beaten back, came again, and again, and again, though he had to come alone from the bloody field where his troops were being slaughtered, since he knew that he alone could ultimately triumph! They said that he thought only of himself. Bah! what good are peasants without a leader? Where ends the war without a brain and heart to conduct it? Again, when, after the battle of Mohács, we threw off the Hungarian yoke, we of the Dracula blood were amongst their leaders, for our spirit would not brook that we were not free, Ah, young sir, the Szekelys—and the Dracula as their heart's blood, their brains, and their swords—can boast a record that mushroom growths like the Hapsburgs and the Romanoffs can never reach. The warlike days are over. Blood is too precious a thing in these days of dishonourable peace; and the glories of the great races are as a tale that is told."

It was by this time close on morning, and we went to bed. (*Mem.,* this diary seems horribly like the beginning of the "Arabian Nights," for everything has to break off at cockcrow—or like the ghost of Hamlet's father.)

12 May.—Let me begin with facts—bare, meagre facts, verified by books and figures, and of which there can be no doubt. I must not confuse them with experiences which will have to rest on my own observation, or my memory of them. Last evening when the Count came from his room he began by asking me questions on legal matters and on the doing of certain kinds of business. I had spent the day wearily over books, and, simply to keep my mind occupied, went over some of the matters I had been examined in at Lincoln's Inn. There was a certain method in the Count's inquiries, so I shall try to put them down in sequence; the knowledge may somehow or some time be useful to me.

First, he asked if a man in England might have two solicitors or more. I told him he might have a dozen if he wished, but that it would not be wise to have more than one solicitor engaged in one transaction, as only one could act at a time, and that to change would be certain to militate against his interest. He seemed thoroughly to understand, and went on to ask if there would be any practical difficulty in having one man to attend, say, to banking, and another to look after shipping, in case local help were needed in a place far from the home of the banking solicitor. I asked him to explain fully, so that I might not by any chance mislead him, so he said:—

"I shall illustrate. Your friend and mine, Mr. Peter Hawkins, from under the shadow of your beautiful cathedral at Exeter, which is far from London, buys for me through your good self my place at London. Good! Now here let me say frankly, lest you should think it strange that I have sought the services of one so far off from London instead of some one resident there, that my motive was that no local interest might be served save my wish only; and as one of London residence might, perhaps, have some purpose of himself or friend to serve, I went thus afield to seek my agent, whose labours should be only to my interest. Now, suppose I, who have much of affairs, wish to ship goods, say, to Newcastle, or Durham, or Harwich, or Dover, might it not be that it could with more ease be done by consigning to one in these ports?" I answered that certainly it would be most easy, but that we solicitors had a system of agency one for the other, so that local work could be done locally on instruction from any solicitor, so that the client, simply placing himself in the hands of one man, could have his wishes carried out by him without further trouble.

"But," said he, "I could be at liberty to direct myself. Is it not so?"

"Of course," I replied; and "such is often done by men of business, who do not like the whole of their affairs to be known by any one person."

"Good!" he said, and then went on to ask about the means of making consignments and the forms to be gone through, and of all sorts of difficulties which might arise, but by forethought could be guarded against. I explained all these things to him to the best of my ability, and he certainly left me under the impression that he would have made a wonderful solicitor, for there was nothing that he did not think of or foresee. For a man who was never in the country, and who did not evidently do much in the way of business, his knowledge and acumen were wonderful. When he had satisfied himself on these points of which he had spoken, and I had verified all as well as I could by the books available, he suddenly stood up and said:—

"Have you written since your first letter to our friend Mr. Peter Hawkins, or to any other?" It was with some bitterness in my heart that I answered that I had not, that as yet I had not seen any opportunity of sending letters to anybody.

"Then write now, my young friend," he said, laying a heavy hand on my shoulder: "write to our friend and to any other; and say, if it will please you, that you shall stay with me until a month from now."

"Do you wish me to stay so long?" I asked, for my heart grew cold at the thought.

"I desire it much; nay, I will take no refusal. When your master, employer, what you will, engaged that someone should come on his behalf, it was understood that my needs only were to be consulted. I have not stinted. Is it not so?"

What could I do but bow acceptance? It was Mr. Hawkins's interest, not mine, and I had to think of him, not myself; and besides, while Count Dracula was speaking, there was that in his eyes and in his bearing which made me remember that I was a prisoner, and that if I wished it I could have no choice. The Count saw his victory in my bow, and his mastery in the trouble of my face, for he began at once to use them, but in his own smooth, resistless way:—

"I pray you, my good young friend, that you will not discourse of things other than business in your letters. It will doubtless please your friends to know that you are well, and that you look forward to getting home to them. Is it not so?" As he spoke he handed me three sheets of note-paper and three envelopes. They were all of the thinnest foreign post, and looking at them, then at him, and noticing his quiet smile, with the sharp, canine teeth lying over the red underlip, I understood as well as if he had spoken that I should be careful what I wrote, for he would be able to read it. So I determined to write only formal notes now, but to write fully to Mr. Hawkins in secret, and also to Nina, for to her I could write in shorthand, which would puzzle the Count, if he did see it. When I had written my two letters I sat quiet, reading a book whilst the Count wrote several notes, referring as he wrote to some books on his table. Then he took up my two and placed them with his own, and put by his writing materials, after which, the instant the door had closed behind him, I leaned over and looked at the letters, which were face down on the table. I felt no compunction in doing so, for under the circumstances I felt that I should protect myself in every way I could.

One of the letters was directed to Samuel F. Billington, No. 7, The Crescent, Whitby, another to Herr Leutner, Varna; the third was to Coutts & Co., London, and the fourth to Herren Klopstock & Billreuth, bankers, Buda-Pesth. The second and fourth were unsealed. I was just about to look at them when I saw the door-handle move. I sank back in my seat, having just had time to replace the letters as they had been and to resume my book before the Count, holding still another letter in his hand, entered the room. He took up the letters on the table and stamped them carefully, and then turning to me, said:—

"I trust you will forgive me, but I have much work to do in private this evening. You will, I hope, find all things as you wish." At the door he turned, and after a moment's pause said:—

"Let me advise you, my dear young friend—nay, let me warn you with all seriousness, that should you leave these rooms you will not by any chance go to sleep in any other part of the castle. It is old, and has many memories, and there are bad dreams for those who sleep unwisely. Be warned! Should sleep now or ever overcome you, or be like to do, then haste to your own chamber or to these rooms, for your rest will then be safe. But if you be not careful in this respect, then"—He finished his speech in a gruesome way, for he motioned with his hands as if he were washing them. I quite understood; my only doubt was as to whether any dream could be more terrible than the unnatural, horrible net of gloom and mystery which seemed closing around me.

Later—I endorse the last words written, but this time there is no doubt in question. I shall not fear to sleep in any place where he is not. I have placed the crucifix over the head of my bed—I imagine that my rest is thus freer from dreams; and there it shall remain.

When he left me I went to my room. After a little while, not hearing any sound, I came out and went up the stone stairs to where I could look out towards the South. There was some sense of freedom in the vast expanse, inaccesible though it was to me, as compared with the narrow darkness of the courtyard. Looking out on this, I felt that I was indeed in prison, and I seemed to want a breath of fresh air, though it were of the night. I am beginning to feel this nocturnal existence tell on me. It is destroying my nerve. I start at my own shadow, and am full of all sorts of horrible imaginings. God knows that there is ground for my terrible fear in this accursed place! I looked out over the beautiful expanse, bathed in soft yellow moonlight till it was almost as light as day. In the soft light the distant hills became melted, and the shadows in the valleys and gorges of velvety blackness. The mere beauty seemed to cheer me; there was peace and comfort in every breath I drew. As I leaned from the window my eye was caught by something moving a storey below me, and somewhat to my left, where I imagined, from the order of the rooms, that the windows of the Count's own room would look out. The window at which I stood was tall and deep, stone-mullioned, and though weatherworn, was still complete; but it was evidently many a day since the case had been there. I drew back behind the stonework, and looked carefully out.

What I saw was the Count's head coming out from the window. I did not see the face, but I knew the man by the neck and the movement of his back and arms. In any case I could not mistake the hands which I had so many opportunities of studying. I was at first interested and somewhat amused, for it is wonderful how small a matter will interest and amuse a man when he is a prisoner. But my very feelings changed to repulsion and terror when I saw the whole man slowly emerge from the window and begin to crawl down the castle wall over that dreadful abyss, *face down* with his cloak spreading out around him like great wings. At first I could not believe my eyes. I thought it was some trick of the moonlight, some weird effect of shadow; but I kept looking, and it could be no delusion. I saw the fingers and toes grasp the corners of the stones, worn clear of the mortar by the stress of years, and by thus using every projection and inequality move downwards with considerable speed, just as a lizard moves along a wall.

What manner of man is this, or what manner of creature is it in the semblance of man? I feel the dread of this horrible place overpowering me; I am in fear—in awful fear—and there is no escape for me; I am encompassed about with terrors that I dare not think of. . . .

15 May.—Once more have I seen the Count go out in his lizard fashion. He moved downwards in a sidelong way; some hundred feet down, and a good deal to the left. He vanished into some hole or window. When his head had disappeared, I leaned out to try and see more, but without avail—the distance was too great to allow a proper angle of sight. I knew he had left the castle now, and thought to use the opportunity to explore more than I had dared to do as yet. I went back to the room, and taking a lamp, tried all the doors. They were all locked, as I had expected, and the locks were comparatively new; but I went down the stone stairs to the hall where I had entered originally. I found I could pull back the bolts easily enough and unhook the great chains; but the door was locked, and the key was gone. The key must be in the Count's room; I must watch should his door be unlocked, so that I may get it and escape. I went on to make a thorough examination of the various stairs and passages, and to try the doors that opened from them. One or two small rooms near the hall were open, but there was nothing to see in them except old furniture, dusty with age and moth-eaten. At last, however, I found one door at the top of the stairway which, though it seemed to be locked, gave a little under pressure. I tried it harder, and found that it was not really locked, but that the resistance came from the fact that the hinges had fallen somewhat, and the heavy door rested on the floor. Here was an opportunity which I might not have again, so I exerted myself, and with many efforts forced it back so that I could enter. I was now in a wing of the castle further to the right than the rooms I knew and a storey lower down. From the windows I could see that the suite of rooms lay along to the south of the castle, the windows of the end room looking out both west and south. On the latter side, as well as to the former, there was a great precipice. The castle was built on the corner of a great rock, so that on three sides it was quite impregnable, and great windows were placed here where sling, or bow, or culverin could not reach, and consequently light and comfort, impossible to a position which had to be guarded, were secured. To the west was a great valley, and then, rising far away, great jagged mountain fastnesses, rising peak on peak, the sheer rock studded with mountain ash and thorn, whose roots clung in cracks and crevices and crannies of the stone. This was evidently the portion of the castle occupied by the ladies in bygone days, for the furniture had more air of comfort than any I had seen. The windows were curtainless, and the yellow moonlight, flooding in through the diamond panes, enabled one to see even colours, whilst it softened the wealth of dust which lay over all and disguised in some measure the ravages of time and the moth. My lamp seemed to be of little effect in the brilliant moonlight, but I was glad to have it with me, for there was a dread loneliness in the place which chilled my heart and made my nerves tremble. Still, it was better than living alone in the rooms which I had come to hate from the presence of the Count, and after trying a little to school my nerves, I found a soft quietude come over me. Here I am, sitting at a little oak table where in old times possibly some fair lady sat to pen, with much thought and many blushes, her ill-spelt love-letter, and writing in my diary in short hand all that has happened since I closed it last. It is nineteenth century up-to-date with a vengeance. And yet, unless my senses deceive me, the old centuries had, and have, powers of their own which mere "modernity" cannot kill.

Later: the Morning of 16 May.—God preserve my sanity, for to this I am reduced. Safety and the assurance of safety are things of the past. Whilst I live on here there is but one thing to hope for, that I may not go mad, if, indeed, I be not mad already. If I be sane, then surely it is maddening to think that of all the foul things that lurk in this hateful place the Count is the least dreadful to me; that to him alone I can look for safety, even though this be only whilst I can serve his purpose. Great God! merciful God! Let me be calm, for out of that way lies madness indeed. I begin to get new lights on certain things which have puzzled me. Up to now I never quite knew what Shakespeare meant when he made Hamlet say:—

> "My tablets! quick, my tablets!
> 'Tis meet that I put it down," etc.,

for now, feeling as though my own brain were unhinged or as if the shock had come which must end in its undoing, I turn to my diary for repose. The habit of entering accurately must help to soothe me.

The Count's mysterious warning frightened me at the time; it frightens me more now when I think of it, for in future he has a fearful hold upon me. I shall fear to doubt what he may say!

When I had written in my diary and had fortunately replaced the book and pen in my pocket I felt sleepy. The Count's warning came into my mind, but I took a pleasure in disobeying it. The sense of sleep was upon me, and with it the obstinacy which sleep brings as outrider. The soft moonlight soothed, and the wide expanse without gave a sense of freedom which refreshed me. I determined not to return to-night to the gloom-haunted rooms, but to sleep here, where, of old, ladies had sat and sung and lived sweet lives whilst their gentle breasts were sad for their menfolk away in the midst of remorseless wars. I drew a great couch out of its place near the corner, so that as I lay, I could look at the lovely view east and south, and unthinking of and uncaring for the dust, composed myself for sleep. I suppose I must have fallen asleep; I hope so, but I fear, for all that followed was startlingly real—so real that now sitting here in the broad, full sunlight of the morning, I cannot in the least believe that it was all sleep.

I was not alone. The room was the same, unchanged in any way since I came into it; I could see along the floor, in the brilliant moonlight, my own footsteps marked where I had disturbed the long accumulation of dust. In the moonlight opposite me were three young· women, ladies by their dress and manner. I thought at the time that I must be dreaming when I saw them, for, though the moonlight was behind them, they threw no shadow on the floor. They came close to me, and looked at me for some time, and then whispered together. Two were dark, and had high aquiline noses, like the Count, and great dark, piercing eyes that seemed to be almost red when contrasted with the pale yellow moon. The other was fair, as fair as can be, with great wavy masses of golden hair and eyes like pale sapphires. I seemed somehow to know her face, and to know it in connection with some dreamy fear, but I could not recollect at the moment how or where. All three had brilliant white teeth that shone like pearls against the ruby of their voluptuous lips. There was something about them that made me uneasy, some longing and at the same time some deadly fear. I felt in my heart a wicked, burning desire that they would kiss me with those red lips. It is not good to note this down, lest some day it should meet Mina's eyes and cause her pain; but it is the truth. They whispered together, and then they all three laughed—such a silvery, musical laugh, but as hard as though the sound never could have come through the softness of human lips. It was like the intolerable, tingling sweetness of water-glasses when played on by a cunning hand. The fair girl shook her head coquettishly, and the other two urged her on. One said:—

"Go on! You are first, and we shall follow; yours is the right to begin." The other added:—

"He is young and strong; there are kisses for us all." I lay quiet, looking out under my eyelashes in an agony of delightful anticipation. The fair girl advanced and bent over me till I could feel the movement of her breath upon me. Sweet it was in one sense, honey-sweet, and sent the same tingling through the nerves as her voice, but with a bitter underlying the sweet, a bitter offensiveness, as one smells in blood.

I was afraid to raise my eyelids, but looked out and saw perfectly under the lashes. The girl went on her knees, and bent over me, simply gloating. There was a deliberate voluptuousness which was both thrilling and repulsive, and as she arched her neck she actually licked her lips like an animal, till I could see in the moonlight the moisture shining on the scarlet lips and on the red tongue as it lapped the white sharp teeth. Lower and lower went her head as the lips went below the range of my mouth and chin and seemed about to fasten on my throat. Then she paused, and I could hear the churning sound of her tongue as it licked her teeth and lips, and could feel the hot breath on my neck. Then the skin of my throat began to tingle as one's flesh does when the hand that is to tickle it approaches nearer—nearer. I could feel the soft, shivering touch of the lips on the supersensitive skin of my throat, and the hard dents of two sharp teeth, just touching and pausing there. I closed my eyes in a languorous ecstasy and waited—waited with beating heart.

But at that instant, another sensation swept through me as quick as lightning. I was conscious of the presence of the Count, and of his being as if lapped in a storm of fury. As my eyes opened involuntarily I saw his strong hand grasp the slender neck of the fair woman and with giant's power draw it back, the blue eyes transformed with fury, the white teeth champing with rage, and the fair cheeks blazing red with passion. But the Count! Never did I imagine such wrath and fury, even to the demons of the pit. His eyes were positively blazing. The red light in them was lurid, as if the flames of hell-fire blazed behind them. His face was deathly pale, and the lines of it were hard like drawn wires; the thick eyebrows that met over the nose now seemed like a heaving bar of white-hot metal. With a fierce sweep of his arm, he hurled the woman from him, and then motioned to the others, as though he were beating them back; it was the same imperious gesture that I had seen used to the wolves. In a voice which, though low and almost in a whisper seemed to cut through the air and then round the room he said:—

"How dare you touch him, any of you? How dare you cast eyes on him when I had forbidden it? Back, I tell you all! This man belongs to me! Beware how you meddle with him, or you'll have to deal with me." The fair girl, with a laugh of ribald coquetry, turned to answer him:—

"You yourself never loved; you never love!" On this the other women joined, and such a mirthless, hard, soulless laughter rang through the room that it almost made me faint to hear; it seemed like the pleasure of fiends. Then the Count turned, after looking at my face attentively, and said in a soft whisper:—

"Yes, I too can love; you yourselves can tell it from the past. Is it not so? Well, now I promise you that when I am done with him you shall kiss him at your will. Now go! go! I must awaken him, for there is work to be done."

"Are we to have nothing to-night?" said one of them, with a low laugh, as she pointed to the bag which he had thrown upon the floor; and which moved as though there were some living thing within it. For answer he nodded his head. One of the women jumped forward and opened it. If my ears did not deceive me there was a gasp and a low wail, as of a half-smothered child. The women closed round, whilst I was aghast with horror; but as I looked they disappeared, and with them the dreadful bag. There was no door near them, and they could not have passed me without my noticing. They simply seemed to fade into the rays of the moonlight and pass out through the window, for I could see outside the dim, shadowy forms for a moment before they entirely faded away.

Then the horror overcame me, and I sank down unconscious.

from

𝕱𝖗𝖆𝖓𝖐𝖊𝖓𝖘𝖙𝖊𝖎𝖓:
or,
𝕿𝖍𝖊 𝕸𝖔𝖉𝖊𝖗𝖓 𝕻𝖗𝖔𝖒𝖊𝖙𝖍𝖊𝖚𝖘

𝖇𝖞 𝕸𝖆𝖗𝖞 𝖂. 𝕾𝖍𝖊𝖑𝖑𝖊𝖞

[*Frankenstein, in attempting to create life, has produced a monster so hideous that no one can bear to look at him. The monster however has warm, human feelings and his exclusion from the society of man makes him miserable. He asks Frankenstein to create a female companion. At first the scientist agrees but then abandons the plan, and the monster vows vengeance on Frankenstein on his wedding night. The scientist, who has already felt the monster's fatal hand upon his family, tries unsuccessfully to protect his bride Elizabeth. Months later he tells the story of that awful night to a ship captain who has rescued him from an ice floe in the far North.*]

CHAPTER XXIII.

It was eight o'clock when we landed; we walked for a short time on the shore, enjoying the transistory light, and then retired to the inn, and contemplated the lovely scene of waters, woods, and mountains, obscured in darkness, yet still displaying their black outlines.

The wind, which had fallen in the south, now rose with great violence in the west. The moon had reached her summit in the heavens, and was beginning to descend; the clouds swept across it swifter than the flight of the vulture, and dimmed her rays, while the lake reflected the scene of the busy heavens, rendered still busier by the restless waves that were beginning to rise. Suddenly a heavy storm of rain descended.

I had been calm during the day; but so soon as night obscured the shapes of objects, a thousand fears arose in my mind. I was anxious and watchful, while my right hand grasped a pistol which was hidden in my bosom; every sound terrified me; but I resolved that I would sell my life dearly, and not shrink from the conflict until my own life, or that of my adversary, was extinguished.

Elizabeth observed my agitation for some time in timid and fearful silence; but there was something in my glance which communicated terror to her, and trembling she asked "What is it that agitates you, my dear Victor? What is it you fear?"

"Oh! peace, peace, my love," replied I; "this night, and all will be safe: but this night is dreadful, very dreadful."

I passed an hour in this state of mind, when suddenly I reflected how fearful the combat which I momentarily expected would be to my wife, and I earnestly entreated her to retire, resolving not to join her until I had obtained some knowledge as to the situation of my enemy.

She left me, and I continued some time walking up and down the passages of the house, and inspecting every corner that might afford a retreat to my adversary. But I discovered no trace of him, and was beginning to conjecture that some fortunate chance had intervened to prevent the execution of his menaces; when suddenly I heard a shrill and dreadful scream. It came from the room into which Elizabeth had retired. As I heard it, the whole truth rushed into my mind, my arms dropped, the motion of every muscle fibre was suspended; I could feel the blood trickling in my veins, and tingling in the extremities of my limbs. This state lasted but for an instant; the scream was repeated, and I rushed into the room.

Great God! Why did I not then expire! Why am I here to relate the destruction of the best hope, and the purest creature of earth? She was there, lifeless and inanimate, thrown across the bed, her head hanging down, and her pale and distorted features half covered by her hair. Every where I turn I see the same figure—her bloodless arms and relaxed form flung by the murderer on its bridal bier. Could I behold this, and live? Alas! life is obstinate, and clings closest where it is most hated. For a moment only did I lose recollection; I fell senseless on the ground.

When I recovered, I found myself surrounded by the people of the inn; their countenances expressed a breathless terror: but the horror of others appeared only as a mockery, a shadow of the feelings that oppressed me. I escaped from them to the room where lay the body of Elizabeth, my love, my wife, so lately living, so dear, so worthy. She had been moved from the posture in which I had first beheld her; and now, as she lay, her head upon her arm, and a handkerchief thrown across her face and neck, I might have supposed her asleep. I rushed towards her, and embraced her with ardour; but the deadly languor and coldness of the limbs told me, that what I now held in my arms had ceased to be the Elizabeth whom I had loved and cherished. The murderous mark of the fiend's grasp was on her neck, and the breath had ceased to issue from her lips.

While I still hung over her in the agony of despair, I happened to look up. The windows of the room had before been darkened, and I felt a kind of panic on seeing the pale yellow light of the moon illuminate the chamber. The shutters had been thrown back; and, with a sensation of horror not to be described, I saw at the open window a figure the most hideous and abhorred. A grin was on the face of the monster; he seemed to jeer, as with his fiendish finger he pointed towards the corpse of my wife. I rushed towards the window, and drawing a pistol from my bosom, fired; but he eluded me, leaped from his station, and, running with the swiftness of lightning, plunged into the lake.

The report of the pistol brought a crowd into the room. I pointed to the spot where he had disappeared, and we followed the track with boats; nets were cast, but in vain. After passing several hours, we returned hopeless, most of my companions believing it to have been a form conjured up by my fancy. After having landed, they proceeded to search the country, parties going in different directions among the woods and vines.

I attempted to accompany them, and proceeded a short distance from the house; but my head whirled round, my steps were like those of a drunken man, I fell at last in a state of utter exhaustion; a film covered my eyes, and my skin was parched with the heat of fever. In this state I was carried back, and placed on a bed, hardly conscious of what had happened; my eyes wandered round the room, as if to seek something that I had lost.

After an interval, I arose, and, as if by instinct, crawled into the room where the corpse of my beloved lay. There were women weeping around—I hung over it, and joined my sad tears to theirs—all this time no distinct idea presented itself to my mind; but my thoughts rambled to various subjects, reflecting confusedly on my misfortunes, and their cause. I was bewildered in a cloud of wonder and horror. The death of William, the execution of Justine, the murder of Clerval, and lastly of my wife; even at that moment I knew not that my only remaining friends were safe from the malignity of the fiend; my father even now might be writhing under his grasp, and Ernest might be dead at his feet. This idea made me shudder, and recalled me to action. I started up, and resolved to return to Geneva with all possible speed.

There were no horses to be procured, and I must return by the lake; but the wind was unfavourable, and the rain fell in torrents. However, it was hardly morning, and I might reasonably hope to arrive by night. I hired men to row, and took an oar myself; for I had always experienced relief from mental torment in bodily exercise. But the overflowing misery I now felt, and the excess of agitation that I endured, rendered me incapable of any exertion. I threw down the oar; and leaning my head upon my hands, gave way to every gloomy idea that arose. If I looked up, I saw the scenes which were familiar to me in my happier time, and which I had contemplated but the day before in the company of her who was now but a shadow and a recollection. Tears streamed from my eyes. The rain had ceased for a moment, and I saw the fish play in the waters as they had done a few hours before; they had then been observed by Elizabeth. Nothing is so painful to the human mind as a great and sudden change. The sun might shine, or the clouds might lower: but nothing could appear to me as it had done the day before. A fiend had snatched from me every hope of future happiness: no creature had ever been so miserable as I was; so frightful an event is single in the history of man.

But why should I dwell upon the incidents that followed this last overwhelming event? Mine has been a tale of horrors; I have reached their *acme,* and what I must now relate can but be tedious to you. Know that, one by one, my friends were snatched away; I was left desolate. My own strength is exhausted; and I must tell, in a few words, what remains of my hideous narration.

I arrived at Geneva. My father and Ernest yet lived; but the former sunk under the tidings that I bore. I see him now, excellent and venerable old man! his eyes wandered in vacancy, for they had lost their charm and their delight—his Elizabeth, his more than daughter, whom he doated on with all that affection which a man feels, who in the decline of life, having few affections, clings more earnestly to those that remain. Cursed, cursed be the fiend that brought misery on his grey hairs, and doomed him to waste in wretchedness! He could not live under the horrors that were accumulated around him; the springs of existence suddenly gave way: he was unable to rise from his bed, and in a few days he died in my arms.

What then became of me? I know not; I lost sensation, and chains and darkness were the only objects that pressed upon me. Sometimes, indeed, I dreamt that I wandered in flowery meadows and pleasant vales with the friends of my youth; but I awoke, and found myself in a dungeon. Melancholy followed, but by degrees I gained a clear conception of my miseries and situation, and was then released from my prison. For they had called me mad; and during many months, as I understood, a solitary cell had been my habitation.

.Liberty, however, had been an useless gift to me, had I not, as I awakened to reason, at the same time awakened to revenge. As the memory of past misfortunes pressed upon me, I began to reflect on their cause—the monster whom I had created, the miserable dæmon whom I had sent abroad into the world for my destruction. I was possessed by a maddening rage when I thought of him, and desired and ardently prayed that I might have him within my grasp to wreak a great and signal revenge on his cursed head.

* * * * * * * * * * * * * * * *

CHAPTER XXIV.

When I quitted Geneva, my first labour was to gain some clue by which I might trace the steps of my fiendish enemy. But my plan was unsettled; and I wandered many hours round the confines of the town, uncertain what path I should pursue. As night approached, I found myself at the entrance of the cemetery where William, Elizabeth, and my father reposed. I entered it, and approached the tomb which marked their graves. Every thing was silent, except the leaves of the trees, which were gently agitated by the wind; the night was nearly dark; and the scene would have been solemn and affecting even to an uninterested observer. The spirits of the departed seemed to flit around, and to cast a shadow, which was felt but not seen, around the head of the mourner.

The deep grief which this scene had at first excited quickly gave way to rage and despair. They were dead, and I lived; their murderer also lived, and to destroy him I must drag out my weary existence. I knelt on the grass, and kissed the earth, and with quivering lips exclaimed, "By the sacred earth on which I kneel, by the shades that wander near me, by the deep and eternal grief that I feel, I swear; and by thee, O Night, and the spirits that preside over thee, to pursue the dæmon, who caused this misery, until he or I shall perish in mortal conflict. For this purpose I will preserve my life: to execute this dear revenge, will I again behold the sun, and tread the green herbage of earth, which otherwise should vanish from my eyes for ever. And I call on you, spirits of the dead; and on you, wandering ministers of vengeance, to aid and conduct me in my work. Let the cursed and hellish monster drink deep of agony; let him feel the despair that now torments me."

I had begun my adjuration with solemnity, and an awe which almost assured me that the shades of my murdered friends heard and approved my devotion; but the furies possessed me as I concluded, and rage choked my utterance.

I was answered through the stillness of night by a loud and fiendish laugh. It rung on my ears long and heavily; the mountains re-echoed it, and I felt as if all hell surrounded me with mockery and laughter. Surely in that moment I should have been possessed by frenzy, and have destroyed my miserable existence, but that my vow was heard, and that I was reserved for vengeance. The laughter died away; when a well-known and abhorred voice, apparently close to my ear, addressed me in an audible whisper—"I am satisfied: miserable wretch! you have determined to live, and I am satisfied."

I darted towards the spot from which the sound proceeded; but the devil eluded my grasp. Suddenly the broad disk of the moon arose, and shone full upon his ghastly and distorted shape, as he fled with more than mortal speed.

I pursued him; and for many months this has been my task. Guided by a slight clue, I followed the windings of the Rhone, but vainly. The blue Mediterranean appeared; and, by a strange chance, I saw the fiend enter by night, and hide himself in a vessel bound for the Black Sea. I took my passage in the same ship; but he escaped, I know not how.

Amidst the wilds of Tartary and Russia, although he still evaded me, I have ever followed in his track. Sometimes the peasants, scared by this horrid apparition, informed me of his path; sometimes he himself, who feared that if I lost all trace of him, I should despair and die, left some mark to guide me. The snows descended on my head, and I saw the print of his huge step on the white plain. To you first entering on life, to whom care is new, and agony unknown, how can you understand what I have felt, and still feel? Cold, want, and fatigue, were the least pains which I was destined to endure; I was cursed by some devil, and carried about with me my eternal hell; yet still a spirit of good followed and directed my steps; and, when I most murmured, would suddenly extricate me from seemingly insurmountable difficulties. Sometimes, when nature, overcome by hunger, sunk under the exhaustion, a repast was prepared for me in the desert, that restored and inspirited me. The fare was, indeed, coarse, such as the peasants of the country ate; but I will not doubt that it was set there by the spirits that I had invoked to aid me. Often, when all was dry, the heavens cloudless, and I was parched by thirst, a slight cloud would bedim the sky, shed the few drops that revived me, and vanish.

I followed, when I could, the courses of the rivers; but the dæmon generally avoided these, as it was here that the population of the country chiefly collected. In other places human beings were seldom seen; and I generally subsisted on the wild animals that crossed my path. I had money with me, and gained the friendship of the villagers by distributing it; or I brought with me some food that I had killed, which, after taking a small part, I always presented to those who had provided me with fire and utensils for cooking.

My life, as it passed thus, was indeed hateful to me, and it was during sleep alone that I could taste joy. O blessed sleep! often, when most miserable, I sank to repose, and my dreams lulled me even to rapture. The spirits that guarded me had provided these moments, or rather hours, of happiness, that I might retain strength to fulfil my pilgrimage. Deprived of this respite, I should have sunk under my hardships. During the day I was sustained and inspirited by the hope of night: for in sleep I saw my friends, my wife, and my beloved country; again I saw the benevolent countenance of my father, heard the silver tones of my Elizabeth's voice, and beheld Clerval enjoying health and youth. Often, when wearied by a toilsome march, I persuaded myself that I was dreaming until night should come, and that I should then enjoy reality in the arms of my dearest friends. What agonising fondness did I feel for them! how did I cling to their dear forms, as sometimes they haunted even my waking hours, and persuade myself that they still lived! At such moments vengeance, that burned within me, died in my heart, and I pursued my path towards the destruction of the dæmon, more as a task enjoined by heaven, as the mechanical impulse of some power of which I was unconscious, than as the ardent desire of my soul.

What his feelings were whom I pursued I cannot know. Sometimes, indeed, he left marks in writing on the barks of the trees, or cut in stone, that guided me, and instigated my fury. "My reign is not yet over," (these words were legible in one of these inscriptions;) "you live, and my power is complete. Follow me; I seek the everlasting ices of the north, where you will feel the misery of cold and frost, to which I am impassive. You will find near this place, if you follow not too tardily, a dead hare; eat, and be refreshed. Come on, my enemy; we have yet to wrestle for our lives; but many hard and miserable hours must you endure until that period shall arrive."

Scoffing devil! Again do I vow vengeance; again do I devote thee, miserable fiend, to torture and death. Never will I give up my search, until he or I perish; and then with what ecstasy shall I join my Elizabeth, and my departed friends, who even now prepare for me the reward of my tedious toil and horrible pilgrimage!

As I still pursued my journey to the northward, the snows thickened, and the cold increased in a degree almost too severe to support. The peasants were shut up in their hovels, and only a few of the most hardy ventured forth to seize the animals whom starvation had forced from their hiding-places to seek for prey. The rivers were covered with ice, and no fish could be procured; and thus I was cut off from my chief article of maintenance.

The triumph of my enemy increased with the difficulty of my labours. One inscription that he left was in these words:—"Prepare! your toils only begin: wrap yourself in furs, and provide food; for we shall soon enter upon a journey where your sufferings will satisfy my everlasting hatred."

My courage and perseverance were invigorated by these scoffing words; I resolved not to fail in my purpose; and, calling on Heaven to support me, I continued with unabated fervour to traverse immense deserts, until the ocean appeared at a distance, and formed the utmost boundary of the horizon. Oh! how unlike it was to the blue seas of the south! Covered with ice, it was only to be distinguished from land by its superior wildness and ruggedness. The Greeks wept for joy when they beheld the Mediterranean from the hills of Asia, and hailed with rapture the boundary of their toils. I did not weep; but I knelt down, and with full heart, thanked my guiding spirit for conducting me in safety to the place where I hoped, notwithstanding my adversary's gibe, to meet and grapple with him.

Some weeks before this period I had procured a sledge and dogs, and thus traversed the snows with inconceivable speed. I know not whether the fiend possessed the same advantages; but I found that, as before I had daily lost ground in the pursuit, I now gained on him: so much so, that when I first saw the ocean, he was but one day's journey in advance, and I hoped to intercept him before he should reach the beach. With new courage, therefore, I pressed on, and in two days arrived at a wretched hamlet on the sea-shore. I enquired of the inhabitants concerning the fiend, and gained accurate information. A gigantic monster, they said, had arrived the night before, armed with a gun and many pistols; putting to flight the inhabitants of a solitary cottage, through fear of his terrific appearance. He had carried off their store of winter food, and, placing it in a sledge, to draw which he had seized on a numerous drove of trained dogs, he had harnessed them, and the same night, to the joy of the horror-struck villagers, had pursued his journey across the sea in a direction that led to no land; and they conjectured that he must speedily be destroyed by the breaking of the ice, or frozen by the eternal frosts.

On hearing this information, I suffered a temporary access of despair. He had escaped me; and I must commence a destructive and almost endless journey across the mountainous ices of the ocean,—amidst cold that few of the inhabitants could long endure, and which I, the native of a genial and sunny climate, could not hope to survive. Yet at the idea that the fiend should live and be triumphant, my rage and vengeance returned, and, like a mighty tide, overwhelmed every other feeling. After a slight repose, during which the spirits of the dead hovered round, and instigated me to toil and revenge, I prepared for my journey.

I exchanged my land-sledge for one fashioned for the inequalities of the Frozen Ocean; and purchasing a plentiful stock of provisions, I departed from land.

I cannot guess how many days have passed since then; but I have endured misery, which nothing but the eternal sentiment of a just retribution burning within my heart could have enabled me to support. Immense and rugged mountains of ice often barred my passage, and I often heard the thunder of the ground sea, which threatened my destruction. But again the frost came, and made the paths of the sea secure.

By the quantity of provision which I had consumed, I should guess that I had passed three weeks in this journey; and the continual protraction of hope, returning back upon the heart, often wrung bitter drops of despondency and grief from my eyes. Despair had indeed almost secured her prey, and I should soon have sunk beneath this misery. Once, after the poor animals that conveyed me had with incredible toil gained the summit of a sloping ice-mountain, and one, sinking under his fatigue, died, I viewed the expanse before me with anguish, when suddenly my eye caught a dark speck upon the dusky plain. I strained my sight to discover what it could be, and uttered a wild cry of ecstasy when I distinguished a sledge, and the distorted proportions of a well-known form within. Oh! with what a burning gush did hope revisit my heart! warm tears filled my eyes, which I hastily wiped away, that they might not intercept the view I had of the dæmon; but still my sight was dimmed by the burning drops, until, giving way to the emotions that oppressed me, I wept aloud.

But this was not the time for delay: I disencumbered the dogs of their dead companion, gave them a plentiful portion of food; and, after an hour's rest, which was absolutely necessary, and yet which was bitterly irksome to me, I continued my route. The sledge was still visible; nor did I again lose sight of it, except at the moments when for a short time some ice-rock concealed it with its intervening crags. I indeed perceptibly gained on it; and when, after nearly two days' journey, I beheld my enemy at no more than a mile distant, my heart bounded within me.

But now, when I appeared almost within grasp of my foe, my hopes were suddenly extinguished, and I lost all traces of him more utterly than I had ever done before. A ground sea was heard; the thunder of its progress, as the waters rolled and swelled beneath me, became every moment more ominous and terrific. I pressed on, but in vain. The wind arose; the sea roared; and, as with the mighty shock of an earthquake, it split, and cracked with a tremendous and overwhelming sound. The work was soon finished: in a few minutes a tumultuous sea rolled between me and my enemy, and I was left drifting on a scattered piece of ice, that was continually lessening, and thus preparing for me a hideous death.

In this manner many appalling hours passed; several of my dogs died; and I myself was about to sink under the accumulation of distress, when I saw your vessel riding at anchor, and holding forth to me hopes of succour and life. I had no conception that vessels ever came so far north, and was astounded at the sight. I quickly destroyed part of my sledge to construct oars; and by these means was enabled, with infinite fatigue, to move my ice-raft in the direction of your ship. I had determined, if you were going southward, still to trust myself to the mercy of the seas rather than abandon my purpose. I hoped to induce you to grant me a boat with which I could pursue my enemy. But your direction was northward. You took me on board when my vigour was exhausted, and I should soon have sunk under my multiplied hardships into a death which I still dread—for my task is unfulfilled.

* * * * * * * * * * * * * * *

[The ship captain continues the narrative.]

His voice became fainter as he spoke; and at length, exhausted by his effort, he sunk into silence. About half an hour afterwards he attempted again to speak, but was unable; he pressed my hand feebly, and his eyes closed for ever, while the irradiation of a gentle smile passed away from his lips.

* * * * * * * * * * * * * * *

I am interrupted. What do these sounds portend? It is midnight; the breeze blows fairly, and the watch on deck scarcely stir. Again; there is a sound as of a human voice, but hoarser; it comes from the cabin where the remains of Frankenstein still lie. I must arise, and examine. . . .

Great God! what a scene has just take place! I am yet dizzy with the remembrance of it. I hardly know whether I shall have the power to detail it; yet the tale which I have recorded would be incomplete without this final and wonderful catastrophe.

I entered the cabin, where lay the remains of my ill-fated and admirable friend. Over him hung a form which I cannot find words to describe; gigantic in stature, yet uncouth and distorted in its proportions. As he hung over the coffin, his face was concealed by long locks of ragged hair; but one vast hand was extended, in colour and apparent texture like that of a mummy. When he heard the sound of my approach, he ceased to utter exclamations of grief and horror, and sprung towards the window.

Never did I behold a vision so horrible as his face, of such loathsome yet appalling hideousness. I shut my eyes involuntarily, and endeavoured to recollect what were my duties with regard to this destroyer. I called on him to stay.

He paused, looking on me with wonder; and, again turning towards the lifeless form of his creator, he seemed to forget my presence, and every feature and gesture seemed instigated by the wildest rage of some uncontrollable passion.

"That is also my victim!" he exclaimed: "in his murder my crimes are consummated; the miserable series of my being is wound to its close! Oh, Frankenstein! generous and self-devoted being! what does it avail that I now ask thee to pardon me? I, who irretrievably destroyed thee by destroying all thou lovedst. Alas! he is cold, he cannot answer me."

His voice seemed suffocated; and my first impulses, which had suggested to me the duty of obeying the dying request of my friend, in destroying his enemy, were now suspended by a mixture of curiosity and compassion. I approached this tremendous being; I dared not again raise my eyes to his face, there was something so scaring and unearthly in his ugliness. I attempted to speak, but the words died away on my lips. The monster continued to utter wild and incoherent self-reproaches. At length I gathered resolution to address him in a pause of the tempest of his passion: "Your repentance," I said, "is now superfluous. If you had listened to the voice of conscience, and heeded the stings of remorse, before you had urged your diabolical vengeance to this extremity, Frankenstein would yet have lived."

"And do you dream?" said the dæmon; "do you think that I was then dead to agony and remorse?—He," he continued, pointing to the corpse, "he suffered not in the consummation of the deed—oh! not the ten-thousandth portion of the anguish that was mine during the lingering detail of its execution. A frightful selfishness hurried me on, while my heart was poisoned with remorse. Think you that the groans of Clerval were music to my ears? My heart was fashioned to be susceptible of love and sympathy; and, when wrenched by misery to vice and hatred, it did not endure the violence of the change, without torture such as you cannot even imagine.

"After the murder of Clerval, I returned to Switzerland, heart-broken and overcome. I pitied Frankenstein; my pity amounted to horror: I abhorred myself. But when I discovered that he, the author at once of my existence and of its unspeakable torments, dared to hope for happiness; that while he accumulated wretchedness and despair upon me, he sought his own enjoyment in feelings and passions from the indulgence of which I was for ever barred, then impotent envy and bitter indignation filled me with an insatiable thirst for vengeance. I recollected my threat, and resolved that it should be accomplished. I knew that I was preparing for myself a deadly torture; but I was the slave, not the master, of an impulse, which I detested, yet could not disobey. Yet when she died!— nay, then I was not miserable. I had cast off all feeling, subdued all anguish, to riot in the excess of my despair. Evil thenceforth became my good. Urged thus far, I had no choice but to adapt my nature to an element which I had willingly chosen. The completion of my demoniacal design became an insatiable passion. And now it is ended; there is my last victim!"

I was at first touched by the expressions of his misery; yet, when I called to mind what Frankenstein had said of his powers of eloquence and persuasion, and when I again cast my eyes on the lifeless form of my friend, indignation was rekindled within me. "Wretch!" I said, "it is well that you come here to whine over the desolation that you have made. You throw a torch into a pile of buildings; and, when they are consumed, you sit among the ruins, and lament the fall. Hypocritical fiend! if he whom you mourn still lived, still would he be the object, again would he become the prey, of your accursed vengeance. It is not pity that you feel; you lament only because the victim of your malignity is withdrawn from your power."

"Oh, it is not thus—not thus," interrupted the being; "yet such must be the impression conveyed to you by what appears to be the purport of my actions. Yet I seek not a fellow-feeling in my misery. No sympathy may I ever find. When I first sought it, it was the love of virtue, the feelings of happiness and affection with which my whole being overflowed, that I wished to be participated. But now, that virtue has become to me a shadow, and that happiness and affection are turned into bitter and loathing despair, in what should I seek for sympathy? I am content to suffer alone, while my sufferings shall endure: when I die, I am well satisfied that abhorrence and opprobrium should load my memory. Once my fancy was soothed with dreams of virtue, of fame, and of enjoyment. Once I falsely hoped to meet with beings, who, pardoning my outward form, would love me for the excellent qualities which I was capable of unfolding. I was nourished with high thoughts of honour and devotion. But now crime has degraded me beneath the meanest animal. No guilt, no mischief, no malignity, no misery, can be found comparable to mine. When I run over the frightful catalogue of my sins, I cannot believe that I am the same creature whose thoughts were once filled with sublime and transcendent visions of the beauty and the majesty of goodness. But it is even so; the fallen angel becomes a malignant devil. Yet even that enemy of God and man had friends and associates in his desolation; I am alone.

"You, who call Frankenstein your friend, seem to have a knowledge of my crimes and his misfortunes. But, in the detail which he gave you of them, he could not sum up the hours and months of misery which I endured, wasting in impotent passions. For while I destroyed his hopes, I did not satisfy my own desires. They were for ever ardent and craving; still I desired love and fellowship, and I was still spurned. Was there no injustice in this? Am I to be thought the only criminal, when all human kind sinned against me? Why do you not hate Felix, who drove his friend from his door with contumely? Why do you not execrate the rustic who sought to destroy the saviour of his child? Nay, these are virtuous and immaculate beings! I, the miserable and the abandoned, am an abortion, to be spurned at, and kicked, and trampled on. Even now my blood boils at the recollection of this injustice.

"But it is true that I am a wretch. I have murdered the lovely and the helpless; I have strangled the innocent as they slept, and grasped to death his throat who never injured me or any other living thing. I have devoted my creator, the select specimen of all that is worthy of love and admiration among men, to misery; I have pursued him even to that irremediable ruin. There he lies, white and cold in death. You hate me; but your abhorrence cannot equal that with which I regard myself. I look on the hands which executed the deed; I think on the heart in which the imagination of it was conceived, and long for the moment when these hands will meet my eyes, when that imagination will haunt my thoughts no more.

"Fear not that I shall be the instrument of future mischief. My work is nearly complete. Neither yours nor any man's death is needed to consummate the series of my being, and accomplish that which must be done; but it requires my own. Do not think that I shall be slow to perform this sacrifice. I shall quit your vessel on the ice-raft which brought me thither, and shall seek the most northern extremity of the globe; I shall collect my funeral pile, and consume to ashes this miserable frame, that its remains may afford no light to any curious and unhallowed wretch, who would create such another as I have been. I shall die. I shall no longer feel the agonies which now consume me, or be the prey of feelings unsatisfied, yet unquenched. He is dead who called me into being; and when I shall be no more, the very remembrance of us both will speedily vanish. I shall no longer see the sun or stars, or feel the winds play on my cheeks. Light, feeling, and sense will pass away; and in this condition must I find my happiness. Some years ago, when the images which this world affords first opened upon me, when I felt the cheering warmth of summer, and heard the rustling of the leaves and the warbling of the birds, and these were all to me, I should have wept to die; now it is my only consolation. Polluted by crimes, and torn by the bitterest remorse, where can I find rest but in death?

"Farewell! I leave you, and in you the last of human kind whom these eyes will ever behold. Farewell, Frankenstein! If thou wert yet alive, and yet cherished a desire of revenge against me, it would be better satiated in my life than in my destruction. But it was not so; thou didst seek my extinction, that I might not cause greater wretchedness; and if yet, in some mode unknown to me, thou hadst not ceased to think and feel, thou wouldst not desire against me a vengeance greater than that which I feel. Blasted as thou wert, my agony was still superior to thine; for the bitter sting of remorse will not cease to rankle in my wounds until death shall close them for ever.

"But soon," he cried, with sad and solemn enthusiasm, "I shall die, and what I now feel be no longer felt. Soon these burning miseries will be extinct. I shall ascend my funeral pile triumphantly, and exult in the agony of the torturing flames. The light of that conflagration will fade away; my ashes will be swept into the sea by the winds. My spirit will sleep in peace; or if it thinks, it will not surely think thus. Farewell."

He sprung from the cabin-window, as he said this, upon the ice-raft which lay close to the vessel. He was soon borne away by the waves, and lost in darkness and distance.

from

The Strange Case of Dr. Jekyll and Mr. Hyde

by Robert Louis Stevenson

HENRY JEKYLL'S FULL
STATEMENT OF THE CASE

[*Dr. Jekyll, a London scientist, writes a manuscript describing the creation of Mr. Hyde.*]

I was born in the year 18— to a large fortune, endowed besides with excellent parts, inclined by nature to industry, fond of the respect of the wise and good among my fellow-men, and thus, as might have been supposed, with every guarantee of an honourable and distinguished future. And indeed the worst of my faults was a certain impatient gaiety of disposition, such as has made the happiness of many, but such as I found it hard to reconcile with my imperious desire to carry my head high, and wear a more than commonly grave countenance before the public. Hence it came about that I concealed my pleasures; and that when I reached years of reflection, and began to look round me and take stock of my progress and position in the world, I stood already committed to a profound duplicity of life. Many a man would have even blazoned such irregularities as I was guilty of; but from the high views that I had set before me, I regarded and hid them with an almost morbid sense of shame. It was thus rather the exacting nature of my aspirations than any particular degradation in my faults, that made we what I was and, with even a deeper trench than in the majority of men, severed in me those provinces of good and ill which divide and compound man's dual nature. In this case, I was driven to reflect deeply and inveterately on that hard law of life, which lies at the root of religion and is one of the most plentiful springs of distress. Though so profound a double-dealer, I was in no sense a hypocrite; both sides of me were in dead earnest; I was no more myself when I laid aside restraint and plunged in shame, than when I laboured, in the eye of day, at the furtherance of knowledge or the relief of sorrow and suffering. And it chanced that the direction of my scientific studies, which led wholly towards the mystic and the transcendental, reacted and shed a strong light on this consciousness of the perennial war among my members. With every day, and from both sides of my intelligence, the moral and the intellectual, I thus drew steadily nearer to that truth, by whose partial discovery I have been doomed to such a dreadful shipwreck: that man is not truly one, but truly two. I say two, because the state of my own knowledge does not pass beyond that point. Others will follow, others will outstrip me on the same lines; and I hazard the guess that man will be ultimately known for a mere polity of multifarious, incongruous and independent denizens. I for my part, from the nature of my life, advanced infallibly in one direction and in one direction only. It was on the moral side, and in my own person, that I learned to recognise the thorough and primitive duality of man; I saw that, of the two natures that contended in the field of my consciousness, even if I could rightly be said to be either, it was only because I was radically both; and from an early date, even before the course of my scientific discoveries had begun to suggest the most naked possibility of such a miracle, I had learned to dwell with pleasure, as a beloved daydream, on the thought of the separation of these elements. If each, I told myself, could but be housed in separate identities, life would be relieved of all that was unbearable; the unjust might go his way, delivered from the aspirations and remorse of his more upright twin; and the just could walk steadfastly and securely on his upward path, doing the good things in which he found his pleasure, and no longer exposed to disgrace and penitence by the hands of this extraneous evil. It was the curse of mankind that these incongruous faggots were thus bound together—that in the agonised womb of consciousness, these polar twins should be continuously struggling. How, then, were they dissociated?

I was so far in my reflections when, as I have said, a side light began to shine upon the subject from the laboratory table. I began to perceive more deeply than it has ever yet been stated, the trembling immateriality, the mistlike transcience, of this seemingly so solid body in which we walk attired. Certain agents I found to have the power to shake and to pluck back that fleshy vestment, even as a wind might toss the curtains of a pavilion. For two good reasons, I will not enter deeply into this scientific branch of my confession. First, because I have been made to learn that the doom and burden of our life is bound forever on man's shoulders, and when the attempt is made to cast it off, it but returns upon us with more unfamiliar and more awful pressure. Second, because as my narrative will make alas! too evident, my discoveries were incomplete. Enough, then, that I not only recognised my natural body for the mere aura and effulgence of certain of the powers that made up my spirit, but managed to compound a drug by which these powers should be dethroned from their supremacy, and a second form and countenance substituted, none the less natural to me because they were the expression, and bore the stamp, of lower elements in my soul.

I hesitated long before I put this theory to the test of

practice. I knew well that I risked death; for any drug that so potently controlled and shook the very fortress of identity, might by the least scruple of an overdose or at the least inopportunity in the moment of exhibition, utterly blot out that immaterial tabernacle which I looked to it to change. But the temptation of a discovery so singular and profound, at last overcame the suggestions of alarm. I had long since prepared my tincture; I purchased at once, from a firm of wholesale chemists, a large quantity of a particular salt which I knew, from my experiments, to be the last ingredient required; and late one accursed night, I compounded the elements, watched them boil and smoke together in the glass, and when the ebullition had subsided, with a strong glow of courage, drank off the potion.

The most racking pangs succeeded: a grinding in the bones, deadly nausea, and a horror of the spirit that cannot be exceeded at the hour of birth or death. Then these agonies began swiftly to subside, and I came to myself as if out of a great sickness. There was something strange in my sensations, something indescribably new and, from its very novelty, incredibly sweet. I felt younger, lighter, happier in body; within I was conscious of a heady recklessness, a current of disordered sensual images running like a mill race in my fancy, a solution of the bonds of obligation, an unknown but not an innocent freedom of the soul. I knew myself, at the first breath of this new life, to be more wicked, tenfold more wicked, sold a slave to my original evil; and the thought, in that moment, braced and delighted me like wine. I stretched out my hands, exulting in the freshness of these sensations; and in the act, I was suddenly aware that I had lost in stature.

There was no mirror, at that date, in my room; that which stands beside me as I write, was brought there later on and for the very purpose of these transformations. The night, however, was far gone into the morning —the morning, black as it was, was nearly ripe for the conception of the day—the inmates of my house were locked in the most rigorous hours of slumber; and I determined, flushed as I was with hope and triumph, to venture in my new shape as far as to my bedroom. I crossed the yard, wherein the constellations looked down upon me, I could have thought, with wonder, the first creature of that sort that their unsleeping vigilance had yet disclosed to them; I stole through the corridors, a stranger in my own house; and coming to my room, I saw for the first time the appearance of Edward Hyde.

I must here speak by theory alone, saying not that which I know, but that which I suppose to be most probable. The evil side of my nature, to which I had now transferred the stamping efficacy, was less robust and less developed than the good which I had just deposed. Again, in the course of my life, which had been, after all, nine tenths a life of effort, virtue and control, it had been much less exercised and much less exhausted. And hence, as I think, it came about that Edward Hyde was so much smaller, slighter and younger than Henry Jekyll. Even as good shone upon the countenance of the one, evil was written broadly and plainly on the face of the other. Evil besides (which I must still believe to be the lethal side of man) had left on that body an imprint of deformity and decay. And yet when I looked upon that ugly idol in the glass, I was conscious of no repugnance, rather of a leap of welcome. This, too, was myself. It seemed natural and human. In my eyes it bore a livelier image of the spirit, it seemed more express and single, than the imperfect and divided countenance, I had been hitherto accustomed to call mine. And in so far I was doubtless right. I have observed that when I wore the semblance of Edward Hyde, none could come near to me at first without a visible misgiving of the flesh. This, as I take it, was because all human beings, as we meet them, are commingled out of good and evil: and Edward Hyde, alone in the ranks of mankind, was pure evil.

I lingered but a moment at the mirror: the second and

conclusive experiment had yet to be attempted; it yet remained to be seen if I had lost my identity beyond redemption and must flee before daylight from a house that was no longer mine; and hurrying back to my cabinet, I once more prepared and drank the cup, once more suffered the pangs of dissolution, and came to myself once more with the character, the stature and the face of Henry Jekyll.

That night I had come to the fatal cross roads. Had I approached my discovery in a more noble spirit, had I risked the experiment while under the empire of generous or pious aspirations, all must have been otherwise, and from these agonies of death and birth, I had come forth an angel instead of a fiend. The drug had no discriminating action; it was neither diabolical nor divine; it but shook the doors of the prisonhouse of my disposition; and like the captives of Philippi, that which stood within ran forth. At that time my virtue slumbered; my evil, kept awake by ambition, was alert and swift to seize the occasion; and the thing that was projected was Edward Hyde. Hence, although I had now two characters as well as two appearances, one was wholly evil, and the other was still the old Henry Jekyll, that incongruous compound of whose reformation and improvement I had already learned to despair. The movement was thus wholly toward the worse.

Even at that time, I had not yet conquered my aversion to the dryness of a life of study. I would still be merrily disposed at times; and as my pleasures were (to say the least) undignified, and I was not only well known and highly considered, but growing towards the elderly man, this incoherency of my life was daily growing more unwelcome. It was on this side that my new power tempted me until I fell in slavery. I had but to drink the cup, to doff at once the body of the noted professor, and to assume, like a thick cloak, that of Edward Hyde. I smiled at the notion; it seemed to me at the time to be humorous;

and I made my preparations with the most studious care. I took and furnished that house in Soho, to which Hyde was tracked by the police; and engaged as housekeeper a creature whom I well knew to be silent and unscrupulous. On the other side, I announced to my servants that a Mr. Hyde (whom I described) was to have full liberty and power about my house in the square; and to parry mishaps, I even called and made myself a familiar object, in my second character. I next drew up that will to which you so much objected; so that if anything befell me in the person of Doctor Jekyll, I could enter on that of Edward Hyde without pecuniary loss. And thus fortified, as I supposed, on every side, I began to profit by the strange immunities of my position.

Men have before hired bravos to transact their crimes, while their own person and reputation sat under shelter. I was the first that ever did so for his pleasures. I was the first that could thus plod in the public eye with a load of genial respectability, and in a moment, like a schoolboy, strip off these lendings and spring headlong into the sea of liberty. But for me, in my impenetrable mantle, the safety was complete. Think of it—I did not even exist! Let me but escape into my laboratory door, give me a second or two to mix and swallow the draught that I had always standing ready; and whatever he had done, Edward Hyde would pass away like the stain of breath upon a mirror; and there in his stead, quietly at home, trimming the midnight lamp in his study, a man who could afford to laugh at suspicion, would be Henry Jekyll.

The pleasures which I made haste to seek in my disguise were, as I have said, undignified; I would scarce use a harder term. But in the hands of Edward Hyde, they soon began to turn towards the monstrous. When I would come back from these excursions, I was often plunged into a kind of wonder at my vicarious depravity. This familiar that I called out of my own soul, and sent forth alone to do his good pleasure, was a being inherently malign and villainous; his every act and thought centered on self; drinking pleasure with bestial avidity from any degree of torture to another; relentless like a man of stone. Henry Jekyll stood at times aghast before the acts of Edward Hyde; but the situation was apart from ordinary laws, and insidiously relaxed the grasp of conscience. It was Hyde, after all, and Hyde alone, that was guilty. Jekyll was no worse; he woke again to his good qualities seemingly unimpaired; he would even make haste, where it was possible to undo the evil done by Hyde. And thus his conscience slumbered.

Into the details of the infamy at which I thus connived (for even now I can scarce grant that I committed it) I have no design of entering; I mean but to point out the warnings and the successive steps with which my chastisement approached. I met with one accident which, as it brought on no consequence, I shall no more than mention. An act of cruelty to a child aroused against me the anger of a passer by, whom I recognised the other day in the person of your kinsman; the doctor and the child's family joined him; there were moments when I feared for my life; and at last, in order to pacify their too just resentment, Edward Hyde had to bring them to the door, and pay them in a cheque drawn in the name of Henry Jekyll. But this danger was easily eliminated from the future, by opening an account at another bank in the name of Edward Hyde himself; and when, by sloping my own hand backward, I had supplied my double with a signature, I thought I sat beyond the reach of fate.

Some two months before the murder of Sir Danvers, I had been out for one of my adventures, had returned at a late hour, and woke the next day in bed with somewhat odd sensations. It was in vain I looked about me; in vain I saw the decent furniture and tall proportions of my room in the square; in vain that I recognised the pattern of the bed curtains and the design of the mahogany frame; something still kept insisting that I was not where I was, that I had not wakened where I seemed to be, but in the little room in Soho where I was accustomed to sleep in the body of Edward Hyde. I smiled to myself, and, in my psychological way, began lazily to inquire into the elements of this illusion, occasionally, even as I did so, dropping back into a comfortable morning doze. I was still so engaged when, in one of my more wakeful moments, my eye fell upon my hand. Now the hand of Henry Jekyll (as you have often remarked) was professional in shape and size: it was large, firm, white and comely. But the hand which I now saw, clearly enough, in the yellow light of a mid-London morning, lying half shut on the bed clothes, was lean, corded, knuckly, of a dusky pallor and thickly shaded with a swart growth of hair. It was the hand of Edward Hyde.

I must have stared upon it for near half a minute, sunk as I was in the mere stupidity of wonder, before terror woke up in my breast as sudden and startling as the crash of cymbals; and bounding from my bed, I rushed to the mirror. At the sight that met my eyes, my blood was changed into something exquisitely thin and icy. Yes, I had gone to bed Henry Jekyll, I had awakened Edward Hyde. How was this to be explained? I asked myself; and then, with another bound of terror—how was it to be remedied? It was well on in the morning; the servants were up; all my drugs were in the cabinet—a long journey, down two pair of stairs, through the back passage, across the open court and through the anatomical theatre, from where I was then standing horror-struck. It might indeed be possible to cover my face; but of what use was that, when I was unable to conceal the alteration in my stature? And then with an overpowering sweetness of relief, it came back upon my mind that the servants were already used to the coming and going of my second self. I had soon dressed, as well as I was able, in clothes of my own size: had soon passed through the house, where Bradshaw stared and drew back at seeing Mr. Hyde at such an hour and in such a strange array; and ten minutes later, Dr. Jekyll had returned to his own shape and was sitting down, with a darkened brow, to make a feint of breakfasting.

Small indeed was my appetite. This inexplicable incident, this reversal of my previous experience, seemed, like the Babylonian finger on the wall, to be spelling out the letters of my judgment; and I began to reflect more seriously than ever before on the issues and possibilities of my double existence. That part of me which I had the power of projecting, had lately been much exercised and nourished; it had seemed to me of late as though the body of Edward Hyde had grown in stature, as though (when I wore that form) I were conscious of a more generous tide of blood; and I began to spy a danger that, if this were much prolonged, the balance of my nature might be permanently overthrown, the power of voluntary change be forfeited, and the character of Edward Hyde become irrevocably mine. The power of the drug had not been always equally displayed. Once, very early in my career, it had totally failed me; since then I had been obliged on more than one occasion to double, and once, with infinite risk of death, to treble the amount, and these rare uncertainties had cast hitherto the sole shadow on my contentment. Now, however, and in the light of that morning's accident, I was led to remark that whereas, in the beginning, the difficulty had been to throw off the body of Jekyll, it had of late gradually but decidedly transferred itself to the other side. All things therefore seemed to point to this: that I was slowly losing hold of my original and better self, and becoming slowly incorporated with my second and worse.

Between these two, I now felt I had to choose. My two natures had memory in common, but all other faculties were most unequally shared between them. Jekyll (who was composite) now with the most sensitive apprehensions, now with a greedy gusto, projected and shared in the pleasures and adventures of Hyde; but Hyde was indifferent to Jekyll, or but remembered him as the mountain bandit remembers the cavern in which he conceals himself from pursuit. Jekyll had more than a father's interest; Hyde had more than a son's indifference. To cast in my lot with Jekyll, was to die to those appetites which I had long secretly indulged and had of late begun to pamper. To cast it in with Hyde, was to die to a thousand interests and aspirations, and to become, at a blow and forever, despised and friendless. The bargain might appear unequal; but there was still another consideration in the scales; for while Jekyll would suffer smartingly in the fires of abstinence, Hyde would be not even conscious of all that he had lost. Strange as my circumstances were, the terms of this debate are as old and commonplace as man; much the same inducements and alarms cast the die for any tempted and trembling sinner; and it fell out with me, as it falls with so vast a majority of my fellows, that I chose the better part and was found wanting in the strength to keep to it.

Yes, I preferred the elderly and discontented doctor, surrounded by friends and cherishing honest hopes; and bade a resolute farewell to the liberty, the comparative youth, the light step, leaping pulses and secret pleasures, that I had enjoyed in the disguise of Hyde. I made this choice perhaps with some unconscious reservation, for I neither gave up the house in Soho, nor destroyed the clothes of Edward Hyde, which still lay ready in my cabinet. For two months, however, I was true to my determination; for two months, I led a life of such severity as I had never before attained to, and enjoyed the compensations of an approving conscience. But time began at last to obliterate the freshness of my alarm; the praises of conscience began to grow into a thing of course; I began to be tortured with throes and longings, as of Hyde struggling after freedom; and at last in an hour of moral weakness, I once again compounded and swallowed the transforming draught.

I do not suppose that, when a drunkard reasons with himself upon his vice, he is once out of five hundred times affected by the dangers that he runs through his brutish, physical insensibility; neither had I, long as I had considered my position, made enough allowance for the complete moral insensibility and insensate readiness to evil, which were the leading characters of Edward Hyde. Yet it was by these that I was punished. My devil had been long caged, he came out roaring. I was conscious, even when I took the draught, of a more unbridled, a more furious propensity to ill. It must have been this, I suppose, that stirred in my soul that tempest of impatience with which I listened to the civilities of my unhappy victim; I declare at least, before God, no man morally sane could have been guilty of that crime upon so pitiful a provocation; and that I struck in no more reasonable spirit than that in which a sick child may break a plaything. But I had voluntarily stripped myself of all those balancing instincts, by which even the worst of us continues to walk with some degree of steadiness among temptations; and in my case, to be tempted, however slightly, was to fall.

Instantly the spirit of hell awoke in me and raged. With a transport of glee, I mauled the unresisting body, tasting delight from every blow; and it was not till weariness had begun to succeed, that I was suddenly, in the top fit of my delirium, struck through the heart by a cold thrill of terror. A mist dispersed; I saw my life to be forfeit; and fled from the scene of these excesses, at once glorying and trembling, my lust of evil gratified and stimulated, my love of life screwed to the topmost peg. I ran to the house in Soho, and (to make assurance doubly sure) destroyed my papers; thence I set out through the lamplit streets, in the same divided ecstasy of mind, gloating on my crime, light-headedly devising others in the future, and yet still hastening and still hearkening in my wake for the steps of the avenger. Hyde had a song upon his lips as he compounded the draught, and as he drank it, pledged the dead man. The pangs of transformation had not done tearing him, before Henry Jekyll, with streaming tears of gratitude and remorse, had fallen upon his knees and lifted his clasped hands to God. The veil of self-indulgence was rent from head to foot, I saw my life as a whole: I followed it up from the days of childhood, when I had walked with my father's hand, and through the self-denying toils of my professional life, to arrive again and again, with the same sense of unreality, at the damned horrors of the evening. I could have screamed aloud; I sought with tears and prayers to smother down the crowd of hideous images and sounds with which my memory swarmed against me; and still, between the petitions, the ugly face of my iniquity stared into my soul. As the acuteness of this remorse began to die away, it was succeeded by a sense of joy. The problem of my conduct was solved. Hyde was thenceforth impossible; whether I would or not, I was now confined to the better part of my existence; and O, how I rejoiced to think it! with what willing humility, I embraced anew the restrictions of natural life! with what sincere renunciation, I locked the door by which I had so often gone and come, and ground the key under my heel!

The next day, came the news that the murder had been overlooked, that the guilt of Hyde was patent to the world, and that the victim was a man high in public estimation. It was not only a crime, it had been a tragic folly. I think I was glad to know it; I think I was glad to have my better impulses thus buttressed and guarded by the terrors of the scaffold. Jekyll was now my city of refuge; but let Hyde peep out an instant, and the hands of all men would be raised to take and slay him.

I resolved in my future conduct to redeem the past; and I can say with honesty that my resolve was fruitful of some good. You know yourself how earnestly in the last months of last year, I laboured to relieve suffering; you know that much was done for others, and that the days passed quietly, almost happily for myself. Nor can I truly say that I wearied of this beneficent and innocent life; I think instead that I daily enjoyed it more completely; but I was still cursed with my duality of purpose; and as the first edge of my penitence wore off, the lower side of me, so long indulged, so recently chained down, began to growl for license. Not that I dreamed of resuscitating Hyde, the bare idea of that would startle me to frenzy: no, it was in my own person, that I was once more tempted to trifle with my conscience; and it was as an ordinary secret sinner, that I at last fell before the assaults of temptation.

There comes an end to all things; the most capacious measure is filled at last; and this brief condescension to my evil finally destroyed the balance of my soul. And yet I was not alarmed; the fall seemed natural, like a return to the old days before I had made my discovery. It was a fine, clear, January day, wet under foot where the frost had melted, but cloudless overhead; and the Regent's park was full of winter chirruppings and sweet with Spring odours. I sat in the sun on a bench; the animal within me licking the chops of memory; the spiritual side a little drowsed, promising subsequent penitence, but not yet moved to begin. After all, I reflected I was like my neighbours; and then I smiled, comparing myself with other men, comparing my active good will with the lazy cruelty of their neglect. And at the very moment of that vainglorious thought, a qualm come over me, a horrid nausea and the most deadly shuddering. These passed away, and left me faint; and then as in its turn the faintness subsided, I began to be aware of a change in the temper of my thoughts, a greater boldness, a contempt of danger, a solution of the bonds of obligation. I looked down; my clothes hung formlessly on my shrunken limbs; the hand that lay on my knee was corded and hairy. I was once more Edward Hyde. A moment before I had been safe of all men's respect, wealthy, beloved——the cloth laying for me in the dining room at home; and now I was the common quarry of mankind, hunted, houseless, a known murderer, thrall to the gallows.

My reason wavered, but it did not fail me utterly. I have more than once observed that, in my second character, my faculties seemed sharpened to a point and my spirits more tensely elastic; thus it came about that, where Jekyll perhaps might have succumbed, Hyde rose to the importance of the moment. My drugs were in one of the presses of my cabinet; how was I to reach them? That was the problem that (crushing my temples in my hands) I set myself to solve. The laboratory door I had closed. If I sought to enter by the house, my own servants would consign me to the gallows. I saw I must employ another hand, and thought of Lanyon. How was he to be reached? how persuaded? Supposing that I escaped capture in the streets, how was I to make my way into his presence? and how should I, an unknown and displeasing visitor, prevail on the famous physician to rifle the study of his colleague, Dr. Jekyll? Then I remembered that of my original character, one part remained to me: I could write my own hand; and once I had conceived that kindling spark, the way that I must follow became lighted up from end to end.

Thereupon, I arranged my clothes as best as I could, and summoning a passing hansom, drove to an hotel in Portland street, the name of which I chanced to remember. At my appearance (which was indeed comical enough, however tragic a fate the garments covered) the driver could not conceal his mirth. I gnashed my teeth upon him with a gust of devilish fury; and the smile withered from his face——happily for him——yet more happily for myself, for in another instant I had certainly dragged him from his perch. At the inn, as I entered, I looked about me with so black a countenance as made the attendants tremble; not a look did they exchange in my presence; but obsequiously took my orders, led me to a private room, and brought me wherewithal to write. Hyde in danger of his life was a creature new to me: shaken with inordinate anger, strung to the pitch of murder, lusting to inflict pain. Yet the creature was astute; mastered his fury with a great effort of the will; composed his two important letters, one to Lanyon and one to Poole; and that he might receive actual evidence of their being posted, sent them out with directions that they should be registered.

Thenceforward, he sat all day over the fire in the private room gnawing his nails; there he dined, sitting alone with his fears, the waiter visibly quailing before his eye; and thence, when the night was fully come, he set forth in the corner of a closed cab, and was driven to and fro about the streets of the city. He, I say—I cannot say, I. That child of Hell had nothing human; nothing lived in him but fear and hatred. And when at last, thinking the driver had begun to grow suspicious, he discharged the cab and ventured on foot, attired in his misfitting clothes, an object marked out for observation, into the midst of the nocturnal passengers, these two base passions raged within him like a tempest. He walked fast, hunted by his fears, chattering to himself, skulking through the less frequented thoroughfares, counting the minutes that still divided him from midnight. Once a woman spoke to him, offering, I think, a box of lights. He smote her in the face, and she fled.

When I came to myself at Lanyon's, the horror of my old friend perhaps affected me somewhat: I do not know; it was at least but a drop in the sea to the abhorrence with which I looked back upon these hours. A change had come over me. It was no longer the fear of the gallows, it was the horror of being Hyde that racked me. I received Lanyon's condemnation partly in a dream; it was partly in a dream that I came home to my own house and got into bed. I slept after the prostration of the day, with a stringent and profound slumber which not even the nightmares that wrung me could avail to break. I awoke in the morning shaken, weakened, but refreshed. I still hated and feared the thought of the brute that slept within me, and I had not of course forgotten the appalling dangers of the day before; but I was once more at home, in my own house and close to my drugs; and gratitude for my escape shone so strong in my soul that it almost rivalled the brightness of hope.

I was stepping leisurely across the court after breakfast, drinking the chill of the air with pleasure, when I was seized again with those indescribable sensations that heralded the change; and I had but the time to gain the shelter of my cabinet, before I was once again raging and freezing with the passions of Hyde. It took on this occasion a double dose to recall me to myself; and alas, six hours after, as I sat looking sadly in the fire, the pangs returned, and the drug had to be re-administered. In short, from that day forth it seemed only by a great effort as of gymnastics, and only under the immediate stimulation of the drug, that I was able to wear the countenance of Jekyll. At all hours of the day and night, I would be taken with the premonitory shudder; above all, if I slept, or even dozed for a moment in my chair, it was always as Hyde that I awakened. Under the strain of this continually impending doom and by the sleeplessness to which I now condemned myself, ay, even beyond what I had thought possible to man, I became, in my own person, a creature eaten up and emptied by fever, languidly weak both in body and mind, and solely occupied by one thought: the horror of my other self. But when I slept, or when the virtue of the medicine wore off, I would leap almost without transition (for the pangs of transformation grew daily less marked) into the possession of a fancy brimming with images of terror, a soul boiling with causeless hatreds, and a body that seemed not strong enough to contain the raging energies of life. The powers of Hyde seemed to have grown with the sickliness of Jekyll. And certainly the hate that now divided them was equal on each side. With Jekyll, it was a thing of vital instinct. He had now seen the full deformity of that creature that shared with him some of the phenomena of consciousness, and was co-heir with him to death: and beyond these links of community, which in themselves made the most poignant part of his distress, he thought of Hyde, for all his energy of life, as of something not only hellish but inorganic. This was the shocking thing; that the slime of the pit seemed to utter cries and voices; that the amorphous dust gesticulated and sinned; that what was dead, and had no shape, should usurp the offices of life. And this again, that that insurgent horror was knit to him closer than a wife, closer than an eye; lay caged in his flesh, where he heard it mutter and felt it struggle to be born; and at every hour of weakness, and in the confidence of slumber, prevailed against him, and deposed him out of life. The hatred of Hyde for Jekyll, was of a different order. His terror of the gallows drove him continually to commit temporary suicide, and return to his subordinate station of a part instead of a person; but he loathed the necessity, he loathed the despondency into which Jekyll was now fallen, and he resented the dislike with which he was himself regarded. Hence the apelike tricks that he would play me, scrawling in my own hand blasphemies on the pages of my books, burning the letters and destroying the portrait of my father; and indeed, had it not been for his fear of death, he would long ago have ruined himself in order to involve me in the ruin. But his love of life is wonderful; I go further: I, who sicken and freeze at the mere thought of him, when I recall the abjection and passion of this attachment, and when I know how he fears my power to cut him off by suicide, I find it in my heart to pity him.

It is useless, and the time awfully fails me, to prolong

this description; no one has ever suffered such torments, let that suffice; and yet even to these, habit brought—no, not alleviation—but a certain callousness of soul, a certain acquiescence of despair; and my punishment might have gone on for years, but for the last calamity which has now fallen, and which has finally severed me from my own face and nature. My provision of the salt, which had never been renewed since the date of the first experiment, began to run low. I sent out for a fresh supply, and mixed the draught; the ebullition followed, and the first change of colour, not the second; I drank it and it was without efficiency. You will learn from Poole how I have had London ransacked; it was in vain; and I am now persuaded that my first supply was impure, and that it was that unknown impurity which lent efficacy to the draught.

About a week has passed, and I am now finishing this statement under the influence of the last of the old powders. This, then, is the last time, short of a miracle, that Henry Jekyll can think his own thoughts or see his own face (now how sadly altered!) in the glass. Nor must I delay too long to bring my writing to an end; for if my narrative has hitherto escaped destruction, it has been by a combination of great prudence and great good luck. Should the throes of change take me in the act of writing it, Hyde will tear it in pieces; but if some time shall have elapsed after I have laid it by, his wonderful selfishness and circumscription to the moment will probably save it once again from the action of his apelike spite. And indeed the doom that is closing on us both, has already changed and crushed him. Half an hour from now, when I shall again and forever reindue that hated personality, I know how I shall sit shuddering and weeping in my chair, or continue, with the most strained and fearstruck ecstasy of listening, to pace up and down this room (my last earthly refuge) and give ear to every sound of menace. Will Hyde die upon the scaffold? or will he find the courage to release himself at the last moment? God knows; I am careless; this is my true hour of death, and what is to follow concerns another than myself. Here then, as I lay down the pen and proceed to seal up my confession, I bring the life of that unhappy Henry Jekyll to an end.

from

Wagner, the Wehr-Wolf

by George W. M. Reynolds

PROLOGUE.

It was the month of January, 1516.

The night was dark and tempestuous;—the thunder growled around;—the lightning flashed at short intervals; —and the wind swept furiously along, in sudden and fitful gusts.

The streams of the great Black Forest of Germany bubbled in playful melody no more, but rushed on with deafening din, mingling their torrent-roar with the wild creaking of the huge oaks, the rustling of the firs, the howling of the affrighted wolves, and the hollow voices of the storm.

The dense black clouds were driven restlessly athwart the sky; and when the vivid lightning gleamed forth with rapid and eccentric glare, it seemed as if the dark jaws of some hideous monster, floating high above, opened to vomit flame.

And as the abrupt but furious gusts of wind swept through the forest they raised strange echoes—as if the impervious mazes of that mighty wood were the abode of hideous fiends and evil spirits, who responded in shrieks, moans, and lamentations, to the fearful din of the tempest.

It was indeed an appalling sight!

An old—old man sat in his little cottage on the verge of the Black Forest.

He had numbered ninety years: his head was completely bald—his mouth was toothless—his long beard was white as snow—and his limbs were feeble and trembling.

He was alone in the world: his wife—his children—his grand-children—all his relations, in fine, *save one*—had preceded him on that long last voyage from which no traveller returns.

And that *one* was a grand-daughter—a beauteous girl of sixteen, who had hitherto been his solace and his comfort, but who had suddenly disappeared—he knew not how—a few days previously to the time when we discover him seated thus lonely in his poor cottage.

But perhaps she also was dead? An accident might have snatched her away from him, and sent her spirit to join those of her father and mother, her sisters, and her brothers, whom a terrible pestilence—*the Black Death*—hurried to the tomb a few years before?

No: the old man could not believe that his darling grand-daughter was no more—for he had sought her throughout the neighbouring district of the Black Forest, and not a trace of her was to be seen. Had she fallen down a precipice, or perished by the ruthless murderer's hand, he would have discovered her mangled corpse: had she become the prey of the ravenous wolves, certain signs of her fate would have doubtless somewhere appeared.

The sad—the chilling conviction therefore went to the old man's heart, that the only being left to solace him on earth, had deserted him; and his spirit was bowed down in despair.

Who now would prepare his food, while he tended his little flock? who was there to collect the dry branches in the forest, for the winter's fuel, while the aged shepherd watched a few sheep that he possessed? who would now spin him warm clothing to protect his weak and trembling limbs?

"Oh! Agnes," he murmured, in a tone indicative of a breaking heart, "how could'st thou have thus abandoned me? Didst thou quit the old man to follow some youthful lover, who will buoy thee up with bright hopes, and then deceive thee? O Agnes—my darling! hast thou left me to perish without a soul to close my eyes?"

It was painful how that aged shepherd wept.

Suddenly a loud knock at the door of the cottage aroused him from his painful reverie; and he hastened, as fast as his trembling limbs would permit him, to answer the summons.

He opened the door; and a tall man, apparently about forty years of age, entered the humble dwelling. His light hair would have been magnificent indeed, were it not sorely neglected; his blue eyes were naturally fine and intelligent, but fearful now to meet, so wild and wandering were their glances;—his form was tall and admirably symmetrical, but prematurely bowed by the weight of sorrow;—and his attire was of costly material, but indicative of inattention even more than it was travel-soiled.

The old man closed the door, and courteously drew a stool near the fire for the stranger who had sought in his cottage a refuge against the fury of the storm.

He also placed food before him; but the stranger touched it not—horror and dismay appearing to have taken possession of his soul.

Suddenly the thunder, which had hitherto growled at a distance, burst above the humble abode; and the wind swept by with so violent a gust, that it shook the little tenement to its foundation, and filled the neighbouring forest with strange, unearthly noises.

Then the countenance of the stranger expressed such ineffable horror, amounting to a fearful agony, that the old man was alarmed, and stretched out his hand to grasp a crucifix that hung over the chimney piece: but this mysterious guest made a forbidding sign of so much earnestness, mingled with such proud authority, that the aged shepherd sank back into his seat without touching the sacred symbol.

The roar of the thunder past—the shrieking, whistling, gushing wind became temporarily lulled into low moans and subdued lamentations amidst the mazes of the Black Forest;—and the stranger grew more composed.

"Dost thou tremble at the storm?" inquired the old man.

"I am unhappy," was the evasive and somewhat impatient reply. "Seek not to know more of me—beware how you question me. But you, old man, are *you* happy? The traces of care seem to mingle with the wrinkles of age upon your brow."

The shepherd narrated, in brief and touching terms, the unaccountable disappearance of his much-loved granddaughter Agnes.

The stranger listened abstractedly at first; but afterwards he appeared to reflect profoundly for several minutes.

"Your lot is a wretched one, old man," he said, at length: "if you live a few years longer, that period must be passed in solitude and cheerlessness;—if you suddenly fall ill, you must die the lingering death of famine, without a soul to place a morsel of food, or the cooling cup to your lips;—and when you shall be no more, who will follow you to the grave? There are no habitations nigh; the nearest village is half-a-day's journey distant;—and ere the peasants of that hamlet or some passing traveller might discover that the inmate of this hut had breathed his last, the wolves from the forest would have entered and mangled your corpse."

"Talk not thus!" cried the old man, with a visible shudder: then, darting a half-terrified, half-curious glance at his guest, said, "But who are you that speak in this awful strain—this warning voice?"

Again the thunder rolled, with crashing sound above

the cottage; and once more the wind swept by, laden, as it seemed, with the shrieks and groans of human beings in the agonies of death.

The stranger maintained a certain degree of composure only by means of a desperate effort; but he could not altogether subdue a wild flashing of the eyes and a ghastly change of the countenance,—signs of a profoundly-felt terror.

"Again I say, ask me not who I am!" he exclaimed when the thunder and the gust had passed. "My soul recoils from the bare idea of pronouncing my own accursed name! But—unhappy as you see me—crushed, overwhelmed with deep affliction as you behold me,—anxious, but unable, to repent for the past as I am, and filled with appalling dread for the future as I now proclaim myself to be,—still is my power far, far beyond that limit which hems mortal energies within so small a sphere. Speak, old man—would'st thou change thy condition? For to me— and to me alone of all human beings—belong the means of giving thee new life—of bestowing upon thee the vigour of youth—of rendering that stooping frame upright and strong—of restoring fire to those glazing eyes, and beauty to that wrinkled, sunken, withered countenance, of endowing thee, in a word, with a fresh tenure of existence, and making that existence sweet by the aid of treasures so vast that no extravagance can dissipate them!"

A strong though indefinite dread assailed the old man as this astounding proffer was rapidly opened, in all its alluring details, to his mind;—and various images of terror presented themselves to his imagination;—but these feelings were almost immediately dominated by a wild and ardent hope, which became the more attractive and exciting in proportion as a rapid glance at his helpless, wretched, deserted condition led him to survey the contrast between what he then was, and what, if the stranger spoke truly, he might so soon become.

The stranger saw that he had made the desired impression;—and he continued thus:—

"Give but your assent, old man,—and not only will I render thee young, handsome and wealthy; but I will endow thy mind with an intelligence to match that proud position. Thou shalt go forth into the world to enjoy all those pleasures—those delights—and those luxuries, the names of which are even now scarcely known to thee!"

"And what is the price of this glorious boon?" asked the old man, trembling with mingled joy and terror throughout every limb.

"There are two conditions," answered the stranger, in a low mysterious tone. "The first is, that you become the companion of my wanderings for one year and a half from the present time—until the hour of sunset on the 30th of July, 1517—when we must part for ever,—you to go whithersoever your inclinations may guide you—and I—— But of *that,* no matter!" he added, hastily, with a sudden motion, as if of deep mental agony and with wildly flashing eyes.

The old man shrank back in dismay from his mysterious guest: the thunder rolled again—the rude gust swept fiercely by—the dark forest rustled awfully—and the stranger's torturing feelings were evidently prolonged by the voices of the storm.

A pause ensued; and the silence was at length broken by the old man, who said, in a hollow and tremulous tone, "To the first condition I would willingly accede. But the second?"

"That you prey upon the human race, whom I hate— because of all the world I alone am so deeply, so terribly accurst!" was the ominously fearful yet only dimly significant reply.

The old man shook his head—scarcely comprehending the words of his guest, and yet daring not to ask to be more enlightened.

"Listen!" said the stranger, in a hasty, but impressive voice. "I require a companion—one who has no human ties, and who will minister to my caprices,—who will devote himself wholly and solely to watch me in my dark hours, and endeavour to recall me back to enjoyment and pleasure,—who, when he shall be acquainted with my power, will devise new means in which to exercise it for the purpose of conjuring up those scenes of enchantment and delight that may for a season win me away from thought. Such a companion do I need for a period of one year and a half; and you are, of all men, the best suited to my design. But the Spirit whom I must invoke to effect the promised change in thee, and by whose aid you can be given back to youth and comeliness, will demand some fearful sacrifice at your hands. And the nature of that sacrifice—the nature of the condition to be imposed—I can well divine!"

"Name the sacrifice—name the condition!" cried the old man, eagerly. "I am so miserable—so spirit broken—so totally without hope in this world, that I greedily long to enter upon that new existence which you promise me! Say, then—what is the condition!"

"That you prey upon the human race whom *he* hates as well as I," answered the stranger.

"Again those awful words!" ejaculated the old man casting trembling glances around him.

"Yes—again those words!" echoed the mysterious guest, looking with his fierce, burning eyes into the glazed orbs of the aged shepherd. "And now learn their import!" he continued, in a solemn tone. "Knowest thou not that there is a belief in many parts of our native land, that at particular seasons certain doomed men throw off the human shape, and take that of ravenous wolves?"

"Oh! yes—yes—I have indeed heard of those strange legends in which the Wehr-Wolf is represented in such appalling colours!" exclaimed the old man, a terrible suspicion crossing his mind. " 'Tis said that at sunset on the last day of every month the mortal to whom belongs the destiny of the Wehr-Wolf, must change his natural form for that of the savage animal; in which horrible shape he must remain until the moment when the morrow's sun dawns upon the earth."

"The legend that told thee this, spoke truly," said the stranger. "And now dost thou comprehend the condition which must be imposed upon thee?"

"I do—I do!" murmured the old man, with a fearful shudder. "But he who accepts that condition makes a compact with the Evil One, and thereby endangers his immortal soul!"

"Not so," was the reply. "There is naught involved in this condition which——But hesitate not," added the stranger, hastily; "I have not time to waste in bandying words. Consider all I offer you: in another hour you shall be another man!"

"I accept the boon—and on the conditions stipulated!" exclaimed the shepherd.

" 'Tis well, Wagner——"

"What! you know my name!" cried the old man. "And yet, meseem, I did not mention it to thee?"

"Canst thou not already perceive that I am no common mortal?" demanded the stranger, bitterly. "And who I am—and whence I derive my power,—all, all shall be revealed to thee so soon as the bond is formed that must link us for eighteen months together! In the meantime, await me here!"

And the mysterious stranger quitted the cottage abruptly, and plunged into the depths of the Black Forest.

One hour elapsed ere he returned,—one mortal hour, during which Wagner sat bowed over his miserably scanty fire, dreaming of pleasure—youth—riches—and enjoyment;—converting, in imagination, the myriad sparks which shone upon the extinguishing embers into piles of gold,—and allowing his now uncurbed fancy to change the one single room of the wretched hovel into a splendid saloon, surrounded by resplendent mirrors and costly hangings,—while the untasted fare spread for the stranger on the rude fir table, became transformed, in his idea, into a magnificent banquet laid out on a board glittering with plate, lustrous with innumerable lamps, and surrounded by an atmosphere fragrant with the most exquisite perfumes.

The return of the stranger awoke the old man from this charming dream, during which he had never once thought of the conditions whereby he was to purchase the complete realization of the vision.

"Oh! what a glorious reverie you have dissipated!" exclaimed Wagner. "Fulfil but one tenth part of that delightful dream——"

"I will fulfil it all!" interrupted the stranger; then, producing a small phial from the bosom of his doublet, he said, "Drink!"

The old man seized the bottle, and greedily drained it to the dregs.

He immediately fell back upon the seat, in a state of complete lethargy.

But it lasted not for many minutes; and when he awoke again, he experienced new and extraordinary sensations. His limbs were vigorous—his form was upright as an arrow—his eyes, for many years dim and failing, seemed gifted with the sight of an eagle—his head was warm with a natural covering—not a wrinkle remained upon his brow nor on his cheeks—and, as he smiled with mingled wonderment and delight, the parting lips revealed a set of brilliant teeth. And it seemed, too, as if by one magic touch, the long fading tree of his intellect had suddenly burst into full foliage; and every cell of his brain was instantaneously stored with an amount of knowledge, the accumulation of which stunned him for an instant, and in the next appeared as familiar to him as if he had never been without it.

"Oh! great and powerful being whosoever thou art!" exclaimed Wagner, in the full melodious voice of a young man of twenty-one, "how can I manifest to thee my deep

—my boundless gratitude for this boon which thou hast conferred upon me?"

"By thinking no more of thy lost grand-child Agnes, but by preparing to follow me whither I shall now lead thee," replied the stranger.

"Command me: I am ready to obey in all things," cried Wagner. "But one word ere we set forth——who art thou, wondrous man?"

"Henceforth I have no secrets from thee, Wagner," was the answer, while the stranger's eyes gleamed with unearthly lustre; then, bending forward, he whispered a few words in the other's ear.

Wagner started with a cold and fearful shudder as if at some appalling announcement; but he uttered not a word of reply—for his master beckoned him imperiously away from the humble cottage.

* * * * * * * * * * * * * * *

CHAPTER XII.

THE WEHR-WOLF.

'Twas the hour of sunset.

The eastern horizon, with its gloomy and sombre twilight, offered a strange contrast to the glorious glowing hues of vermillion, and purple, and gold, that blended in long streaks athwart the western sky.

For even the winter sunset of Italy is accompanied with resplendent tints,—as if an Emperor, decked with a refulgent diadem, were repairing to his imperial couch.

The declining rays of the orb of light bathed in molten gold the pinnacles, steeples, and lofty palaces of proud Florence, and toyed with the limpid waves of the Arno, on whose banks innumerable villas and casinos already sent forth delicious streams of music, broken only by the mirth of joyous revellers.

And by degrees, as the sun went down, the palaces of the superb city began to shed light from their lattices set in richly sculptured masonry; and here and there where festivity prevailed, grand illuminations sprang up with magical quickness,—the reflection from each separate galaxy rendering it bright as day,—far—far around.

Vocal and instrumental melody floated through the still air; and the perfume of exotics, decorating the halls of the Florentine nobles, poured from the widely opened portals, and rendered that air delicious.

For Florence was gay that evening—the last day of each month being the one which the wealthy lords and high-born ladies set apart for the reception of their friends.

The sun sunk behind the western hills; and even the hot-house flowers closed up their buds—as if they were eye-lids weighed down by slumber, and not to awake until the morning should arouse them again to welcome the return of their lover—that glorious sun!

Darkness seemed to dilate upon the sky like an image in the midst of a mirage, expanding into superhuman dimensions,—then rapidly losing its shapeliness, and covering the vault above densely and confusedly.

But by degrees countless stars began to stud the colourless canopy of heaven, like gems of orient splendour; for the last—last flickering ray of the twilight in the west had expired in the increasing obscurity.

But, hark! what is that wild and fearful cry?

In the midst of a wood of evergreens on the banks of the Arno, a man—young, handsome, and splendidly attired—has thrown himself upon the ground, where he writhes like a stricken serpent, in horrible convulsions.

He is the prey of a demoniac excitement: an appalling consternation is on him;—madness is in his brain—his mind is on fire.

Lightnings appear to gleam from his eyes—as if his soul were dismayed, and withering within his breast.

"Oh! no—no!" he cries, with a piercing shriek, as if

wrestling madly—furiously—but vainly, against some unseen fiend that holds him in his grasp.

And the wood echoes to that terrible wail: and the
startled bird flies from its bough.

But, lo! what awful change is taking place in the form
of that doomed being? His handsome countenance elon-
gates into one of savage and brute-like shape;—the rich
garment which he wears becomes a rough, shaggy, and
wiry skin;—his body loses its human contours—his arms
and limbs take another form;—and, with a frantic howl
of misery, to which the woods give horribly faithful reverberations, and with a rush like a hurling wind, the
wretch starts wildly away—no longer a man, but a monstrous wolf!

On—on he goes: the wood is cleared—the open country is gained. Tree—hedge—and isolated cottage appear
but dim points in the landscape—a moment seen, the
next left behind: the very hills appear to leap after each
other.

A cemetery stands in the monster's way; but he turns
not aside:—through the sacred enclosure, on—on he goes.
There are situate many tombs, stretching up the slope of
a gentle acclivity, from the dark soil of which the white
monuments stand forth with white and ghastly gleaming;
and on the summit of the hill is the church of St. Benedict
the Blessed.

From the summit of the ivy-grown tower the very
rooks, in the midst of their cawing, are scared away by the
furious rush and the wild howl with which the Wehr-Wolf
thunders over the hallowed ground.

At the same instant a train of monks appear round the
angle of the church—for there is a funeral at that hour;
and their torches, flaring with the breeze that is now
springing up, cast an awful and almost magical light upon
the dark grey walls of the edifice,—the strange effect being
enhanced by the prismatic reflection of the lurid blaze
from the stained glass of the oriel window.

The solemn spectacle seemed to madden the Wehr-Wolf. His speed increased—he dashed through the funeral train—appalling cries of terror and alarm burst from the lips of the holy fathers and the solemn procession was thrown into confusion. The coffin-bearers dropped their burden—and the corpse rolled out upon the ground—its decomposing countenance seeming horrible by the glare of the torchlight.

The monk who walked nearest the head of the coffin was thrown down by the violence with which the ferocious monster cleared its passage; and the venerable father—on whose brow sat the snow of eighty winters—fell with his head against a monument, and his brains were dashed out.

On—on fled the Wehr-Wolf—over mead and hill, through valley and dale. The very wind seemed to make way: he clove the air—he appeared to skim the ground —to fly.

Through the romantic glades and rural scenes of Etruria the monster sped—sounds resembling shrieking howls, bursting ever and anon from his foaming mouth—his red eyes glaring in the dusk of the evening like ominous meteors—and his whole aspect so full of appalling ferocity, that never was seen so monstrous—so terrific a spectacle!

A village is gained: he turns not aside—but dashes madly through the little street formed by the huts and cottages of the Tuscan vine-dressers.

A little child in his path—a sweet, blooming, ruddy, noble boy, with violet-coloured eyes and flaxen hair,— disporting merrily at a short distance from his parents who are seated at the threshold of their dwelling.

Suddenly a strange and ominous rush—an unknown trampling of rapid feet falls upon their ears: then with a savage cry, a monster sweeps past.

"My child! my child!" screams the affrighted mother; and simultaneously the shrill cry of an infant in the sudden agony of death carries desolation to the ear!

'Tis done—'twas but the work of a moment: the wolf has swept by—the quick rustling of his feet is no longer heard in the village. But those sounds are succeeded by awful wails and heart-rending lamentations;—for the child —the blooming, violet-eyed, flaxen haired boy—the darling of his poor but tender parents, is weltering in his blood!

On—on speeds the destroyer, urged by an infernal influence which maddens the more intensely because its victim strives vainly to struggle against it:—on—on, over the beaten road—over the fallow field—over the cottager's garden—over the grounds of the rich one's rural villa!

And now, to add to the horror of the scene, a pack of dogs have started in pursuit of the wolf,—dashing—crushing—hurrying—pushing—pressing upon one another in all the anxious ardour of the chase.

The silence and shade of the open country, in the mild starlight, seem eloquently to proclaim the peace and happiness of a rural life:—but now that silence is broken by the mingled howling of the wolf and the deep baying of the hounds,—and that shade is crossed and darkened by the forms of the animals as they scour so fleetly—oh! with such whirlwind speed along!

But that Wehr-Wolf bears a charmed life;—for though the hounds overtake him—fall upon him—and attack him with all the courage of their nature,—yet does he hurl them from him—toss them aside—spurn them away —and at length free himself from their pursuit altogether!

And now the moon rises with unclouded splendour like a maiden looking from her lattice screened with purple curtains; and still the monster hurries madly on with unrelaxing speed.

For hours has he pursued his way thus madly;—and, on a sudden, as he passes the outskirts of a sleeping town, the church bell is struck by the watcher's hand, to proclaim midnight.

Over the town—over the neighbouring fields—through the far-off forest, clanged that iron tongue; and the Wehr-Wolf sped all the faster—as if he were with ominous flapping, like the wings of the fabulous Simoorg.

But, in the midst of appalling spasmodic convulsions,—with direful writhings on the soil, and with cries of bitter anguish,—the Wehr-Wolf gradually threw off his monster shape; and at the very moment when the first sunbeam penetrated the wood and glinted on his face, he rose a handsome—young—and perfect man once more!

from

Melmoth the Wanderer

by Robert Maturin

[Melmoth, who regrets having traded his soul to the devil for an abnormally long life, searches in vain for someone with whom he can in turn barter to regain a soul. In the course of these wanderings, he visits Monçada, who is imprisoned in Madrid by the dreaded Inquisition. Thinking the monk receptive, Melmoth attempts to trade for his soul.]

CHAPTER XI.

Oh! torture me no more, I will confess.
HENRY THE SIXTH
You have betrayed her to her own reproof.
COMEDY OF ERRORS

"And it was true,—I was a prisoner in the Inquisition. Great emergencies certainly inspire us with the feelings they demand; and many a man has braved a storm on the wide wild ocean, who would have shrunk from its voice as it pealed down his chimney. I believe so it fared with me,—the storm had risen, and I braced myself to meet it.

I was in the Inquisition, but I knew that my crime, heinous as it was, was not one that came properly under the cognizance of the Inquisition. It was a conventual fault of the highest class, but liable only to be punished by the ecclesiastical power. The punishment of a monk who had dared to escape from his convent, might be dreadful enough, immurement, or death perhaps, but still I was not legitimately a prisoner of the Inquisition. I had never, under all my trials, spoken a disrespectful word of the holy Catholic church, or a doubtful one of our most holy faith,—I had not dropped one heretical, obnoxious, or equivocal expression, relative to a single point of duty, or article of faith. The preposterous charges of sorcery and possession, brought against me in the convent, had been completely disproved at the visitation of the Bishop. My aversion to the monastic state was indeed sufficiently known and fatally proved, but that was no subject for the investigation or penalties of the Inquisition. I had nothing to fear from the Inquisition,—at least so I said to myself in my prison, and I believed myself. The seventh day after the recovery of my reason was fixed on for my examination, and of this I received due notice, though I believe it is contrary to the usual forms of the Inquisition to give this notice; and the examination took place on the day and hour appointed.

"You are aware, Sir, that the tales related in general of the interior discipline of the Inquisition, must be in nine out of ten mere fables, as the prisoners are bound by an oath never to disclose what happens within its walls; and they who could violate this oath, would certainly not scruple to violate truth in the details with which their emancipation from it indulges them. I am forbidden, by an oath which I shall never break, to disclose the circumstances of my imprisonment or examination. I am at liberty to mention some general features of both, as they are connected with my extraordinary narrative. My first examination terminated rather favourably; my contumacy and

aversion to monasticism were indeed deplored and repro-
bated, but there was no ulterior hint,—nothing to alarm
the peculiar fears of an inmate of the Inquisition. So I was
as happy as solitude, darkness, straw, bread, and water,
could make me, or any one, till, on the fourth night after
my first examination, I was awoke by a light gleaming so
strongly on my eyes, that I started up. The person then
retired with his light, and I discovered a figure sitting in
the farthest corner of my cell. Delighted at the sight of a
human form, I yet had acquired so much of the habit of
the Inquisition, that I demanded, in a cold and peremptory
voice, who had ventured to intrude on the cell of a
prisoner? The person answered in the blandest tones that
ever soothed the human ear, that he was, like myself, a
prisoner in the Inquisition;—that, by its indulgence, he
had been permitted to visit me, and hoped——'And is
hope to be named here?' I could not help exclaiming. He
answered in the same soft and deprecatory tone; and, without adverting to our peculiar circumstances, suggested
the consolation that might be derived from the society of
two sufferers who were indulged with the power of meeting and communicating with each other.

"This man visited me for several successive nights; and
I could not help noticing three extraordinary circumstances in his visits and his appearance. The first was, that
he always (when he could) concealed his eyes from me;
he sat sideways and backwards, shifted his position, changed
his seat, held up his hand before his eyes; but when at
times he was compelled or *surprised* to turn their light on
me, I felt that I had never beheld such eyes blazing in a
mortal face,—in the darkness of my prison, I held up my
hand to shield myself from their preternatural glare. The
second was, that he came and retired apparently without
help or hindrance,—that he came, like one who had a
key to the door of my dungeon, at all hours, without leave
or forbiddance,—that he traversed the prisons of the Inquisition, like one who had a master-key to its deepest

recesses. Lastly, he spoke not only in a tone of voice clear and audible, totally unlike the whispered communications of the Inquisition, but spoke his abhorrence of the whole system,—his indignation against the Inquisition, Inquisitors, and all their aiders and abettors, from St Dominic down to the lowest official,—with such unqualified rage or vituperation, such caustic inveteracy of satire, such unbounded license of ludicrous and yet withering severity, that I trembled.

"You know, Sir, or perhaps have yet to know, that there are persons *accredited* in the Inquisition, who are permitted to solace the solitude of the prisoners, on the condition of obtaining, under the pretence of friendly communication, those secrets which even torture has failed to extort. I discovered in a moment that my visitor was not one of these,—his abuse of the system was too gross, his indignation too unfeigned. Yet, in his continued visits, there was one circumstance more, which struck me with a feeling of terror that actually paralyzed and annihilated all the terrors of the Inquisition.

"He constantly alluded to events and personages beyond his *possible memory,*—then he checked himself,—then he appeared to go on, with a kind of wild derisive sneer at his own *absence.* But this perpetual reference to events long past, and men long buried, made an impression on me I cannot describe. His conversation was rich, various, and intelligent, but it was interspersed with such reiterated mention of the dead, that I might be pardoned for feeling as if the speaker was one of them. He dealt much in anecdotical history, and I, who was very ignorant of it, was delighted to listen to him, for he told every thing with the fidelity of an eye-witness. He spoke of the *Restoration* in England, and repeated the well-remembered observation of the queen-mother, Henriette of France,—that, had she known as much of the English on her first arrival, as she did on her second, she never would have been driven from the throne; then he added, to my astonishment,

I was beside her carriage, *it was the only one then in London*. He afterwards spoke of the superb fetes given by Louis Quatorze, and described, with an accuracy that made me start, the magnificent chariot in which that monarch personated the god of day, while all the titled pimps and harlots of the court followed as the rabble of Olympus. Then he reverted to the death of the Duchesse d'Orleans, sister to Charles II.—to Pere Bourdaloue's awful sermon, preached at the death-bed of the royal beauty, dying of poison, (as suspected); and added, I saw the roses heaped on her toilette, to array her for a fete that very night, and near them stood the pix, and tapers, and oil, shrouded with the lace of that very toilette. Then he passed to England; he spoke of the wretched and well-rebuked pride of the wife of James II. who "thought it scorn" to sit at the same table with an Irish officer who informed her husband (then Duke of York) that *he* had sat at table, as an officer in the Austrian service, where the Duchess's father (Duke of Modena) had stood behind a chair, as a vassal to the Emperor of Germany.

"These circumstances were trifling, and might be told by any one, but there was a minuteness and circumstantiality in his details, that perpetually forced on the mind the idea that he had himself seen what he described, and been conversant with the personages he spoke of. I listened to him with an indefinable mixture of curiosity and terror. At last, while relating a trifling but characteristic circumstance that occurred in the reign of Louis the Thirteenth, he used the following expressions: 'One night that the king was at an entertainment, where Cardinal Richelieu also was present, the Cardinal had the insolence to rush out of the apartment before his Majesty, just as the coach of the latter was announced. The King, without any indignant notice of the arrogance of the minister, said, with much *bon hommie*, "His Eminence the Cardinal will always be first."—"The first to attend your Majesty," answered the Cardinal, with admirable polite presence of mind; and snatching a flambeau from a page who *stood near me,* he lighted the King to his carriage.' I could not help catching at the extraordinary words that had escaped him; and I asked him, 'Were you there?' He gave some indirect answer; and, avoiding the subject, went on to amuse me with some other curious circumstances of the private history of that age, of which he spoke with a minute fidelity somewhat *alarming.* I confess my pleasure in listening to them was greatly diminished by the singular sensation with which this man's presence and conversation inspired me. He departed, and I regretted his absence, though I could not account for the extraordinary feeling which I experienced during his visits.

"A few days later I was to encounter my second examination. The night before it one of the *officials* visited me. These are men who are not the common officers of a prison, but accredited in some degree by the higher powers of the Inquisition, and I paid due respect to his communications, particularly as they were delivered more in detail, and with more emphasis and energy than I could have expected from an inmate of that speechless mansion. This circumstance made me expect something extraordinary, and his discourse verified all, and more than I expected. He told me in plain terms, that there had been lately a cause of disturbance and inquietude, which had never before occurred in the Inquisition. That it was reported a human figure had appeared in the cells of some of the prisoners, uttering words not only hostile to the Catholic religion, and the discipline of the most holy Inquisition, but to religion in general, to the belief of a God and a future state. He added, that the utmost vigilance of the officials, on the rack for discovery, had never been able to trace this being in his visits to the cells of the prisoners; that the guards had been doubled, and every precaution that the circumspection of the Inquisition could employ, was had recourse to, hitherto without success; and that the only intimation they had of this singular visitor, was from some of the prisoners whose cells he had entered, and whom he had addressed in language that seemed lent him by the enemy of mankind, to accomplish the perdition of these unhappy beings. He himself had hitherto eluded all discovery; but he trusted, that, with the means lately adopted, it was impossible for this agent of the evil one to insult and baffle the holy tribunal much longer. He advised me to be prepared on this point, as it would undoubtedly be touched on at my next examination, and perhaps more urgently than I might otherwise imagine; and so, commending me to the holy keeping of God, he departed.

"Not wholly unconscious of the subject alluded to in this extraordinary communication, but perfectly innocent of any ulterior signification, as far as related to myself, I awaited my next examination rather with hope than fear. After the usual questions of—Why I was there? who had accused me? for what offense? whether I could recollect any expression that had ever intimated a disregard for the tenets of the holy church? &c. &c. &c.—after all this had been gone through, in a detail that may be spared the hearer, certain extraordinary questions were proposed to me, that appeared to relate indirectly to the appearance of my late visitor. I answered them with a sincerity that seemed to make a frightful impression on my judges. I stated plainly, in answer to their questions, that a person had appeared in my dungeon. "You must call it cell," said the Supreme. "In my cell, then. He spoke with the utmost severity of the holy office,—he uttered words that it would not be respectful for me to repeat. I could scarcely believe that such a person would be permitted to visit the dungeons (cells, I should say) of the holy Inquisition." As I uttered these words, one of the judges, trembling on his seat (while his shadow, magnified by the imperfect light, pictured the figure of a paralytic giant on the wall opposite to me), attempted to address some question to me. As he spoke, there came a hollow sound from his throat, his eyes were rolled upwards in their sockets,—he was in an apoplectic paroxysm, and died before he could be removed to another apartment. The examination terminated suddenly, and in some confusion; but, as I was remanded back to my cell, I could perceive, to my consternation, that I had left an impression the most unfavourable on the minds of the judges. They interpreted this accidental circumstance in a manner the most extraordinary and unjust, and I felt the consequences of it at my next examination.

"That night I received a visit in my cell from one of the judges of the Inquisition, who conversed with me a considerable time, and in an earnest and dispassionate manner. He stated the atrocious and revolting character under which I appeared from the first before the Inquisition,—that of a monk who had apostatized, had been accused of the crime of sorcery in his convent, and, in his impious attempt at escape, had caused the death of his brother, whom he had seduced to join in it, and had overwhelmed one of the first families with despair and disgrace. Here I was going to reply, but he stopped me, and observed, that he came not to listen, but to speak; and went on to inform me, that though I had been acquitted of the charge of communication with the evil spirit at the visitation of the Bishop, certain suspicions attached to me had been fearfully strengthened, by the fact that the visits of the extraordinary being, of whom I had heard enough to assure me of his actuality, had never been known in the prison of the Inquisition till my entrance into it. That the fair and probable conclusion was, that I was really the victim of the enemy of mankind, whose power (through the reluctant permission of God and St Dominic, and he crossed himself as he spoke) had been suffered to range even through the walls of the holy office. He cautioned me, in severe but plain terms, against the danger of the situation in which I was placed, by the suspicions universally and (he feared) too justly attached to me; and, finally, adjured me, as I valued my salvation, to place my entire confidence in the mercy of the holy office, and, if *the figure* should visit me again, to watch what its impure lips might suggest, and faithfully report it to the holy office.

"When the Inquisitor had departed, I reflected on what he had said. I conceived it was something like the conspiracies so often occurring in the convent. I conceived that this might be an attempt to involve me in some plot against myself, something in which I might be led to be active in my own condemnation,—I felt the necessity of vigilant and breathless caution. I knew myself innocent, and this is a consciousness that defies even the Inquisition itself; but, within the walls of the Inquisition, the consciousness, and the defiance it inspires, are alike vain. I finally resolved, however, to watch every circumstance that might occur within the walls of my cell very closely, threatened as I was at once by the powers of the Inquisition, and those of the infernal demon, and I had not long to watch. It was on the second night after my examination, that I saw this person enter my cell. My first impulse was to call aloud for the officials of the Inquisition. I felt a kind of vacillation I cannot describe, between throwing myself into the power of the Inquisition, or the power of this extraordinary being, more formidable perhaps than all the Inquisitors on earth, from Madrid to Goa. I dreaded imposition on both sides. I believed that they were playing off terror against terror; I knew not what to believe or think. I felt myself surrounded by enemies on every side, and would have given my heart to those who would first throw off the mask, and announce themselves as my decided and avowed enemy. After some reflection, I judged it best *to distrust the Inquisition,* and to hear all that this extraordinary visitor had to say. In my secret soul I believed him their secret agent,—I did them great injustice. His conversation on this second visit was more than usually amusing, but it was certainly such as might justify all the suspicions of the Inquisitors. At every sentence he uttered, I was disposed to start up and call for the officials. Then I represented to myself his turning accuser, and pointing *me* out as the victim of their condemnation. I trembled at the idea of committing myself by a word, while in the power of that dreadful body that might condemn me to expire under the torture,—or, worse, to die the long and lingering death of inanity,—the mind famished, the body scarcely fed,—the annihilation of hopeless and interminable solitude,—the terrible inversion of natural feeling, that makes life the object of deprecation, and death of indulgence.

"The result was, that I sat and listened to the conversation (if it may be called so) of this extraordinary visitor, who appeared to regard the walls of the Inquisition no more than those of a domestic apartment, and who seated himself beside me as quietly as if he had been reposing on the most luxurious sofa that ever was arrayed by the fingers of voluptuousness. My senses were so bewildered, my mind so disarranged, that I can hardly remember his conversation. Part of it ran thus: 'You are a prisoner of the Inquisition. The holy office, no doubt, is instituted for wise purposes, beyond the cognizance of sinful beings like us; but, as far as we can judge, its prisoners are not only insensible of, but shamefully ungrateful for, the benefits they might derive from its provident vigilance. For instance, you, who are accused of sorcery, fratricide, and plunging an illustrious and affectionate family in despair, by your atrocious misconduct, and who are now fortunately restrained from farther outrages against nature, religion, and society, by your salutary confinement here;— you, I venture to say, are so unconscious of these blessings, that it is your earnest desire to escape from the further enjoyment of them. In a word, I am convinced that the secret wish of your heart (unconverted by all the profusion of charity which has been heaped on you by the holy office) is not on any account to increase the burden of your obligation to them, but, on the contrary, to diminish as much as possible the grief these worthy persons must feel, as long as your residence pollutes their holy walls, by abridging its period, even long before they intend you should do so. Your wish is to escape from the prison of the holy office, if possible,—you know it is." I did not answer a word. I felt a terror at this wild and fierce irony, —I felt a terror at the mention of escape, (I had fatal reasons for this feeling),—a terror of every thing, and every one near me, indescribable. I believed myself tottering on a narrow ridge,—an Al-araf, between the alternate gulphs which the infernal spirit and the Inquisition (not less dreaded) disclosed on each side of my trembling march. I compressed my lips,—I hardly suffered my breath to escape.

"The speaker went on. 'With regard to your escape, though I can promise that to you, (and that is what no *human power* can promise you), you must be aware of the difficulty which will attend it,—and, should that difficulty terrify you, will you hesitate?' Still I was silent;— my visitor perhaps took this for the silence of doubt. He went on. 'Perhaps you think that your lingering here, amid the dungeons of the Inquisition, will infallibly secure your salvation. There is no error more absurd, and yet more rooted in the heart of man, than the belief that his sufferings will promote his spiritual safety.' Here I thought myself safe in rejoining, that I felt,—I trusted, my sufferings here would indeed be accepted as a partial mitigation of my well-merited punishment hereafter. I acknowledged my many errors,—I professed myself as penitent for my misfortunes as if they had been crimes; and the energy of my grief combining with the innocence of my heart, I commended myself to the Almighty with an unction I really felt,—I called on the names of God, the Saviour, and the Virgin, with the earnest supplication of sincere devoutness. When I had risen from my knees, my visitor had retired.

"Examination followed examination before the judges, with a rapidity unexampled in the annals of the Inquisition. Alas! that they should be *annals,*—that they should be more than records of *one day* of abuse, oppression, falsehood, and torture. At my next examination before the judges, I was interrogated according to the usual forms, and afterwards was led, by questions as artfully constructed, as if there was any necessity for art to lead me, to speak to the question on which I longed to disburden myself. The moment the subject was mentioned, I entered on my narrative with an eagerness of sincerity that would have undeceived any but Inquisitors. I announced that I had received another visit from this unknown being. I repeated, with breathless and trembling eagerness every word of our late conference. I did not suppress a syllable of the insults on the holy office, the wild and fiend-like acrimony of his satire, the avowed atheism, the diabolism of his conversation,—I dwelt on every particular. I hoped to *make merit* with the Inquisition, by accusing their enemy, and that of mankind. Oh! there is no telling the agony of zeal with which we work between two mortal adversaries, hoping to make a friend of one of them! I had suffered enough already from the Inquisition, but at this moment I would have crouched at the knees of the Inquisitors,—I would have pleaded for the place of the meanest official in their prison,—I would have supplicated for the loathsome office of their executioner,—I would have encountered any thing that the Inquisition could inflict, to be spared the horror of being imagined the ally of the enemy of souls. To my distraction, I perceived that every word I uttered, in all the agony of truth,—in all the hopeless eloquence of a soul struggling with the fiends who are bearing it beyond the reach of mercy, was disregarded. The judges appeared struck, indeed, by the earnestness with which I spoke. They gave, for a moment, a kind of instinctive credit to my words, extorted by terror; but, a moment after, I could perceive that *I*, and not my communication, was the object of that terror. They seemed to view me through a distorting atmosphere of mystery and suspicion. They urged me, over and over again, for further particulars,—for ulterior circumstances,—for something that was in *their* minds, but not in mine. The more pains they took to construct their questions skillfully, the more unintelligible they became to me. I had told all I knew, I was anxious to tell all, but I could not tell more than I knew, and the agony of my solicitude to meet the object of the judges, was aggravated in proportion to my ignorance of it. On being remanded to my cell, I was warned, in the most solemn manner, that if I neglected to watch, remember, and report every word uttered by the extraordinary being, whose visits they tacitly acknowledged they could neither prevent or detect, I might expect the utmost severity of the holy office. I promised all this,—all that could be demanded, and, finally, as the last proof I could give of my sincerity, I implored that some one might be allowed to pass the night in my cell,— or, if that was contrary to the rules of the Inquisition, that one of the guard might be stationed in the passage communicating with my cell, to whom I could, by a signal agreed on, intimate when this nameless being burst on me, and his impious intrusion might be at once detected and punished. In speaking thus, I was indulged with a privilege very unusual in the Inquisition, where the prisoner is only to answer questions, but never to speak unless when called on. My proposal, however, caused some consultation; and it was with horror I found, on its termination, that not one of the officials, even under the discipline of the Inquisition, would undertake the task of watching at the door of *my* cell.

"I went back to it in an agony inexpressible. The more I had laboured to clear myself, the more I had become involved. My only resource and consolation was in a determination to obey, to the strictest letter, the injunctions of the Inquisition. I kept myself studiously awake,—*he* came not all that night. Towards the morning I slept,— Oh what sleep was mine!—the genii, or the demons of the place, seemed busy in the dream that haunted me. I am convinced that a real victim of an *auto da fe* (so called) never suffered more during his horrible procession to flames temporal and eternal, than I did during that dream. I dreamed that the judgment had passed,—the bell had tolled,—and we marched out from the prison of the Inquisition;—my crime was proved, and my sentence determined, as an apostate monk and a *diabolical* heretic. The procession commenced,—the Dominicans went first, then followed the penitents, arms and feet bare, each hand holding a wax taper, some with *san benitos,* some without, all pale, haggard, and breathless, the hue of their faces frightfully resembling that of their clay-coloured arms and feet. Then followed those who had on their black dresses the *fuego revolto.* Then followed—I saw *myself;* and this horrid tracing of yourself in a dream,—this haunting of yourself by your own spectre, while you still live, is perhaps a curse almost equal to your crimes visiting you in the punishments of eternity. I saw myself in the garment of condemnation, *the flames pointing upwards,* while the demons painted on my dress were mocked by the demons who beset my feet, and hovered round my temples. The Jesuits on each side of me, urged me to consider the difference between these painted fires, and those which were about to enwrap my writhing soul for an eternity of ages. All the bells of Madrid seemed to be ringing in my ears. There was no light but a dull twilight, such as one always sees in his sleep, (no man ever dreamed of sun-light);—there was a dim and smoky blaze of torches in my eyes, whose flames were soon to *be in my eyes.* I saw the stage before me,—I was chained to the chair, amid the ringing of bells, the preaching of the Jesuits, and the shouts of the multitude. A splendid amphitheatre stood opposite,—the king and queen of Spain, and all the nobility and hierarchy of the land, were there to see us burn. Our thoughts in dreams wander; I had heard a story of an *auto da fe,* where a young Jewess, not sixteen, doomed to be burnt alive, had prostrated herself before the queen, and exclaimed, "Save me,—save me, do not let me burn, my only crime is believing in the God of my fathers;"—the queen (I believe Elizabeth of France, wife of Philip) wept, but the procession went on. Something like this crossed my dream. I saw the supplicant rejected; the next moment the figure was that of my brother Juan, who clung to me, shrieking, "Save me, save me." The next moment I was chained to my chair again,— the fires were lit, the bells rang out, the litanies were sung;—my feet were scorched to a cinder,—my muscles cracked, my blood and marrow hissed, my flesh consumed like shrinking leather,—the bones of my legs hung two black withering and moveless sticks in the ascending blaze;—it ascended, caught my hair,—I was crowned with fire,—my head was a ball of molten metal, my eyes flashed and melted in their sockets;—I opened my mouth, it drank fire,—I closed it, the fire was within,—and still the bells rung on, and the crowd shouted, and the king and queen, and all the nobility and priesthood, looked on, and we burned, and burned!—I was a cinder body and soul in my dream.

"I awoke from it with the horrible exclamation—ever shrieked, never heard—of those wretches, when the fires are climbing fast and fell,—*Misericordia por amor di Dios!* My own screams awoke me,—I was in my prison, and beside me stood the tempter. With an impulse I could not resist,—an impulse borrowed from the horrors of my dream, I flung myself at his feet, and called on him to 'save me.'

"I know not, Sir, nor is it a problem to be solved by human intellect, whether this inscrutable being had not the power to influence my dreams, and dictate to a tempting demon the images which had driven me to fling myself at his feet for hope and safety. However it was, he certainly took advantage of my agony, half-visionary, half-real as it was, and, while proving to me that he had the power of effecting my escape from the Inquisition, proposed to me that incommunicable condition which I am forbid to reveal, except in the act of confession."

* * * * * * * * * * * * * * * *

"At my next examination, the questions were more eager and earnest than ever, and I was more anxious to be heard than questioned; so, in spite of the eternal circumspection and formality of an inquisitorial examination, we soon came to understand each other. I had an object to gain, and they had nothing to lose by my gaining that object. I confessed, without hesitation, that I had received another visit from that most mysterious being, who could penetrate the recesses of the Inquisition, without either its leave or prevention, (the judges trembled on their seats, as I uttered these words);—that I was most willing to disclose all that had transpired at our last conference, but that I required to first confess to a priest, and receive absolution. This, though quite contrary to the rules of the Inquisition, was, on this extraordinary occasion, complied with. A black curtain was dropt before one of the recesses; I knelt down before a priest, and confided to him that tremendous secret, which, according to the rules of the Catholic church, can never be disclosed by the confessor but to the Pope. I do not understand how the business was managed, but I was called on to repeat the same confession before the Inquisitors. I repeated it word for word, saving only the words that my oath, and my consciousness of the holy secret of confession, forbade me to disclose. The sincerity of this confession, I thought, would have worked a miracle for me,—and so it did, but not the miracle that I expected. They required from me that incommunicable secret; I announced it was in the bosom of the priest to whom I had confessed. They whispered, and seemed to debate about the torture.

"At this time, as may be supposed, I cast an anxious and miserable look round the apartment, where the large crucifix, thirteen feet high, stood bending above the seat of the Supreme. At this moment I saw a person seated at the table covered with black cloth, intensely busy as a secretary, or person employed in taking down the depositions of the accused. As I was led near the table, this person flashed a look of recognition on me,—he was my dreaded companion,—he was an official now of the Inquisition. I gave all up the moment I saw his ferocious and lurking scowl, like that of the tiger before he springs from his jungle, or the wolf from his den. This person threw on me looks, from time to time, which I could not mistake, and I dared not interpret;—and I had reason to believe that the tremendous sentence pronounced against me, issued, if not from his lips, at least from his dictation.—'You, Alonzo di Monçada, monk, professed of the order of——, accused of the crimes of heresy, apostacy, fratricide, ('Oh no,—no!' I shrieked, but no one heeded me), and conspiracy with the enemy of mankind against the peace of the community in which you professed yourself a votary of God, and against the authority of the holy office; accused, moreover, of intercourse in your cell, the prison of the holy office, with an infernal messenger of the foe of God, man, and your own apostatized soul; condemned on your own confession of the infernal spirit having had access to your cell,—are hereby delivered to——'

"I heard no more. I exclaimed, but my voice was drowned in the murmur of the officials. The crucifix suspended behind the chair of the judge, rocked and reeled before my eyes; the lamp that hung from the ceiling, seemed to send forth twenty lights. I held up my hands in abjuration—they were held down by stronger hands. I tried to speak—my mouth was stopped. I sunk on my knees—on my knees I was about to be dragged away, when an aged Inquisitor giving a sign to the officials, I was released for a few moments, and he addressed me in these words—words rendered terrible by the sincerity of the speaker. From his age, from his sudden interposition, I had expected mercy. He was a very old man—he had been blind for twenty years; and as he rose to speak my malediction, my thoughts wandered from Appius Claudius of Rome,—blessing the loss of sight, that saved him from beholding the disgrace of his country,—to that blind chief Inquisitor of Spain, who assured Philip, that in sacrificing his son, he imitated the Almighty, who had sacrificed his Son also for the salvation of mankind.— Horrid profanation! yet striking application to the bosom of a Catholic. The words of the Inquisitor were these: 'Wretch, apostate, and excommunicate, I bless God that these withered balls can no longer behold you. The demon has haunted you from your birth—you were born in sin— fiends rocked your cradle, and dipt their talons in the holy font, while they mocked the sponsors of your unsanctified baptism. Illegitimate and accursed, you were always the burden of the holy church; and now, the infernal spirit comes to claim his own, and you acknowledge him as your lord and master. He has sought and sealed you as his own, even amid the prison of the Inquisition. Begone, accursed, we deliver you over to the secular arm, praying that it may deal with you not too severely." At these terrible words, whose meaning I understood but too well, I uttered one shriek of agony—the only *human* sound ever heard within the walls of the Inquisition. But I was borne away; and that cry into which I had thrown the whole strength of nature, was heeded no more than a cry from the torture room. On my return to my cell, I felt convinced the whole was a scheme of inquisitorial art, to involve me in self-accusation, (their constant object when they can effect it), and punish me for a crime, while I was guilty only of an extorted confession.

"With compunction and anguish unutterable, I execrated my own beast-like and credulous stupidity. Could any but an idiot, a driveller, have been the victim of such a plot? Was it in nature to believe that the prisons of the Inquisition could be traversed at will by a stranger whom no one could discover or apprehend? That such a being could enter cells impervious to human power, and hold conversation with the prisoners at his pleasure—appear and disappear—insult, ridicule, and blaspheme—propose escape, and point out the means with a precision and facility, that must be the result of calm and profound calculation—and this within the walls of the Inquisition, almost in the hearing of the judges—actually in the hearing of the guards, who night and day paced the passages with sleepless and inquisitorial vigilance?—ridiculous, monstrous, impossible! it was all a plot to betray me to self-condemnation. My visitor was an agent and accomplice of the Inquisition, and I was my own betrayer and executioner. Such was my conclusion; and, hopeless as it was, it certainly seemed probable.

"I had now nothing to await but the most dreadful of all destinations, amid the darkness and silence of my cell, where the total suspension of the stranger's visits confirmed me every hour in my conviction of their nature and purport, when an event occurred, whose consequences alike defeated fear, hope, and calculation. This was the great fire that broke out within the walls of the Inquisition, about the close of the last century.

"It was on the night of the 29th November 17—, that this extraordinary circumstance took place—extraordinary from the well-known precautions adopted by the vigilance of the holy office against such an accident, and also from the very small quantity of fuel consumed within its walls. On the first intimation that the fire was spreading rapidly, and threatened danger, the prisoners were ordered to be brought from their cells, and guarded in a court of the prison. I must acknowledge we were treated with great humanity and consideration. We were conducted deliberately from our cells; placed each of us between two guards, who did us no violence, nor used harsh language, but assured us, from time to time, that if the danger became imminent, we would be permitted every fair opportunity to effect our escape. It was a subject worthy of the pencil of Salvador Rosa, or of Murillo, to sketch us as we stood. Our dismal garbs and squalid looks, contrasted with the equally dark, but imposing and authoritative looks of the guards and officials, all displayed by the light of torches, which burned, or appeared to burn, fainter and fainter, as the flames rose and roared in triumph above the towers of the Inquisition. The heavens were all on fire—and the torches, held no longer in firm hands, gave a tremulous and pallid light. It seemed to me like a wildly painted picture of the last day. God appeared descending in the light that enveloped the skies—and we stood pale and shuddering in the light below.

"Among the groupe of prisoners, there were fathers and sons, who perhaps had been inmates of adjacent cells for years, without being conscious of each others vicinity or existence—but they did not dare to recognize each other. Was not this like the day of judgment, where similar mortal relations may meet under different classes of the sheep and goats, without presuming to acknowledge the strayed one amid the flock of a different shepherd? There were also parents and children who *did* recognize and stretch out their wasted arms to each other, though feeling they must never meet,—some of them condemned to the flames, some to imprisonment, and some to the official duties of the Inquisition, as a mitigation of their sentence,—and was not this like the day of judgement, where parent and child may be allotted different destinations, and the arms that would attest the last proof of mortal affection, are expanded in vain over the gulph of eternity. Behind and around us stood the officials and guards of the Inquisition, all watching and intent on the progress of the flames, but fearless of the result with regard to themselves. Such may be the feeling of those spirits who watch the doom of the Almighty, and know the destination of those they are appointed to watch. And is not this like the day of judgement? Far, far, above us, the flames burst out in volumes, in solid masses of fire, spiring up to the burning heavens. The towers of the Inquisition shrunk into cinders —that tremendous monument of the power, and crime, and gloom of the human mind, was wasting like a scroll in the fire. Will it not be thus also at the day of judgement? Assistance was slowly brought—Spaniards are very indolent—the engines played imperfectly—the danger increased—the fire blazed higher and higher—the persons employed to work the engines, paralyzed by terror, fell to the ground, and called on every saint they could think of, to arrest the progress of the flames. Their exclamations were so loud and earnest, that really the saints must have been deaf, or must have felt a particular predilection for a conflagration, not to attend to them. However it was, the fire went on. Every bell in Madrid rang out.—Orders were issued to every Alcaide to be had.—The king of Spain himself, (after a hard day's shooting), attended in person. The churches were all lit up, and thousands of the devout supplicated on their knees by torch-light, or whatever light they could get, that the reprobate souls confined in the Inquisition might feel the fires that were consuming its walls, as merely a slight foretaste of the fires that glowed for them for ever and ever. The fire went on, doing its dreadful work, and heeding kings and priests no more than if they were firemen. I am convinced twenty able men, accustomed to such business, could have quenched the fire; but when our workmen should have played their engines, they were all on their knees.

"The flames at last began to descend into the court. Then commenced a scene of horror indescribable. The wretches who had been doomed to the flames, imagined their hour was come. Idiots from long confinement, and submissive as the holy office could require, they became delirious as they saw the flames approaching, and shrieked audibly, "Spare me—spare me—put me to as little torture as you can." Others, kneeling to the approaching flames, invoked them as saints. They dreamt they saw the visions they had worshipped,—the holy angels, and even the blessed virgin, descending in flames to receive their souls as parting from the stake; and they howled out their allelujahs half in horror, half in hope. Amid this scene of distraction, the Inquisitors stood their ground. It was admirable to see their firm and solemn array. As the flames prevailed, they never faultered with foot, or gave a sign with hand, or winked with eye;—their duty, their stern and heartless duty, seemed to be the only principle and motive of their existence. They seemed a phalanx clad in iron impenetrable. When the fires roared, they crossed themselves calmly;—when the prisoners shrieked, they gave a signal for silence;—when they dared to pray, they tore them from their knees, and hinted the inutility of prayer at such a juncture, when they might be sure that the flames they were deprecating would burn hotter in a region from which there was neither escape or hope of departure. At this moment, while standing amid the groupe of prisoners, my eyes were struck by an extraordinary spectacle. Perhaps it is amid the moments of despair, that imagination has most power, and they who have suffered, can best describe and feel. In the burning light, the steeple of the Dominican church was as visible as at noon-day. It was close to the prison of the Inquisition. The night was intensely dark, but so strong was the light of the conflagration, that I could see the spire blazing, from the reflected lustre, like a meteor. The hands of the clock were as visible as if a torch was held before them; and this calm and silent progress of time, amid the tumultuous confusion of midnight horrors,—this scene of the physical and mental world in an agony of fruitless and incessant motion, might have suggested a profound and singular image, had not my whole attention been rivetted to a human figure placed on a pinnacle of the spire, and surveying the scene in perfect tranquility. It was a figure not to be mistaken—it was the figure of him who had visited me in the cells of the Inquisition. The hopes of my justification made me forget every thing. I called aloud on the guard, and pointed out the figure, visible as it was in that strong light to every eye. No one had time, however, to give a glance towards it. At that very moment, the archway of the court opposite to us gave way, and sunk in ruins at our feet, dashing, as it fell, an ocean of flame against us. One wild shriek burst from every lip at that moment. Prisoners, guards, and Inquisitors, all shrunk together, mingled in one groupe of terror.

"The next instant, the flames being suppressed by the fall of such a mass of stone, there arose such a blinding cloud of smoke and dust, that it was impossible to distinguish the face or figure of those who were next you. The confusion was increased by the contrast of the sudden darkness, to the intolerable light that had been drying up our sight for the last hour, and by the cries of those who, being near the arch, lay maimed and writhing under its fragments. Amid shrieks, and darkness, and flames, a space lay open before me. The thought, the motion, were simultaneous—no one saw—no one pursued;—and hours before my absence could be discovered, or an inquiry be made after me, I had struggled safe and secret through the ruins, and was in the streets of Madrid.

"To those who have escaped present and extreme peril, all other peril seems trifling. The wretch who has swum from a wreck cares not on what shore he is cast; and though Madrid was in fact only a wider prison of the Inquisition to me, in knowing that I was no longer in the hands of the officials, I felt a delirious and indefinite consciousness of safety. Had I reflected for a moment, I must have known, that my peculiar dress and *bare feet* must betray me wherever I went. The conjuncture, however, was very favourable to me—the streets were totally deserted;—every inhabitant who was not in bed, or bed-rid, was in the churches, deprecating the wrath of heaven, and praying for the extinction of the flames.

"I ran on, I know not where, till I could run no longer. The pure air, which I had been so long unaccustomed to breathe, acted like the most torturing spicula on my throat and lungs as I flew along, and utterly deprived me of the power of respiration, which at first it appeared to restore. I saw a building near me, whose large doors were open. I rushed in—it was a church. I fell on the pavement panting. It was the aisle into which I had burst—it was separated from the chancel by large grated railings. Within I could see the priests at the altar, by the lamps recently and rarely lighted, and a few trembling devotees on their knees, in the body of the chancel. There was a strong contrast between the glare of the lamps within the chancel, and the faint light that trembled through the windows of the aisle, scarcely showing me the monuments, on one of which I leaned to rest my throbbing temples for a moment. I could not rest—I dared not—and rising, I cast an involuntary glance on the inscription which the monument bore. The light appeared to increase maliciously, to aid my powers of vision. I read. 'Orate pro anima.' I at last came to the name—'Juan di Monçada.' I flew from the spot as if pursued by demons—my brother's early grave had been my resting place.

Part Five

Monsters of Unknown Origin

If the threatening effect produced by monsters of human origin depends largely on their ugliness, abnormality, and unpredictability, it follows that other creatures more grotesque, alien, and unpredictable should be even more frightening. Hence, Gothic writers, to give free rein to their imaginations, utilized creatures of unknown origin. It might be said, therefore, that the basic difference between the use of monsters of human origin and those of unknown origin is fundamentally one of degree rather than of kind. The same emotional responses on the part of the reader are involved, but the use of monsters of unknown origin removes any basis for rapport or understanding on the part of the potential victim, accentuating that victim's isolation and helplessness. There is an additional value or message in the use of such monsters in that they suggest the very limited perimeters of rational knowledge, providing the reader once again not with the world he encounters in his daily routine but the world as it might be—perhaps is, if the senses could grasp it.

The feeling of alienation in works using monsters of human origin or in human form to evoke fear is lessened; because there is a familiarity about them as well as a physical presence, allowing the reader to make at least a minimal identification with them. One does not, for example, feel the full impact of horror in *Wagner, the Wehr-Wolf* or *Dracula* until the monstrous natures of the two begin to reveal themselves, but there is something sinister from the very beginning about the plants in Wyndham's *The Day of the Triffids*. Furthermore, there is the aspect of communication. Victims can talk to Wagner and to Count Dracula just as Dr. Frankenstein can discuss the monster's problems with him; Dr. Jekyll is fully aware of his metamorphosized self, but there is no possibility for humans to communicate with triffids, no way of understanding the "thing" in "What Was It?" The Martians in Wells's *The War of the Worlds* cannot be appeased; because those creatures are so alien, there is no basis for communication.

When speculation concerns itself with creatures from outer space or other possible origins, it begins to overlap that area of fiction generally regarded as science fiction, and it is true that much Gothic literature is science fiction, or vice versa. The identification depends on whether or not the intended effect in science fiction is the creation of terror. If science is suppressed in favor of terror, the writing is Gothic, and stories such as Wyndham's are "Gothic" science fiction rather than "scientific" science fiction. This is only by way of saying that science fiction and Gothic are not mutually exclusive but are, in fact, frequently identical, and a very large proportion of modern science fiction is Gothic literature in contemporary trappings.

In the modern Gothic, then, the same principles apply in the creation of terror as apply in the early Gothic. Only now the medieval castle is replaced by some other planet, an isolated (and usually dilapidated) farmhouse, a space ship, space platform, electronically isolated nuclear control center, or any other type of isolating device, and this helps to create an ambiance of threat and helplessness. The mouldering furniture, dark dungeons, secret chambers, moonlit cemeteries, and screeching owls have yielded to lunar landscapes, underground cities, and edifices of materials unknown to man, while the wicked uncle, the soulless Melmoth, the incestuous Ambrosio, and other villains have become men from Mars or the Pegasus galaxy, robots, intelligent and mobile plant life, or other malevolent beings. The torture implements of the Inquisition have transformed into computers, death rays, psychological programming, and countless other existing or imagined devices, but the threat and the victim remain. So does the Gothic rebellion against a narrowly scientific or rational approach to life.

Most Gothic science fiction is admonitory in nature, suggesting that science creates as many problems as solutions and that there is more to life than technology. Only now, instead of turning to the supernatural in rebellion against the strictures of empirical knowledge, modern Gothic writers accept man's involvement with technology and are content with pointing out that many of our "solutions" are merely interest payments on the mortgage which the unpredictable and destructive hold on life. Yet this again is merely the old Gothic "evil" or injustice brought up to date and translated into terms a contemporary society can appreciate.

from

The War of the Worlds

by H. G. Wells

[*According to the narrator, early in the twentieth century man was unaware that Mars was inhabited by a race of monsters with intelligence far superior to that of earthlings, and these monsters had long been observing earth with an eye to invasion and conquest. This invasion began with the landing of huge metal cylinders in the vicinity of London, England. The general populace, unafraid and idly curious, gathered around the first cylinder which landed near the village of Woking. Among them was the narrator.*]

CHAPTER IV.

THE CYLINDER OPENS

When I returned to the common the sun was setting. Scattered groups were hurrying from the direction of Woking, and one or two persons were returning. The crowd about the pit had increased, and stood out black against the lemon-yellow of the sky—a couple of hundred people, perhaps. There were raised voices, and some sort of struggle appeared to be going on about the pit. Strange imaginings passed through my mind. As I drew nearer I heard Stent's voice:

"Keep back! Keep back!"

A boy came running towards me.

"It's a-movin'," he said to me as he passed—"a-screwin' and a-screwin' out. I don't like it. I'm a-goin' 'ome, I am."

I went on to the crowd. There were really, I should think, two or three hundred people elbowing and jostling one another, the one or two ladies there being by no means the least active.

"He's fallen in the pit!" cried some one.

"Keep back!" said several.

The crowd swayed a little, and I elbowed my way through. Everyone seemed greatly excited. I heard a peculiar humming sound from the pit.

"I say!" said Ogilvy; "help keep these idiots back. We don't know what's in the confounded thing, you know!"

I saw a young man, a shop assistant in Woking I believe he was, standing on the cylinder and trying to scramble out of the hole again. The crowd had pushed him in.

The end of the cylinder was being screwed out from within. Nearly two feet of shining screw projected. Somebody blundered against me, and I narrowly missed being pitched on to the top of the screw. I turned, and as I did so the screw must have come out, for the lid of the cylinder fell upon the gravel with a ringing concussion. I stuck my elbow into the person behind me, and turned my head towards the Thing again. For a moment that circular cavity seemed perfectly black. I had the sunset in my eyes.

I think every one expected to see a man emerge—possibly something a little unlike us terrestrial men, but in all essentials a man. I know I did. But, looking, I presently saw something stirring within the shadow: greyish billowy movements, one above another, and then two luminous disks—like eyes. Then something resembling a little grey snake, about the thickness of a walking-stick, coiled up out of the writhing middle, and wriggled in the air towards me—and then another.

A sudden chill came over me. There was a loud shriek from a woman behind. I half turned, keeping my eyes fixed upon the cylinder still, from which other tentacles were now projecting, and began pushing my way back from the edge of the pit. I saw astonishment giving place to horror on the faces of the people about me. I heard inarticulate exclamations on all sides. There was a general movement backwards. I saw the shopman struggling still on the edge of the pit. I found myself alone, and saw the people on the other side of the pit running off, Stent among them. I looked again at the cylinder, and ungovernable terror gripped me. I stood petrified and staring.

A big greyish rounded bulk, the size, perhaps, of a bear, was rising slowly and painfully out of the cylinder. As it bulged up and caught the light, it glistened like wet leather.

Two large dark-coloured eyes were regarding me steadfastly. The mass that framed them, the head of the thing, it was rounded, and had, one might say, a face. There was a mouth under the eyes, the lipless brim of which quivered and panted, and dropped saliva. The whole creature heaved and pulsated convulsively. A lank tentacular appendage gripped the edge of the cylinder, another swayed in the air.

Those who have never seen a living Martian can scarcely imagine the strange horror of its appearance. The peculiar V-shaped mouth with its pointed upper lip, the absence of brow ridges, the absence of a chin beneath the wedge-like lower lip, the incessant quivering of this mouth, the Gorgon groups of tentacles, the tumultuous breathing of the lungs in a strange atmosphere, the evident heaviness and painfulness of movement due to the greater gravitational energy of the earth—above all, the extraordinary intensity of the immense eyes—were at once vital, intense, inhuman, crippled and monstrous. There was something fungoid in the oily brown skin, something in the clumsy deliberation of the tedious movements unspeakably nasty. Even at this first encounter, this first glimpse, I was overcome with disgust and dread.

Suddenly the monster vanished. It had toppled over the brim of the cylinder and fallen into the pit, with a thud like the fall of a great mass of leather. I heard it give a peculiar thick cry, and forthwith another of these creatures appeared darkly in the deep shadow of the aperture.

I turned and, running madly, made for the first group of trees, perhaps a hundred yards away; but I ran slantingly and stumbling, for I could not avert my face from these things.

There, among some young pine-trees and furze-bushes, I stopped, panting, and waited further developments. The common round the sand-pits was dotted with people, standing like myself in a half-fascinated terror, staring at these creatures, or rather at the heaped gravel at the edge of the pit in which they lay. And then, with a renewed horror, I saw a round, black object bobbing up and down on the edge of the pit. It was the head of the shopman who had fallen in, but showing as a little black object against the hot western sky. Now he got his shoulder and knee up, and again he seemed to slip back until only his head was visible. Suddenly he vanished, and I could have fancied a faint shriek had reached me. I had a momentary impulse to go back and help him that my fears overruled.

Everything was then quite visible, hidden by the deep pit and the heap of sand that the fall of the cylinder had made. Any one coming along the road from Chobham or Woking would have been amazed at the sight—a dwindling multitude of perhaps a hundred people or more standing in a great irregular circle, in ditches, behind bushes, behind gates and hedges, saying little to one another and that in short, excited shouts, and staring,

staring hard at a few heaps of sand. The barrow of ginger-beer stood, a queer derelict, black against the burning sky, and in the sand-pits was a row of deserted vehicles with their horses feeding out of nose-bags or pawing the ground.

CHAPTER V.

THE HEAT-RAY

After the glimpse I had had of the Martians emerging from the cylinder in which they had come to the earth from their planet, a kind of fascination paralysed my actions. I remained standing knee-deep in the heather, staring at the mound that hid them. I was a battle-ground of fear and curiosity.

I did not dare to go back towards the pit, but I felt a passionate longing to peer into it. I began walking, therefore, in a big curve, seeking some point of vantage and continually looking at the sand-heaps that hid these new-comers to our earth. Once a leash of thin black whips, like the arms of an octopus, flashed across the sunset and was immediately withdrawn, and afterwards a thin rod rose up, joint by joint, bearing at its apex a circular disk that spun with a wobbling motion. What could be going on there?

Most of the spectators had gathered in one or two groups—one a little crowd towards Woking, the other a knot of people in the direction of Chobham. Evidently they shared my mental conflict. There were few near me. One man I approached—he was, I perceived, a neighbour of mine, though I did not know his name—and accosted. But it was scarcely a time for articulate conversation.

"What ugly *brutes!*" he said. "Good God! what ugly brutes!" He repeated this over and over again.

"Did you see a man in the pit?" I said; but he made no answer to that. We became silent, and stood watching for a time side by side, deriving, I fancy, a certain comfort in one another's company. Then I shifted my position to a little knoll that gave me the advantage of a yard or more of elevation, and when I looked for him presently he was walking towards Woking.

The sunset faded to twilight before anything further happened. The crowd far away on the left, towards Woking, seemed to grow, and I heard now a faint murmur from it. The little knot of people towards Chobham dispersed. There was scarcely an intimation of movement from the pit.

It was this, as much as anything, that gave people courage, and I suppose the new arrivals from Woking also helped to restore confidence. At any rate, as the dusk came on a slow, intermittent movement upon the sand-pits began, a movement that seemed to gather force as the stillness of the evening about the cylinder remained unbroken. Vertical black figures in twos and threes would advance, stop, watch and advance again, spreading out as they did so in a thin irregular crescent that promised to enclose the pit in its attenuated horns. I, too, on my side began to move towards the pit.

Then I saw some cabmen and others had walked boldly into the sand-pits, and heard the clatter of hoofs and the gride of wheels. I saw a lad trundling off the barrow of apples. And then, within thirty yards of the pit, advancing from the direction of Horsell, I noted a little black knot of men, the foremost of whom was waving a white flag.

This was the Deputation. There had been a hasty consultation, and since the Martians were evidently, in spite of their repulsive forms, intelligent creatures, it had been resolved to show them, by approaching them with signals, that we too were intelligent.

Flutter, flutter, went the flag, first to the right, then to the left. It was too far for me to recognise any one there, but afterwards I learned that Ogilvy, Stent, and Henderson were with others in this attempt at communication. This little group had in its advance dragged inward, so to speak, the circumference of the now almost complete circle of people, and a number of dim black figures followed it at discreet distances.

Suddenly there was a flash of light, and a quantity of luminous greenish smoke came out of the pit in three distinct puffs, which drove up, one after the other, straight into the still air.

This smoke (or flame, perhaps, would be the better word for it) was so bright that the deep blue sky overhead and the hazy stretches of brown common towards Chertsey, set with black pine-trees, seemed to darken abruptly as these puffs arose, and to remain the darker after their dispersal. At the same time a faint hissing sound became audible.

Beyond the pit stood the little wedge of people with the white flag at its apex, arrested by these phenomena, a little knot of small vertical black shapes upon the black ground. As the green smoke arose, their faces flashed out pallid green, and faded again as it vanished. Then slowly the hissing passed into a humming, into a long, loud, droning noise. Slowly a humped shape rose out of the pit, and the ghost of a beam of light seemed to flicker out from it.

Forthwith flashes of actual flame, a bright glare leaping from one to another, sprang from the scattered group of men. It was as if some invisible jet impinged upon them and flashed into white flame. It was as if each man were suddenly and momentarily turned to fire.

Then, by the light of their own destruction, I saw them staggering and falling, and their supporters turning to run.

I stood staring, not as yet realising that this was death leaping from man to man in that little distant crowd. All I felt was that it was something very strange. An almost noiseless and blinding flash of light, and a man fell headlong and lay still; and as the unseen shaft of heat passed over them, pine-trees burst into fire, and every dry furze-bush became with one dull thud a mass of flames. And far away towards Knaphill I saw the flashes of trees and hedges and wooden buildings suddenly set alight.

It was sweeping round swiftly and steadily, this flaming death, this invisible, inevitable sword of heat. I perceived it coming towards me by the flashing bushes it touched, and was too astounded and stupefied to stir. I heard the crackle of fire in the sand-pits and the sudden squeal of a horse that was as suddenly stilled. Then it was as if an invisible yet intensely heated finger were drawn through the heather between me and the Martians, and all along a curving line beyond the sand-pits the dark ground smoked and crackled. Something fell with a crash far away to the left where the road from Woking station opens out on the common. Forthwith the hissing and humming ceased, and the black, dome-like object sank slowly out of sight into the pit.

All this had happened with such swiftness that I had stood motionless, dumbfounded and dazzled by the flashes of light. Had that death swept through a full circle, it must inevitably have slain me in my surprise. But it passed and spared me, and left the night about me suddenly dark and unfamiliar.

*　*　*　*　*　*　*　*　*　*　*　*　*　*　*

[*A detail of artillerymen is wiped out as it tries to destroy the invading creatures, who protect themselves by crawling behind giant shields on tripod legs. The only survivor escapes and stumbles to the narrator's house, from which they watch the destruction of the countryside by Martian Heat-Rays.*]

CHAPTER XII.

WHAT I SAW OF THE DESTRUCTION OF WEYBRIDGE AND SHEPPERTON

As the dawn grew brighter we withdrew from the window from which we had watched the Martians, and went very quietly downstairs.

The artilleryman agreed with me that the house was no place to stay in. He proposed, he said, to make his way Londonward, and thence rejoin his battery—No. 12, of the Horse Artillery. My plan was to return at once to Leatherhead; and so greatly had the strength of the Martians impressed me that I had determined to take my wife to Newhaven, and go with her out of the country forthwith. For I already perceived clearly that the country about London must inevitably be the scene of a disastrous struggle before such creatures as these could be destroyed.

Between us and Leatherhead, however, lay the Third Cylinder, with its guarding giants. Had I been alone, I think I should have taken my chance and struck across country. But the artilleryman dissuaded me: "It's no kindness to the right sort of wife," he said, "to make her a widow"; and in the end I agreed to go with him, under cover of the woods, northward as far as Street Cobham before I parted with him. Thence I would make a big detour by Epsom to reach Leatherhead.

I should have started at once, but my companion had been in active service and he knew better than that. He made me ransack the house for a flask, which he filled with whiskey; and we lined every available pocket with packets of biscuits and slices of meat. Then we crept out of the house, and ran as quickly as we could down the ill-made road by which I had come overnight. The houses seemed deserted. In the road lay a group of three charred bodies close together, struck dead by the Heat-Ray; and here and there were things that people had dropped—a clock, a slipper, a silver spoon, and the like poor valuables. At the corner turning up towards the post-office a little cart, filled with boxes and furniture, and horseless, heeled over on a broken wheel. A cash-box had been hastily smashed open and thrown under the débris.

Except the lodge at the Orphanage, which was still on fire, none of the houses had suffered very greatly here. The Heat-Ray had shaved the chimney-tops and passed. Yet, save ourselves, there did not seem to be a living soul on Maybury Hill. The majority of the inhabitants had escaped, I suppose, by way of the Old Woking road—the road I had taken when I drove to Leatherhead—or they had hidden.

We went down the lane, by the body of the man in black, sodden now from the overnight hail, and broke into the woods at the foot of the hill. We pushed through these towards the railway without meeting a soul. The woods across the line were but the scarred and blackened ruins of woods; for the most part the trees had fallen, but a certain proportion still stood, dismal grey stems, with dark brown foliage instead of green.

On our side the fire had done no more than scorch the nearer trees; it had failed to secure its footing. In one place the woodmen had been at work on Saturday; trees, felled and freshly trimmed, lay in a clearing, with heaps of sawdust by the sawing machine and its engine. Hard by was a temporary hut, deserted. There was not a breath of wind this morning, and everything was strangely still. Even the birds were hushed, and as we hurried along I and the artilleryman talked in whispers and looked now and again over our shoulders. Once or twice we stopped to listen.

After a time we drew near the road, and as we did so we heard the clatter of hoofs and saw through the tree-stems three cavalry soldiers riding slowly towards Woking.

We hailed them, and they halted while we hurried towards them. It was a lieutenant and a couple of privates of the 8th Hussars, with a stand like a theodolite, which the artilleryman told me was a heliograph.

"You are the first men I've seen coming this way this morning," said the lieutenant. "What's brewing?"

His voice and face were eager. The men behind him stared curiously. The artilleryman jumped down the bank into the road and saluted.

"Gun destroyed last night, sir. Have been hiding. Trying to rejoin battery, sir. You'll come in sight of the Martians, I expect, about half a mile along this road."

"What the dickens are they like?" asked the lieutenant.

"Giants in armour, sir. Hundred feet high. Three legs and a body like 'luminium, with a mighty great head in a hood, sir."

"Get out!" said the lieutenant. "What confounded nonsense!"

"You'll see, sir. They carry a kind of box, sir, that shoots fire and strikes you dead."

"What d'ye mean—a gun?"

"No, sir," and the artilleryman began a vivid account of the Heat-Ray. Half-way through, the lieutenant interrupted him and looked up at me. I was still standing on the bank by the side of the road.

"It's perfectly true," I said.

"Well," said the lieutenant, "I suppose it's my business to see it too. Look here"—to the artilleryman—"we're detailed here clearing people out of their houses. You'd better go along and report yourself to Brigadier-General Marvin, and tell him all you know. He's at Weybridge. Know the way?"

"I do," I said; and he turned his horse southward again.

"Half a mile, you say?" said he.

"At most," I answered, and pointed over the tree-tops

southward. He thanked me and rode on, and we saw them no more.

Farther along we came upon a group of three women and two children in the road, busy clearing out a labourer's cottage. They had got hold of a little hand-truck, and were piling it up with unclean looking bundles and shabby furniture. They were all too assiduously engaged to talk to us as we passed.

By Byfleet station we emerged from the pine-trees, and found the country calm and peaceful under the morning sunlight. We were far beyond the range of the Heat-Ray there, and had it not been for the silent desertion of some of the houses, the stirring movement of packing in others, and the knot of soldiers standing on the bridge over the railway and staring down the line towards Woking, the day would have seemed very like any other Sunday.

Several farm waggons and carts were moving creakily along the road to Addlestone, and suddenly through the gate of a field we saw, across a stretch of flat meadow, six twelve-pounders standing neatly at equal distances pointing toward Woking. The gunners stood by the guns waiting, and the ammunition waggons were at a business-like distance. The men stood almost as if under inspection.

"That's good!" said I. "They will get one fair shot, at any rate."

The artilleryman hesitated at the gate.

"I shall go on," he said.

Farther on towards Weybridge, just over the bridge, there were a number of men in white fatigue jackets throwing up a long rampart, and more guns behind.

"It's bows and arrows against lightning, anyhow," said the artilleryman. "They 'aven't seen that fire-beam yet."

The officers who were not actively engaged stood and stared over the tree-tops south-westward, and the men digging would stop every now and again to stare in the same direction.

Byfleet was in a tumult; people packing, and a score of

hussars, some of them dismounted, some on horseback, were hunting them about. Three of four black government waggons, with crosses in white circles, and an old omnibus, among other vehicles, were being loaded in the village street. There were scores of people, most of them sufficiently sabbatical to have assumed their best clothes. The soldiers were having the greatest difficulty in making them realise the gravity of their position. We saw one shrivelled old fellow with a huge box and a score or more of flower-pots containing orchids, angrily expostulating with the corporal who would leave them behind. I stopped and gripped his arm.

"Do you know what's over there?" I said, pointing at the tree-tops that hid the Martians.

"Eh?" said he, turning. "I was explainin' these is vallyble."

"Death!" I shouted. "Death is coming! Death!" and leaving him to digest that if he could, I hurried on after the artilleryman. At the corner I looked back. The soldier had left him, and he was still standing by his box, with the pots of orchids on the lid of it, and staring vaguely over the trees.

No one in Weybridge could tell us where the headquarters were established; the whole place was in such confusion as I had never seen in any town before. Carts, carriages everywhere, the most astonishing miscellany of conveyances and horseflesh. The respectable inhabitants of the place, men in golf and boating costumes, wives prettily dressed, were packing, river-side loafers energetically helping, children excited, and, for the most part, highly delighted at this astonishing variation of their Sunday experiences. In the midst of it all the worthy vicar was very pluckily holding an early celebration, and his bell was jangling out above the excitement.

I and the artilleryman, seated on the step of the drinking-fountain, made a very passable meal upon what we had brought with us. Patrols of soldiers—here no longer hussars, but grenadiers in white—were warning people to move now or to take refuge in their cellars as soon as the firing began. We saw as we crossed the railway bridge that a growing crowd of people had assembled in and about the railway station, and the swarming platform was piled with boxes and packages. The ordinary traffic had been stopped, I believe, in order to allow of the passage of troops and guns to Chertsey, and I have heard since that a savage struggle occurred for places in the special trains that were put on at a later hour.

We remained at Weybridge until mid-day, and at that hour we found ourselves at the place near Shepperton Lock where the Wey and Thames join. Part of the time we spent helping two old women to pack a little cart. The Wey has a treble mouth, and at this point boats are to be hired, and there was a ferry across the river. On the Shepperton side was an inn with a lawn, and beyond that the tower of Shepperton Church—it has been replaced by a spire—rose above the trees.

Here we found an excited and noisy crowd of fugitives. As yet the flight had not grown to a panic, but there were already far more people than all the boats going to and fro could enable to cross. People came panting along under heavy burdens; one husband and wife were even carrying a small outhouse door between them, with some of their household goods piled thereon. One man told us he meant to try to get away from Shepperton station.

There was a lot of shouting, and one man was even jesting. The idea people seemed to have here was that the Martians were simply formidable human beings, who might attack and sack the town, to be certainly destroyed in the end. Every now and then people would glance nervously across the Wey, at the meadows towards Chertsey, but everything over there was still.

Across the Thames, except just where the boats landed, everything was quiet, in vivid contrast with the Surrey side. The people who landed there from the boats went tramping off down the lane. The big ferry-boat had just made a journey. Three or four soldiers stood on the lawn of the inn, staring and jesting at the fugitives, without offering to help. The inn was closed, as it was now within prohibited hours.

"What's that?" cried a boatman, and "Shut up, you fool!" said a man near me to a yelping dog. Then the sound came again, this time from the direction of Chertsey, a muffled thud—the sound of a gun.

The fighting was beginning. Almost immediately unseen batteries across the river to our right, unseen because of the trees, took up the chorus, firing heavily one after the other. A woman screamed. Everyone stood arrested by the sudden stir of battle, near us and yet invisible to us. Nothing was to be seen save flat meadows, cows feeding unconcernedly for the most part, and silvery pollard willows motionless in the warm sunlight.

"The sojers'll stop 'em," said a woman beside me, doubtfully. A haziness rose over the tree-tops.

Then suddenly we saw a rush of smoke far away up the river, a puff of smoke that jerked up into the air and hung; and forthwith the ground heaved underfoot and a heavy explosion shook the air, smashing two or three windows in the houses near, and leaving us astonished.

"Here they are!" shouted a man in a blue jersey. "Yonder! D'yer see them? Yonder!"

Quickly, one after the other, one, two, three, four of the armoured Martians appeared, far away over the little trees, across the flat meadows that stretched towards Chertsey, and striding hurriedly towards the river. Little cowled figures they seemed at first, going with a rolling motion and as fast as flying birds.

Then, advancing obliquely towards us, came a fifth. Their armoured bodies glittered in the sun as they swept swiftly forward upon the guns, growing rapidly larger as they drew nearer. One on the extreme left, the remotest that is, flourished a huge case high in the air, and the ghostly, terrible Heat-Ray I had already seen on Friday night smote towards Chertsey, and struck the town.

At sight of these strange, swift, and terrible creatures the crowd near the water's edge seemed to be for a moment horror-struck. There was no screaming or shouting, but a silence. Then a hoarse murmur and a movement of feet— a splashing from the water. A man, too frightened to drop the portmanteau he carried on his shoulder, swung round and sent me staggering with a blow from the corner of his burden. A woman thrust at me with her hand and rushed past me. I turned with the rush of the people, but I was not too terrified for thought. The terrible Heat-Ray was in my mind. To get under water! That was it!

"Get under water!" I shouted, unheeded.

I faced about again, and rushed towards the approaching Martian, rushed down the gravelly beach and headlong into the water. Others did the same. A boatload of people putting back came leaping out as I rushed past. The stones under my feet were muddy and slippery, and the river was so low that I ran perhaps twenty feet scarcely waist-deep. Then, as the Martian towered overhead scarcely a couple of hundred yards away, I flung myself forward under the surface. The splashes of the people in the boats leaping into the river sounded like thunderclaps in my ears. People were landing hastily on both sides of the river.

But the Martian machine took no more notice for the moment of the people running this way and that than a man would of the confusion of ants in a nest against which his foot has kicked. When, half suffocated, I raised my head above water, the Martian's hood pointed at the batteries that were still firing across the river, and as it advanced it swung loose what must have been the generator of the Heat-Ray.

In another moment it was on the bank, and in a stride wading half-way across. The knees of its foremost legs bent at the farther bank, and in another moment it had raised itself to its full height again, close to the village of Shepperton. Forthwith the six guns which, unknown to any one on the right bank, had been hidden behind the outskirts of that village, fired simultaneously. The sudden near concussion, the last close upon the first, made my heart jump. The monster was already raising the case generating the Heat-Ray as the first shell burst six yards above the hood.

I gave a cry of astonishment. I saw and thought nothing of the other four Martian monsters; my attention was riveted upon the nearer incident. Simultaneously two other shells burst in the air near the body as the hood twisted round in time to receive, but not in time to dodge, the fourth shell.

The shell burst clean in the face of the Thing. The hood bulged, flashed, was whirled off in a dozen tattered fragments of red flesh and glittering metal.

"Hit!" shouted I, with something between a scream and a cheer.

I heard answering shouts from the people in the water about me. I could have leaped out of the water with that momentary exultation.

The decapitated colossus reeled like a drunken giant; but it did not fall over. It recovered its balance by a miracle, and, no longer heeding its steps and with the camera that fired the Heat-Ray now rigidly upheld, it reeled swiftly upon Shepperton. The living intelligence, the Martian within the hood, was slain and splashed to the four winds of heaven, and the Thing was now but a mere intricate device of metal whirling to destruction. It drove along a straight line, incapable of guidance. It struck the tower of Shepperton Church, smashing it down as the impact of a battering-ram might have done, swerved aside, blundered on, and collapsed with tremendous force into the river out of my sight.

A violent explosion shook the air, and a spout of water, steam, mud, and shattered metal shot far up into the sky. As the camera of the Heat-Ray hit the water, the latter had immediately flashed into steam. In another moment a huge wave, like a muddy tidal bore but almost scaldingly hot, came sweeping round the bend up-stream. I saw people struggling shorewards, and heard their screaming and shouting faintly above the seething and roar of the Martian's collapse.

For a moment I heeded nothing of the heat, forgot the patent need of self-preservation. I splashed through the tumultuous water, pushing aside a man in black to do so, until I could see round the bend. Half a dozen deserted boats pitched aimlessly upon the confusion of the waves. The fallen Martian came into sight down-stream, lying across the river, and for the most part submerged.

Thick clouds of steam were pouring off the wreckage, and through the tumultuously whirling wisps I could see, intermittently and vaguely, the gigantic limbs churning the water and flinging a splash and spray of mud and froth into the air. The tentacles swayed and struck like living arms, and, save for the helpless purposelessness of these movements, it was as if some wounded thing were struggling for its life amid the waves. Enormous quantities of a ruddy-brown fluid were spurting up in noisy jets out of the machine.

My attention was diverted from this death flurry by a furious yelling, like that of the thing called a siren in our manufacturing towns. A man, knee-deep near the towing-path, shouted inaudibly to me and pointed. Looking back, I saw the other Martians advancing with gigantic strides down the river-bank from the direction of Chertsey. The Shepperton guns spoke this time unavailingly.

At that I ducked at once under water, and holding my breath until movement was an agony, blundered painfully ahead under the surface as long as I could. The water was in a tumult about me, and rapidly growing hotter.

When for a moment I raised my head to take breath and throw the hair and water from my eyes, the steam was rising in a whirling white fog that at first hid the Martians altogether. The noise was deafening. Then I saw them dimly, colossal figures of grey, magnified by the mist. They had passed by me, and two were stooping over the frothing, tumultuous ruins of their comrade.

The third and fourth stood beside him in the water, one perhaps two hundred yards from me, the other towards Laleham. The generators of the Heat-Rays waved high, and the hissing beams smote down this way and that.

The air was full of sound, a deafening and confusing conflict of noises—the clangorous din of the Martians, the crash of falling houses, the thud of trees, fences, sheds flashing into flame, and the crackling and roaring of fire. Dense black smoke was leaping up to mingle with the steam from the river, and as the Heat-Ray went to and fro over Weybridge its impact was marked by flashes of incandescent white, that gave place at once to a smoky dance of lurid flames. The nearer houses still stood intact, awaiting their fate, shadowy, faint, and pallid in the steam, with the fire behind them going to and fro.

For a moment perhaps I stood there, breast-high in the almost boiling water, dumbfounded at my position, hopeless of escape. Through the reek I could see the people who had been with me in the river scrambling out of the water through reeds, like little frogs hurrying through grass from the advance of a man, or running to and fro in utter dismay on the towing-path.

Then suddenly the white flashes of the Heat-Ray came leaping towards me. The houses caved in as they dissolved at its touch, and darted out flames; the trees changed to fire with a roar. The Ray flickered up and down the towing-path, licking off people who ran this way and that and came down to the water's edge not fifty yards from where I stood. It swept across the river to Shepperton, and the water in its track rose in a boiling weal crested with steam. I turned shoreward.

In another moment the huge wave, wellnigh at the

boiling-point, had rushed upon me. I screamed aloud, and scalded, half blinded, agonised, I staggered through the leaping, hissing water towards the shore. Had my foot stumbled, it would have been the end. I fell helplessly, in full sight of the Martians, upon the broad, bare gravelly spit that runs down to mark the angle of the Wey and Thames. I expected nothing but death.

I have a dim memory of the foot of a Martian coming down within a score of yards of my head, driving straight into the loose gravel, whirling it this way and that, and lifting again; of a long suspense, and then of the four carrying the débris of their comrade between them, now clear and then presently faint through a veil of smoke, receding interminably, as it seemed to me, across a vast space of river and meadow. And then, very slowly, I realised that by a miracle I had escaped.

[*All seems hopeless for the earthlings because their weaponry is ineffectual against the Martian attack. The invaders, however, are finally confronted and destroyed by the one weapon against which they have no resistance, earth's bacteria.*]

from

Canon Alberic's Scrap-Book

Montague Rhodes James

St. Bertrand de Comminges is a decayed town on the spurs
of the Pyrenees, not very far from Toulouse, and still
nearer to Bagnères-de-Luchon. It was the site of a bishop-
ric until the Revolution, and has a cathedral which is
visited by a certain number of tourists. In the spring of
1883 an Englishman arrived at this old-world place—I
can hardly dignify it with the name of city, for there are
not a thousand inhabitants. He was a Cambridge man,
who had come specially from Toulouse to see St. Bertrand's Church, and had left two friends, who were less
keen archæologists than himself, in their hotel at Toulouse,
under promise to join him on the following morning. Half
an hour at the church would satisfy *them,* and all three
could then pursue their journey in the direction of Auch.
But our Englishman had come early on the day in question, and proposed to himself to fill a note-book and to use
several dozens of plates in the process of describing and
photographing every corner of the wonderful church that
dominates the little hill of Comminges. In order to carry
out this design satisfactorily, it was necessary to monopo-

lize the verger of the church for the day. The verger or sacristan (I prefer the latter appellation, inaccurate as it may be) was accordingly sent for by the somewhat brusque lady who keeps the inn of the Chapeau Rouge; and when he came, the Englishman found him an unexpectedly interesting object of study. It was not in the personal appearance of the little, dry, wizened old man that the interest lay, for he was precisely like dozens of other church-guardians in France, but in a curious furtive, or rather hunted and oppressed, air which he had. He was perpetually half glancing behind him; the muscles of his back and shoulders seemed to be hunched in a continual nervous contraction, as if he were expecting every moment to find himself in the clutch of an enemy. The Englishman hardly knew whether to put him down as a man haunted by a fixed delusion, or as one oppressed by a guilty conscience, or as an unbearably henpecked husband. The probabilities, when reckoned up, certainly pointed to the last idea; but, still, the impression conveyed was that of a more formidable persecutor even than a termagant wife.

However, the Englishman (let us call him Dennistoun) was soon too deep in his note-book and too busy with his camera to give more than an occasional glance to the sacristan. Whenever he did look at him, he found him at no great distance, either huddling himself back against the wall or crouching in one of the gorgeous stalls. Dennistoun became rather fidgety after a time. Mingled suspicions that he was keeping the old man from his *déjeuner*, that he was regarded as likely to make away with St. Bertrand's ivory crozier, or with the dusty stuffed crocodile that hangs over the font, began to torment him.

"Won't you go home?" he said at last; "I'm quite well able to finish my notes alone; you can lock me in if you like. I shall want at least two hours more here, and it must be cold for you, isn't it?"

"Good heavens!" said the little man, whom the suggestion seemed to throw into a state of unaccountable terror, "such a thing cannot be thought of for a moment. Leave monsieur alone in the church? No, no; two hours, three hours, all will be the same to me. I have breakfasted, I am not at all cold, with many thanks to monsieur."

"Very well, my little man," quoth Dennistoun to himself: "you have been warned, and you must take the consequences."

Before the expiration of the two hours, the stalls, the enormous dilapidated organ, the choir-screen of Bishop John de Mauléon, the remnants of glass and tapestry, and the objects in the treasure-chamber, had been well and truly examined; the sacristan still keeping at Dennistoun's heels, and every now and then whipping round as if he had been stung, when one or other of the strange noises that trouble a large empty building fell on his ear. Curious noises they were sometimes.

"Once," Dennistoun said to me, "I could have sworn I heard a thin metallic voice laughing high up in the tower. I darted an inquiring glance at my sacristan. He was white to the lips. 'It is he—that is—it is no one; the door is locked,' was all he said, and we looked at each other for a full minute."

Another little incident puzzled Dennistoun a good deal. He was examining a large dark picture that hangs behind the altar, one of a series illustrating the miracles of St. Bertrand. The composition of the picture is wellnigh indecipherable, but there is a Latin legend below, which runs thus:

"Qualiter S. Bertrandus liberavit hominem quem diabolus diu volebat strangulare." (How St. Bertrand delivered a man whom the Devil long sought to strangle.)

Dennistoun was turning to the sacristan with a smile and a jocular remark of some sort on his lips, but he was confounded to see the old man on his knees, gazing at the picture with the eye of a suppliant in agony, his hands tightly clasped, and a rain of tears on his cheeks. Dennistoun naturally pretended to have noticed nothing, but the question would not away from him, "Why should a daub of this kind affect anyone so strangely?" He seemed to himself to be getting some sort of clue to the reason of the strange look that had been puzzling him all the day: the man must be a monomaniac; but what was his monomania?

It was nearly five o'clock; the short day was drawing in, and the church began to fill with shadows, while the curious noises—the muffled footfalls and distant talking voices that had been perceptible all day—seemed, no doubt because of the fading light and the consequently quickened sense of hearing, to become more frequent and insistent.

The sacristan began for the first time to show signs of hurry and impatience. He heaved a sigh of relief when camera and note-book were finally packed up and stowed away, and hurriedly beckoned Dennistoun to the western door of the church, under the tower. It was time to ring the Angelus. A few pulls at the reluctant rope, and the great bell Bertrande, high in the tower, began to speak, and swung her voice up among the pines and down to the valleys, loud with mountain-streams, calling the dwellers on those lonely hills to remember and repeat the salutation of the angel to her whom he called Blessed among women. With that profound quiet seemed to fall for the first time that day upon the little town, and Dennistoun and the sacristan went out of the church.

On the doorstep they fell into conversation.

"Monsieur seemed to interest himself in the old choir-books in the sacristy."

"Undoubtedly. I was going to ask you if there were a library in the town."

"No, monsieur; perhaps there used to be one belonging to the Chapter, but it is now such a small place——" Here came a strange pause of irresolution, as it seemed;

then, with a sort of plunge, he went on: "But if monsieur is *amateur des vieux livres,* I have at home something that might interest him. It is not a hundred yards."

At once all Dennistoun's cherished dreams of finding priceless manuscripts in untrodden corners of France flashed up, to die down again the next moment. It was probably a stupid missal of Plantin's printing, about 1580. Where was the likelihood that a place so near Toulouse would not have been ransacked long ago by collectors? However, it would be foolish not to go; he would reproach himself for ever after if he refused. So they set off. On the way the curious irresolution and sudden determination of the sacristan recurred to Dennistoun, and he wondered in a shame-faced way whether he was being decoyed into some purlieu to be made away with as a supposed rich Englishman. He contrived, therefore, to begin talking with his guide, and to drag in, in a rather clumsy fashion, the fact that he expected two friends to join him early the next morning. To his surprise, the announcement seemed to relieve the sacristan at once of some of the anxiety that oppressed him.

"That is well," he said quite brightly—"that is very well. Monsieur will travel in company with his friends; they will be always near him. It is a good thing to travel thus in company—sometimes."

The last word appeared to be added as an afterthought, and to bring with it a relapse into gloom for the poor little man.

They were soon at the house, which was one rather larger than its neighbours, stone-built, with a shield carved over the door, the shield of Alberic de Mauléon, a collateral descendant, Dennistoun tells me, of Bishop John de Mauléon. This Alberic was a Canon of Comminges from 1680 to 1701. The upper windows of the mansion were boarded up, and the whole place bore, as does the rest of Comminges, the aspect of decaying age.

Arrived on his doorstep, the sacristan paused a moment.

"Perhaps," he said, "perhaps, after all, monsieur has not the time?"

"Not at all—lots of time—nothing to do till to-morrow. Let us see what it is you have got."

The door was opened at this point, and a face looked out, a face far younger than the sacristan's, but bearing something of the same distressing look: only here it seemed to be the mark, not so much of fear for personal safety as of acute anxiety on behalf of another. Plainly, the owner of the face was the sacristan's daughter; and, but for the expression I have described, she was a handsome girl enough. She brightened up considerably on seeing her father accompanied by an able-bodied stranger. A few remarks passed between father and daughter, of which Dennistoun only caught these words, said by the sacristan, "He was laughing in the church," words which were answered only by a look of terror from the girl.

But in another minute they were in the sitting-room of the house, a small, high chamber with a stone floor, full of moving shadows cast by a wood-fire that flickered on a great hearth. Something of the character of an oratory was imparted to it by a tall crucifix, which reached almost to the ceiling on one side; the figure was painted of the natural colours, the cross was black. Under this stood a chest of some age and solidity, and when a lamp had been brought, and chairs set, the sacristan went to this chest, and produced therefrom, with growing excitement and nervousness, as Dennistoun thought, a large book, wrapped in a white cloth, on which cloth a cross was rudely embroidered in red thread. Even before the wrapping had been removed, Dennistoun began to be interested by the size and shape of the volume. "Too large for a missal," he thought, "and not the shape of an antiphoner; perhaps it may be something good, after all." The next moment the book was open, and Dennistoun felt that he had at last lit upon something better than good. Before him lay a large folio, bound, perhaps, late in the seventeenth century, with the arms of Canon Alberic de Mauléon stamped in gold on the sides. There may have been a hundred and fifty leaves of paper in the book, and on almost every one of them was fastened a leaf from an illuminated manuscript. Such a collection Dennistoun had hardly dreamed of in his wildest moments. Here were ten leaves from a copy of Genesis, illustrated with pictures, which could not be later than 700 A.D. Further on was a complete set of pictures from a Psalter, of English execution, of the very finest kind that the thirteenth century could produce; and, perhaps best of all, there were twenty leaves of uncial writing in Latin, which, as a few words seen here and there told him at once, must belong to some very early unknown patristic treatise. Could it possibly be a fragment of the copy of Papias "On the Words of Our Lord," which was known to have existed as late as the twelfth century at Nîmes?* In any case, his mind was made up: that book must return to Cambridge with him, even if he had to draw the whole of his balance from the bank and stay at St. Bertrand till the money came. He glanced up at the sacristan to see if his face yielded any hint that the book was for sale. The sacristan was pale, and his lips were working.

"If monsieur will turn on to the end," he said.

So monsieur turned on, meeting new treasures at every rise of a leaf; and at the end of the book he came upon two sheets of paper, of much more recent date than anything he had yet seen, which puzzled him considerably. They must be contemporary, he decided, with the unprincipled Canon Alberic, who had doubtless plundered the Chapter library of St. Bertrand to form this priceless scrap-book. On the first of the paper sheets was a plan, carefully drawn and instantly recognisable by a person who knew the ground, of the south aisle and cloisters of St. Bertrand's. There were curious signs looking like

---

* We now know that these leaves did contain a considerable fragment of that work, if not of that actual copy of it.

planetary symbols, and a few Hebrew words in the corners; and in the north-west angle of the cloister was a cross drawn in gold paint. Below the plan were some lines of writing in Latin, which ran thus:

"Responsa 12^{mi} Dec. 1694. Interrogatum est: Inveniamne? Responsum est: Invenies. Fiamne dives? Fies. Vivamne invidendus? Vives. Moriarne in lecto meo? Ita." (Answers of the 12th of December, 1694. It was asked: Shall I find it? Answer: Thou shalt. Shall I become rich? Thou wilt. Shall I live an object of envy? Thou wilt. Shall I die in my bed? Thou wilt.)

"A good specimen of the treasure-hunter's record—quite reminds one of Mr. Minor-Canon Quatremain in 'Old St. Paul's'," was Dennistoun's comment, and he turned the leaf.

What he then saw impressed him, as he has often told me, more than he could have conceived any drawing or picture capable of impressing him. And, though the drawing he saw is no longer in existence, there is a photograph of it (which I possess) which fully bears out that statement. The picture in question was a sepia drawing at the end of the seventeenth century, representing, one would say at first sight, a Biblical scene; for the architecture (the picture represented an interior) and the figures had that semi-classical flavour about them which the artists of two hundred years ago thought appropriate to illustrations of the Bible. On the right was a King on his throne, the throne elevated on twelve steps, a canopy overhead, soldiers on either side—evidently King Solomon. He was bending forward with outstretched sceptre, in attitude of command; his face expressed horror and disgust, yet there was in it also the mark of imperious command and confident power. The left half of the picture was the strangest, however. The interest plainly centred there. On the pavement before the throne were grouped four soldiers, surrounding a crouching figure which must be described in a moment. A fifth soldier lay dead on the pavement, his neck distorted, and his eyeballs starting from his head. The four surrounding guards were looking at the King. In their faces the sentiment of horror was intensified; they seemed, in fact, only restrained from flight by their implicit trust in their master. All this terror was plainly excited by the being that crouched in their midst. I entirely despair of conveying by any words the impression which this figure makes upon anyone who looks at it. I recollect once showing the photograph of the drawing to a lecturer on morphology—a person of, I was going to say, abnormally sane and unimaginative habits of mind. He absolutely refused to be alone for the rest of that evening, and he told me afterwards that for many nights he had not dared to put out his light before going to sleep. However, the main traits of the figure I can at least indicate. At first you saw only a mass of coarse, matted black hair; presently it was seen that this covered a body of fearful thinness, almost a skeleton, but with the muscles standing out like wires. The hands were of a dusky pallor, covered, like the body, with long, coarse hairs, and hideously taloned. The eyes, touched in with a burning yellow, had intensely black pupils, and were fixed upon the throned King with a look of beast-like hate. Imagine one of the awful bird-catching spiders of South America translated into human form, and endowed with intelligence just less than human, and you will have some faint conception of the terror inspired by the appalling effigy. One remark is universally made by those to whom I have shown the picture: "It was drawn from the life."

As soon as the first shock of his irresistible fright had subsided, Dennistoun stole a look at his hosts. The sacristan's hands were pressed upon his eyes; his daughter, looking up at the cross on the wall, was telling her beads feverishly.

At last the question was asked, "Is this book for sale?" There was the same hesitation, the same plunge of determination, that he had noticed before, and then came the welcome answer, "If monsieur pleases."

"How much do you ask for it?"

"I will take two hundred and fifty francs."

This was confounding. Even a collector's conscience is sometimes stirred, and Dennistoun's conscience was tenderer than a collector's.

"My good man!" he said again and again, "your book is worth far more than two hundred and fifty francs, I assure you—far more."

But the answer did not vary: "I will take two hundred and fifty francs, not more."

There was really no possibility of refusing such a chance. The money was paid, the receipt signed, a glass of wine drunk over the transaction, and then the sacristan seemed to become a new man. He stood upright, he ceased to throw those suspicious glances behind him, he actually laughed or tried to laugh. Dennistoun rose to go.

"I shall have the honour of accompanying monsieur to his hotel?" said the sacristan.

"Oh no, thanks! it isn't a hundred yards. I know the way perfectly, and there is a moon."

The offer was pressed three or four times, and refused as often.

"Then, monsieur will summon me if—if he finds occasion; he will keep the middle of the road, the sides are so rough."

"Certainly, certainly," said Dennistoun, who was impatient to examine his prize by himself; and he stepped out into the passage with his book under his arm.

Here he was met by the daughter; she, it appeared, was anxious to do a little business on her own account; perhaps, like Gehazi, to "take somewhat" from the foreigner whom her father had spared.

"A silver crucifix and chain for the neck; monsieur would perhaps be good enough to accept it?"

Well, really, Dennistoun hadn't much use for these things. What did mademoiselle want for it?

"Nothing—nothing in the world. Monsieur is more than welcome to it."

The tone in which this and much more was said was unmistakably genuine, so that Dennistoun was reduced to profuse thanks, and submitted to have the chain put round his neck. It really seemed as if he had rendered the father and daughter some service which they hardly knew how to repay. As he set off with his book they stood at the door looking after him, and they were still looking when he waved them a last good-night from the steps of the Chapeau Rouge.

Dinner was over, and Dennistoun was in his bedroom, shut up alone with his acquisition. The landlady had manifested a particular interest in him since he had told her that he had paid a visit to the sacristan and bought an old book from him. He thought, too, that he had heard a hurried dialogue between her and the said sacristan in the passage outside the *salle à manger;* some words to the effect that "Pierre and Bertrand would be sleeping in the house" had closed the conversation.

At this time a growing feeling of discomfort had been creeping over him—nervous reaction, perhaps, after the delight of his discovery. Whatever it was, it resulted in a conviction that there was someone behind him, and that he was far more comfortable with his back to the wall. All this, of course, weighed light in the balance as against the obvious value of the collection he had acquired. And now, as I said, he was alone in his bedroom, taking stock of Canon Alberic's treasures, in which every moment revealed something more charming.

"Bless Canon Alberic!" said Dennistoun, who had an inveterate habit of talking to himself. "I wonder where he is now? Dear me! I wish that landlady would learn to laugh in a more cheering manner; it makes one feel as if there was someone dead in the house. Half a pipe more, did you say? I think perhaps you are right. I wonder what that crucifix is that the young woman insisted on giving me? Last century, I suppose. Yes, probably. It is rather a nuisance of a thing to have round one's neck—just too heavy. Most likely her father has been wearing it for years. I think I might give it a clean up before I put it away."

He had taken the crucifix off, and laid it on the table, when his attention was caught by an object lying on the red cloth just by his left elbow. Two or three ideas of what it might be flitted through his brain with their own incalculable quickness.

"A penwiper? No, no such thing in the house. A rat? No, too black. A large spider? I trust to goodness not—no. Good God! a hand like the hand in that picture!"

In another infinitesimal flash he had taken it in. Pale, dusky skin, covering nothing but bones and tendons of appalling strength; coarse black hairs, longer than ever grew on a human hand; nails rising from the ends of the fingers and curving sharply down and forward, gray, horny and wrinkled.

He flew out of his chair with deadly, inconceivable terror clutching at his heart. The shape, whose left hand rested on the table, was rising to a standing posture behind his seat, its right hand crooked above his scalp. There was black and tattered drapery about it; the coarse hair covered it as in the drawing. The lower jaw was thin—what can I call it?—shallow, like a beast's; teeth showed behind the black lips; there was no nose; the eyes, of a fiery yellow, against which the pupils showed black and intense, and the exulting hate and thirst to destroy life which shone there, were the most horrifying feature in the whole vision. There was intelligence of a kind in them—intelligence beyond that of a beast, below that of a man.

The feelings which this horror stirred in Dennistoun were the intensest physical fear and the most profound mental loathing. What did he do? What could he do? He has never been quite certain what words he said, but he knows that he spoke, that he grasped blindly at the silver crucifix, that he was conscious of a movement towards him on the part of the demon, and that he screamed with the voice of an animal in hideous pain.

Pierre and Bertrand, the two sturdy little serving-men, who rushed in, saw nothing, but felt themselves thrust aside by something that passed out between them, and found Dennistoun in a swoon. They sat up with him that night, and his two friends were at St. Bertrand by nine o'clock next morning. He himself though still shaken and nervous, was almost himself by that time, and his story found credence with them, though not until they had seen the drawing and talked with the sacristan.

Almost at dawn the little man had come to the inn on some pretence, and had listened with the deepest interest to the story retailed by the landlady. He showed no surprise.

"It is he—it is he! I have seen him myself," was his only comment; and to all questionings but one reply was vouchsafed: "Deux fois je l'ai vu; mille fois je l'ai senti." He would tell them nothing of the provenance of the book, nor any details of his experiences. "I shall soon sleep, and my rest will be sweet. Why should you trouble me?" he said.*

We shall never know what he or Canon Alberic de Mauléon suffered. At the back of that fateful drawing were some lines of writing which may be supposed to throw light on the situation:

"Contradictio Salomonis cum demonio nocturno. Albericus de Mauleone delineavit. V. Deus in adiutorium. Ps. Qui habitat. Sancte Bertrande, demoniorum effugator,

---

* He died that summer; his daughter married, and settled at St. Papoul. She never understood the circumstances of her father's "obsession."

intercede pro me miserrimo. Primum uidi nocte 12^{mi} Dec. 1694: uidebo mox ultimum. Peccaui et passus sum, plura adhuc passurus. Dec. 29, 1701."*

I have never quite understood what was Dennistoun's view of the events I have narrated. He quoted to me once a text from Ecclesiasticus: "Some spirits there be that are created for vengeance, and in their fury lay on sore strokes." On another occasion he said: "Isaiah was a very sensible man; doesn't he say something about night monsters living in the ruins of Babylon? These things are rather beyond us at present."

Another confidence of his impressed me rather, and I sympathized with it. We had been, last year, to Comminges, to see Canon Alberic's tomb. It is a great marble erection with an effigy of the Canon in a large wig and soutane, and an elaborate eulogy of his learning below. I saw Dennistoun talking for some time with the Vicar of St. Bertrand's, and as we drove away he said to me: "I hope it isn't wrong: you know I am a Presbyterian—but I—I believe there will be 'saying of Mass and singing of dirges' for Alberic de Mauléon rest." Then he added, with a touch of the Northern British in his tone, "I had no notion they came so dear."

The book is in the Wentworth Collection at Cambridge. The drawing was photographed and then burnt by Dennistoun on the day when he left Comminges on the occasion of his first visit.

---

* *I.e.*, The Dispute of Solomon with a demon of the night. Drawn by Alberic de Mauléon. *Versicle*. O Lord, make haste to help me. *Psalm.* Whoso dwelleth (xci.).

Saint Bertrand, who puttest devils to flight, pray for me most unhappy. I saw it first on the night of Dec. 12, 1694: soon I shall see it for the last time. I have sinned and suffered, and have more to suffer yet. Dec. 29, 1701.

The "Gallia Christiana" gives the date of the Canon's death as December 31, 1701, "in bed, of a sudden seizure." Details of this kind are not common in the great work of the Sammarthani.

What Was It?

by Fitz-James O'Brien

It is, I confess, with considerable diffidence that I approach the strange narrative which I am about to relate. The events which I purpose detailing are of so extraordinary a character that I am quite prepared to meet with an unusual amount of incredulity and scorn. I accept all such beforehand. I have, I trust, the literary courage to face unbelief. I have, after mature consideration, resolved to narrate, in as simple and straightforward a manner as I can compass, some facts that passed under my observation, in the month of July last, and which, in the annals of the mysteries of physical science, are wholly unparalleled.

I live at No.— Twenty-sixth Street, in New York. The house is in some respects a curious one. It has enjoyed for the last two years the reputation of being haunted. It is a large and stately residence, surrounded by what was once a garden, but which is now only a green enclosure used for bleaching clothes. The dry basin of what has been a fountain, and a few fruit-trees ragged and unpruned, indicate that this spot in past days was a

405

pleasant, shady retreat, filled with fruits and flowers and the sweet murmur of waters.

The house is very spacious. A hall of noble size leads to a large spiral staircase winding through its centre, while the various apartments are of imposing dimensions. It was built some fifteen or twenty years since by Mr. A——, the well-known New York merchant, who five years ago threw the commercial world into convulsions by a stupendous bank fraud. Mr. A——, as everyone knows, escaped to Europe, and died not long after, of a broken heart. Almost immediately after the news of his decease reached this country and was verified, the report spread in Twenty-sixth Street that No.— was haunted. Legal measures had dispossessed the widow of its former owner, and it was inhabited merely by a care-taker and his wife, placed there by the house-agent into whose hands it had passed for purposes of renting or sale. These people declared that they were troubled with unnatural noises. Doors were opened without any visible agency. The remnants of furniture scattered through the various rooms were, during the night, piled one upon the other by unknown hands. Invisible feet passed up and down the stairs in broad daylight, accompanied by the rustle of unseen silk dresses, and the gliding of viewless hands along the massive balusters. The care-taker and his wife declared they would live there no longer. The house-agent laughed, dismissed them, and put others in their place. The noises and supernatural manifestations continued. The neighborhood caught up the story, and the house remained untenanted for three years. Several persons negotiated for it; but somehow, always before the bargain was closed they heard the unpleasant rumors and declined to treat any further.

It was in this state of things that my landlady, who at that time kept a boarding-house in Bleecker Street, and who wished to move further up town, conceived the bold idea of renting No.— Twenty-sixth Street. Hap-

pening to have in her house rather a plucky and philosophical set of boarders, she laid her scheme before us,
stating candidly everything she had heard respecting the
ghostly qualities of the establishment to which she wished
to remove us. With the exception of two timid persons,
—a sea-captain and a returned Californian, who immediately gave notice that they would leave,—all of Mrs.
Moffat's guests declared that they would accompany her
in her chivalric incursion into the abode of spirits.

Our removal was effected in the month of May, and we
were charmed with our new residence. The portion of
Twenty-sixth Street where our house is situated, between
Seventh and Eighth Avenues, is one of the pleasantest
localities in New York. The gardens back of the houses,
running down nearly to the Hudson, form, in the sum-
mertime, a perfect avenue of verdure. The air is pure
and invigorating, sweeping, as it does, straight across the
river from the Weehawken heights, and even the ragged
garden which surrounded the house, although displaying
on washing days rather too much clothes-line, still gave
us a piece of greensward to look at, and a cool retreat
in the summer evenings, where we smoked our cigars in
the dusk, and watched the fire-flies flashing their dark-
lanterns in the long grass.

Of course we had no sooner established ourselves at
No.— than we began to expect the ghosts. We absolutely awaited their advent with eagerness. Our dinner
conversation was supernatural. One of the boarders, who
had purchased Mrs. Crowe's "Night Side of Nature"
for his own private delectation, was regarded as a public
enemy by the entire household for not having bought
twenty copies. The man led a life of supreme wretchedness while he was reading this volume. A system of
espionage was established, of which he was the victim.
If he incautiously laid the book down for an instant
and left the room, it was immediately seized and read
aloud in secret places to a select few. I found myself a

person of immense importance, it having leaked out that I was tolerably well versed in the history of supernaturalism, and had once written a story the foundation of which was a ghost. If a table or a wainscot panel happened to warp when we were assembled in the large drawing-room, there as an instant silence, and every one was prepared for an immediate clanking of chains and a spectral form.

After a month of psychological excitement, it was with the utmost dissatisfaction that we were forced to acknowledge that nothing in the remotest degree approaching the supernatural had manifested itself. Once the black butler asseverated that his candle had been blown out by some invisible agency while he was undressing himself for the night; but as I had more than once discovered this colored gentleman in a condition when one candle must have appeared to him like two, I thought it possible that, by going a step further in his potations, he might have reversed this phenomenon, and seen no candle at all where he ought to have beheld one.

Things were in this state when an incident took place so awful and inexplicable in its character that my reason fairly reels at the bare memory of the occurrence. It was the tenth of July. After dinner was over I repaired, with my friend Dr. Hammond, to the garden to smoke my evening pipe. Independent of certain mental sympathies which existed between the Doctor and myself, we were linked together by a vice. We both smoked opium. We knew each other's secret, and respected it. We enjoyed together that wonderful expansion of thought, that marvellous intensifying of the perceptive faculties, that boundless feeling of existence when we seem to have points of contact with the whole universe,—in short, that unimaginable spiritual bliss, which I would not surrender for a throne, and which I hope you, reader, will never—never taste.

Those hours of opium happiness which the Doctor and

I spent together in secret were regulated with a scientific accuracy. We did not blindly smoke the drug of paradise, and leave our dreams to chance. While smoking, we carefully steered our conversation through the brightest and calmest channels of thought. We talked of the East, and endeavored to recall the magical panorama of its glowing scenery. We criticised the most sensuous poets,—those who painted life ruddy with health, brimming with passion, happy in the possession of youth and strength and beauty. If we talked of Shakespeare's "Tempest," we lingered over Ariel, and avoided Caliban. Like the Guebers, we turned our faces to the east, and saw only the sunny side of the world.

The skilful coloring of our train of thought produced in our subsequent visions a corresponding tone. The splendors of Arabian fairy-land dyed our dreams. We paced that narrow strip of grass with the tread and port of kings. The song of the *rana arborea,* while he clung to the bark of the ragged plum-tree, sounded like the strains of divine musicians. Houses, walls, and streets melted like rain-clouds, and vistas of unimaginable glory stretched away before us. It was a rapturous companionship. We enjoyed the vast delight more perfectly because, even in our most ecstatic moments, we were conscious of each other's presence. Our pleasures, while individual, were still twin, vibrating and moving musical accord.

On the evening in question, the tenth of July, the Doctor and myself drifted into an unusually metaphysical mood. We lit our large meerschaums, filled with fine Turkish tobacco, in the core of which burned a little black nut of opium, that, like the nut in the fairy tale, held within its narrow limits wonders beyond the reach of kings; we paced to and fro, conversing. A strange perversity dominated the currents of our thought. They would *not* flow through the sun-lit channels into which we strove to divert them. For some unaccountable reason, they constantly diverged into dark and lonesome beds, where a continual gloom brooded. It was in vain that, after our old fashion, we flung ourselves on the shores of the East, and talked of its gay bazaars, of the splendors of the time of Haroun, of harems and golden palaces. Black afreets continually arose from the depths of our talk, and expanded, like the one the fisherman released from the copper vessel, until they blotted everything bright from our vision. Insensibly, we yielded to the occult force that swayed us, and indulged in gloomy speculation. We had talked some time upon the proneness of the human mind to mysticism, and the almost universal love of the terrible, when Hammond suddenly said to me, "What do you consider to be the greatest element of terror?"

The question puzzled me. That many things were terrible, I knew. Stumbling over a corpse in the dark; beholding, as I once did, a woman floating down a deep and rapid river, with wildly lifted arms, and awful, upturned face, uttering, as she drifted, shrieks that rent one's heart, while we, the spectators, stood frozen at a window which overhung the river at a height of sixty feet, unable to make the slightest effort to save her, but dumbly watching her last supreme agony and her disappearance. A shattered wreck, with no life visible, encountered floating listlessly on the ocean, is a terrible object, for it suggests a huge terror, the proportions of which are veiled. But it now struck me, for the first time, that there must be one great and ruling embodiment of fear,—a King of Terrors, to which all others must succumb. What might it be? To what train of circumstances would it owe its existence?

"I confess, Hammond," I replied to my friend, "I never considered the subject before. That there must be one Something more terrible than any other thing, I feel. I cannot attempt, however, even the most vague definition."

"I am somewhat like you, Harry," he answered. "I feel my capacity to experience a terror greater than anything yet conceived by the human mind;—something combining in fearful and unnatural amalgamation hitherto supposed incompatible elements. The calling of the voices in Brockden Brown's novel of 'Wieland' is awful; so is the picture of the Dweller of the Threshold, in Bulwer's 'Zanoni'; but," he added, shaking his head gloomily, "there is something more horrible still than these."

"Look here, Hammond," I rejoined, "let us drop this kind of talk, for heaven's sake! We shall suffer for it, depend on it."

"I don't know what's the matter with me to-night," he replied, "but my brain is running upon all sorts of weird and awful thoughts. I feel as if I could write a story like Hoffman, to-night, if I were only master of a literary style."

"Well, if we are going to be Hoffmanesque in our talk, I'm off to bed. Opium and nightmares should never be brought together. How sultry it is! Good-night, Hammond."

"Good-night, Harry. Pleasant dreams to you."

"To you, gloomy wretch, afreets, ghouls, and enchanters."

We parted, and each sought his respective chamber. I undressed quickly and got into bed, taking with me, according to my usual custom, a book, over which I generally read myself to sleep. I opened the volume as soon as I had laid my head upon the pillow, and instantly flung it to the other side of the room. It was Goudon's "History of Monsters,"—a curious French work, which I had lately imported from Paris, but which, in the state of mind I had then reached, was anything but an agreeable companion. I resolved to go to sleep at once; so, turning down my gas until nothing but a little blue point of light glimmered on the top of the tube, I composed myself to rest.

The room was in total darkness. The atom of gas that still remained alight did not illuminate a distance of three inches from the burner. I desperately drew my arm across my eyes, as if to shut out even the darkness, and tried to think of nothing. It was in vain. The confounded themes touched on by Hammond in the garden kept obtruding themselves on my brain. I battled against them. I erected ramparts of would-be blankness of intellect to keep them out. They still crowded upon me. While I was lying still as a corpse, hoping that by a perfect physical inaction I should hasten mental repose, an awful incident occurred. A Something dropped, as it seemed, from the ceiling, plumb upon my chest, and the next instant I felt two bony hands encircling my throat, endeavoring to choke me.

I am no coward, and am possessed of considerable physical strength. The suddenness of the attack, instead of stunning me, strung every nerve to its highest tension. My body acted from instinct, before my brain had time to realize the terrors of my position. In an instant I wound two muscular arms around the creature, and squeezed it, with all the strength of despair, against my chest. In a few seconds the bony hands that had fastened on my throat loosened their hold, and I was free to breathe once more. Then commenced a struggle of awful intensity. Immersed in the most profound darkness, totally ignorant of the nature of the Thing by which I was so suddenly attacked, finding my grasp slipping every moment, by reason, it seemed to me, of the entire nakedness of my assailant, bitten with sharp teeth in the shoulder, neck, and chest, having every moment to protect my throat against a pair of sinewy, agile hands, which my utmost efforts could not confine,—these were a combination of circumstances to combat which required all the strength, skill, and courage that I possessed.

At last, after a silent, deadly, exhausting struggle, I got my assailant under by a series of incredible efforts of strength. Once pinned, with my knee on what I made out to be its chest, I knew that I was victor. I rested for a moment to breathe. I heard the creature beneath me panting in the darkness, and felt the violent throbbing of a heart. It was apparently as exhausted as I was; that was one comfort. At this moment I remembered that I usually placed under my pillow, before going to bed, a large yellow silk pocket-handkerchief. I felt for it instantly; it was there. In a few seconds more I had, after a fashion, pinioned the creature's arms.

I now felt tolerably secure. There was nothing more to be done but to turn on the gas, and, having first seen what my midnight assailant was like, arouse the household. I will confess to being actuated by a certain pride in not giving the alarm before; I wished to make the capture alone and unaided.

Never losing my hold for an instant, I slipped from the bed to the floor, dragging my captive with me. I had but a few steps to make to reach the gas-burner; these I made with the greatest caution, holding the creature in a grip like a vice. At last I got within arm's-length of the tiny speck of blue light which told me where the gas-burner lay. Quick as lightning I released my grasp with one hand and let on the full flood of light. Then I turned to look at my captive.

I cannot even attempt to give any definition of my sensations the instant after I turned on the gas. I suppose I must have shrieked with terror, for in less than a minute afterward my room was crowded with the inmates of the house. I shudder now as I think of that awful moment. *I saw nothing!* Yes; I had one arm firmly clasped round a breathing, panting, corporeal shape, my other hand gripped with all its strength a throat as warm, and apparently fleshly, as my own; and yet, with this living substance in my grasp, with its body pressed against my own, and all in the bright glare of a large jet of gas, I absolutely beheld nothing! Not even an outline,—a vapor!

I do not, even at this hour, realize the situation in which I found myself. I cannot recall the astounding incident thoroughly. Imagination in vain tries to compass the awful paradox.

It breathed. I felt its warm breath upon my cheek. It struggled fiercely. It had hands. They clutched me. Its skin was smooth, like my own. There it lay, pressed close up against me, solid as stone,—and yet utterly invisible!

I wonder that I did not faint or go mad on the instant. Some wonderful instinct must have sustained me; for, absolutely, in place of loosening my hold on the terrible Enigma, I seemed to gain an additional strength in my moment of horror, and tightened my grasp with such wonderful force that I felt the creature shivering with agony.

Just then Hammond entered my room at the head of the household. As soon as he beheld my face—which, I suppose, must have been an awful sight to look at— he hastened forward, crying, "Great heaven, Harry! what has happened?"

"Hammond! Hammond!" I cried, "come here. O, this is awful! I have been attacked in bed by something or other, which I have hold of; but I can't see it,—I can't see it!"

Hammond, doubtless struck by the unfeigned horror expressed in my countenance, made one or two steps forward with an anxious yet puzzled expression. A very audible titter burst from the remainder of my visitors. This suppressed laughter made me furious. To laugh at a human being in my position! It was the worst species of cruelty. *Now,* I can understand why the appearance of a man struggling violently, as it would seem, with an airy nothing, and calling for assistance against a vision, should have appeared ludicrous. *Then,* so great was my rage against the mocking crowd that had I the power I would have stricken them dead where they stood.

"Hammond! Hammond!" I cried again, despairingly,

"for God's sake come to me. I can hold the—the thing but a short while longer. It is overpowering me. Help me! Help me!"

"Harry," whispered Hammond, approaching me, "you have been smoking too much opium."

"I swear to you, Hammond, that this is no vision," I answered, in the same low tone. "Don't you see how it shakes my whole frame with its struggles? If you don't believe me, convince yourself. Feel it,—touch it."

Hammond advanced and laid his hand in the spot I indicated. A wild cry of horror burst from him. He had felt it!

In a moment he had discovered somewhere in my room a long piece of cord, and was the next instant winding it and knotting it about the body of the unseen being that I clasped in my arms.

"Harry," he said, in a hoarse, agitated voice, for, though he preserved his presence of mind, he was deeply moved, "Harry, it's all safe now. You may let go, old fellow, if you're tired. The Thing can't move."

I was utterly exhausted, and I gladly loosed my hold.

Hammond stood holding the ends of the cord that bound the Invisible, twisted round his hand, while before him, self-supporting as it were, he beheld a rope laced and interlaced, and stretching tightly around a vacant space. I never saw a man look so thoroughly stricken with awe. Nevertheless his face expressed all the courage and determination which I knew him to possess. His lips, although white, were set firmly, and one could perceive at a glance that, although stricken with fear, he was not daunted.

The confusion that ensued among the guests of the house who were witnesses of this extraordinary scene between Hammond and myself,—who beheld the pantomime of binding this struggling Something,—who beheld me almost sinking from physical exhaustion when my task of jailer was over,—the confusion and terror that took possession of the bystanders, when they saw all this, was beyond description. The weaker ones fled from the apartment. The few who remained clustered near the door and could not be induced to approach Hammond and his Charge. Still incredulity broke out through their terror. They had not the courage to satisfy themselves, and yet they doubted. It was in vain that I begged of some of the men to come near and convince themselves by touch of the existence in that room of a living being which was invisible. They were incredulous, but did not dare to undeceive themselves. How could a solid, living, breathing body be invisible, they asked. My reply was this. I gave a sign to Hammond, and both of us—conquering our fearful repugnance to touch the invisible creature—lifted it from the ground, manacled as it was, and took it to my bed. Its weight was about that of a boy of fourteen.

"Now, my friends," I said, as Hammond and myself held the creature suspended over the bed, "I can give you self-evident proof that here is a solid, ponderable body, which, nevertheless, you cannot see. Be good enough to watch the surface of the bed attentively."

I was astonished at my own courage in treating this strange event so calmly; but I had recovered from my first terror, and felt a sort of scientific pride in the affair, which dominated every other feeling.

The eyes of the bystanders were immediately fixed on my bed. At a given signal Hammond and I let the creature fall. There was the dull sound of a heavy body alighting on a soft mass. The timbers of the bed creaked. A deep impression marked itself distinctly on the pillow, and on the bed itself. The crowd who witnessed this gave a low cry, and rushed from the room. Hammond and I were left alone with our Mystery.

We remained silent for some time, listening to the low, irregular breathing of the creature on the bed, and watching the rustle of the bed-clothes as it impotently struggled to free itself from confinement. Then Hammond spoke.

"Harry, this is awful."

"Ay, awful."

"But not unaccountable."

"Not unaccountable! What do you mean? Such a thing has never occurred since the birth of the world. I know not what to think, Hammond. God grant that I am not mad, and that this is not an insane fantasy!"

"Let us reason a little, Harry. Here is a solid body which we touch, but which we cannot see. The fact is so unusual that it strikes us with terror. Is there no parallel, though, for such a phenomenon? Take a piece of pure glass. It is tangible and transparent. A certain chemical coarseness is all that prevents its being so entirely transparent as to be totally invisible. It is not *theoretically impossible,* mind you, to make a glass which shall not reflect a single ray of light,—a glass so pure and homogeneous in its atoms than the rays of light from the sun will pass through it as they do through the air, refracted but not reflected. We do not see the air, and yet we feel it."

"That's all very well, Hammond, but these are inanimate substances. Glass does not breathe, air does not breathe. *This* thing has a heart that palpitates,—a will that moves it,—lungs that play, and inspire and respire."

"You forget the phenomena of which we have so often heard of late," answered the Doctor, gravely. "At the meetings called 'spirit circles,' invisible hands have been thrust into the hands of those persons round the table,— warm, fleshly hands that seemed to pulsate with mortal life."

"What? Do you think, then, that this thing is—"

"I don't know what it is," was the solemn reply; "but please the gods I will, with your assistance, thoroughly investigate it."

We watched together, smoking many pipes, all night long, by the bedside of the unearthly being that tossed and panted until it was apparently wearied out. Then we learned by the low, regular breathing that it slept.

The next morning the house was all astir. The boarders congregated on the landing outside my room, and Hammond and myself were lions. We had to answer a thousand questions as to the state of our extraordinary prisoner, for as yet not one person in the house except ourselves could be induced to set foot in the apartment.

The creature was awake. This was evidenced by the convulsive manner in which the bed-clothes were moved in its efforts to escape. There was something truly terrible in beholding, as it were, those second-hand indications of the terrible writhings and agonized struggles for liberty which themselves were invisible.

Hammond and myself had racked our brains during the long night to discover some means by which we might realize the shape and general appearance of the Enigma. As well as we could make out by passing our hands over the creature's form, its outlines and lineaments were human. There was a mouth; a round, smooth head without hair; a nose, which, however, was a little elevated above the cheeks; and its hands and feet felt like those of a boy. At first we thought of placing the being on a smooth surface and tracing its outline with chalk, as shoemakers trace the outline of the foot. This plan was given up as being of no value. Such an outline would give not the slightest idea of its conformation.

A happy thought struck me. We would take a cast of it in plaster of Paris. This would give us the solid figure, and satisfy all our wishes. But how to do it? The movements of the creature would disturb the setting of the plastic covering, and distort the mould. Another thought. Why not give it chloroform? It had respiratory organs,— that was evident by its breathing. Once reduced to a state of insensibility, we could do with it what we would. Doctor X—— was sent for; and after the worthy physician had recovered from the first shock of amazement, he proceeded to administer the chloroform. In three minutes afterward we were enabled to remove the fetters from the creature's body, and a modeller was busily engaged in covering the invisible form with the moist clay. In five minutes more we had a mould, and before evening a rough fac-simile of the Mystery. It was shaped like a man,—distorted, uncouth, and horrible, but still a man. It was small, not over four feet and some inches in height, and its limbs revealed a muscular development that was unparalleled. Its face surpassed in hideousness anything I had ever seen. Gustav Doré, or Callot, or Tony Johannot, never conceived anything so horrible. There is a face in one of the latter's illustrations to *Un Voyage où il vous plaira,* which somewhat approaches the countenance of this creature, but does not equal it. It was the physiognomy of what I should fancy a ghoul might be. It looked as if it was capable of feeding on human flesh.

Having satisfied our curiosity, and bound every one in the house to secrecy, it became a question what was to be done with our Enigma? It was impossible that we should keep such a horror in our house; it was equally impossible that such an awful being should be let loose upon the world. I confess that I would have gladly voted for the creature's destruction. But who would shoulder the responsibility? Who would undertake the execution of this horrible semblance of a human being? Day after day this question was deliberated gravely. The boarders all left the house. Mrs. Moffat was in despair, and threatened Hammond and myself with all sorts of legal penalties if we did not remove the Horror. Our answer was, "We will go if you like, but we decline taking this creature with us. Remove it yourself if you please. It appeared in your house. On you the responsibility rests." To this there was, of course, no answer. Mrs. Moffat could not obtain for love or money a person who would even approach the Mystery.

The most singular part of the affair was that we were entirely ignorant of what the creature habitually fed on. Everything in the way of nutriment that we could think of was placed before it, but was never touched. It was awful to stand by, day after day, and see the clothes toss, and hear the hard breathing, and know that it was starving.

Ten, twelve days, a fortnight passed, and it still lived. The pulsations of the heart, however, were daily growing fainter, and had now nearly ceased. It was evident that the creature was dying for want of sustenance. While this terrible life-struggle was going on, I felt miserable. I could not sleep. Horrible as the creature was, it was pitiful to think of the pangs it was suffering.

At last it died. Hammond and I found it cold and stiff one morning in the bed. The heart had ceased to beat, the lungs to inspire. We hastened to bury it in the garden. It was a strange funeral, the dropping of that viewless corpse into the damp hole. The cast of its form I gave to Doctor X——, who keeps it in his museum in Tenth Street.

As I am on the eve of a long journey from which I may not return, I have drawn up this narrative of an event the most singular that has ever come to my knowledge.

from

The Day of the Triffids

by John Wyndham

[*The story takes place in England.*]

My introduction to a triffid came early. It so happened
that we had one of the first in the locality growing in our
own garden. The plant was quite well developed before
any of us bothered to notice it, for it had taken root along
with a number of other casuals behind the bit of hedge
that screened the rubbish heap. It wasn't doing any harm
there, and it wasn't in anyone's way. So when we did
notice it later on we'd just take a look at it now and then
to see how it was getting along, and let it be.

However, a triffid is certainly distinctive, and we couldn't
help getting a bit curious about it after a time. Not, perhaps, very actively, for there are always a few unfamiliar
things that somehow or other manage to lodge in the
neglected corners of a garden, but enough to mention to
one another that it was beginning to look a pretty queer
sort of thing.

Nowadays when everyone knows only too well what a
triffid looks like it is difficult to recall how odd and some-

how *foreign* the first ones appeared to us. Nobody, as far as I know, felt any misgiving or alarm about them then. I imagine that most people thought of them—when they thought of them at all—in much the same way that my father did.

I have a picture in my memory of him examining ours and puzzling over it at a time when it must have been about a year old. In almost every detail it was a half-size replica of a fully-grown triffid—only it didn't have a name yet, and no one had seen one fully grown. My father leant over, peering at it through his horn-rimmed glasses, fingering its stalk, and blowing gently through his gingery moustache as was his habit when thoughtful. He inspected the straight stem, and the woody bole from which it sprang. He gave curious, if not very penetrative attention to the three small, bare sticks which grew straight up beside the stem. He smoothed the short sprays of leathery green leaves between his finger and thumb as if their texture might tell him something. Then he peered into the curious, funnel-like formation at the top of the stem, still puffing reflectively but inconclusively through his moustache. I remember the first time he lifted me up to look inside that conical cup and see the tightly-wrapped whorl within. It looked not unlike the new, close-rolled frond of a fern, emerging a couple of inches from a sticky mess in the base of the cup. I did not touch it, but I knew the stuff must be sticky because there were flies and other small insects struggling in it.

More than once my father ruminated that it was pretty queer, and observed that one of these days he really must try to find out what it was. I don't think he ever made the effort, nor, at that stage, was he likely to have learned much if he had tried.

The thing would be about four feet high then. There must have been plenty of them about, growing up quietly and inoffensively, with nobody taking any particular notice of them—at least, it seemed so, for if the biological or botanical experts were excited over them no news of their interest percolated to the general public. And so the one in our garden continued its growth peacefully, as did thousands like it in neglected spots all over the world.

It was some little time later that the first one picked up its roots, and walked.

That improbable achievement must, of course, have been known for sime time in Russia where it was doubtless classified as a state secret, but as far as I have been able to confirm its first occurrence in the outside world took place in Indo-China—which meant that people went on taking practically no notice. Indo-China was one of those regions from which such curious and unlikely yarns might be expected to drift in, and frequently did—the kind of thing an editor might conceivably use if news were scarce and a touch of the "mysterious East" would liven the paper up a bit. But in any case the Indo-Chinese specimen can have had no great lead. Within a few weeks reports of walking plants were pouring in from Sumatra, Borneo, Belgian Congo, Columbia, Brazil and most places in the neighbourhood of the equator.

This time they got into print, all right. But the much-handled stories written up with that blend of cautiously defensive frivolity which the Press habitually employed to cover themselves in matters regarding sea-serpents, elementals, thought-transference and other irregular phenomena prevented anyone from realizing that these accomplished plants at all resembled the quiet, respectable weed beside our rubbish heap. Not until the pictures began to appear did we realize that they were identical with it save in size.

The news-reel men were quickly off the mark. Possibly they got some good and interesting pictures for their trouble of flying to outlandish places, but there was a current theory among cutters that more than a few seconds of any one news-subject—except a boxing match—could not fail to paralyse an audience with boredom. My first view, therefore, of a development which was to play such an important part in my future, as well as in so many other people's, was a glimpse sandwiched between a hula contest in Honolulu, and the First Lady launching a battleship. (That is no anachronism. They were still building them; even admirals had to live.) I was permitted to see a few triffids sway across the screen to the kind of accompaniment supposed to be on the level of the great movie-going public:

"And now, folks, get a load of what our cameraman found in Ecuador. Vegetables on vacation! *You've* only seen this kind of thing after a party, but down in sunny Ecuador they see it any time—and no hang-over to follow! Monster plants on the march! Say, now, that's given me a big idea! Maybe if we can educate our potatoes right we can fix it so they'll walk right into the pot. How'd that be, Momma?"

For the short time the scene was on, I stared at it, fascinated. There was our mysterious rubbish-heap plant grown to a height of seven feet or more. There was no mistaking it—and it was "walking!"

The bole, which I now saw for the first time, was shaggy with little rootlet hairs. It would have been almost spherical but for three bluntly-tapered projections extending from the lower part. Supported on these, the main body was lifted about a foot clear of the ground.

When it "walked" it moved rather like a man on crutches. Two of the blunt "legs" slid forward, then the whole thing lurched as the rear one drew almost level with them, then the two in front slid forward again. At each "step" the long stem whipped violently back and forth: it gave one a kind of seasick feeling to watch it. As a method of progress it looked both strenuous and clumsy— faintly reminiscent of young elephants at play. One felt that if it were to go on lurching for long in that fashion it would be bound to strip all its leaves if it did not actually break its stem. Nevertheless, ungainly though it looked, it was contriving to cover the ground at something like an average walking pace.

That was about all I had time to see before the battle-ship launching began. It was not a lot, but it was enough to incite an investigating spirit in a boy. For, if that thing in Ecuador could do a trick like that, why not the one in our garden? Admittedly ours was a good deal smaller but it did *look* the same. . . .

About ten minutes after I got home I was digging round our triffid, carefully loosening the earth near it to encourage it to "walk".

Unfortunately there was an aspect of this self-propelled plant discovery which the news-reel people had either not experienced, or chosen for some reason of their own not to reveal. There was no warning, either. I was bending down, intent on clearing the earth without harming the plant, when something from nowhere hit me one terrific slam, and knocked me out. . . .

I woke up to find myself in bed, with my mother, my father, and the doctor watching me anxiously. My head felt as if it were split open, I was aching all over, and, as I later discovered, one side of my face was decorated with a blotchy-red raised weal. The insistent questions as to how I came to be lying unconscious in the garden were quite useless; I had no faintest idea what it was that had hit me. And some little time passed before I learned that I must have been one of the first persons in England to be stung by a triffid and get away with it. The triffid was, of course, immature. But before I had fully recovered my father had found out what had undoubtedly happened to me, and by the time I went into the garden again he had wreaked stern vengeance on our triffid, and disposed of the remains on a bonfire.

Now that walking plants were established facts the Press lost its former tepidity, and bathed them in publicity. So a name had to found for them. Already there were botanists wallowing after their custom in polysyllabic dog-Latin and Greek to produce variants on *ambulans* and *pseudopodia,* but what the newspapers and the public wanted was something easy on the tongue and not too heavy on the headlines for general use. If you could see the papers of that time you would find them referring to:

Trichots	Trinits
Tricusps	Tripedals
Trigenates	Tripeds
Trigons	Triquets
Trilogs	Tripods
Tridentates	Trippets

and a number of other mysterious things not even beginning with "tri"—though almost all centred on the feature of that active, three-pronged root.

There was argument, public, private, and bar-parlour with heated championship of one term or another on near-scientific, quasi-etymological, and a number of other grounds, but gradually one term began to dominate this philological gymkhana. In its first form it was not quite acceptable, but common usage modified the original long first "i", and custom quickly wrote in a second "f", to leave no doubt about it. And so emerged the standard term. A catchy little name originating in some newspaper office as a handy label for an oddity—but destined one day to be associated with pain, fear and misery—TRIFFID. . . .

The first wave of public interest soon ebbed away. Triffids were, admittedly, a bit weird—but that was, after all, just because they were novelties. People had felt the same about novelties of other days—about kangaroos, giant lizards, black swans. And, when you came to think of it, were triffids all that much queerer than mudfish, ostriches, tadpoles, and a hundred other things? The bat was an animal that had learned to fly: well, here was a plant that had learned to walk—what of that?

But there were features of it to be less casually dismissed. On its origins the Russians, true to type, lay low and said nuffin. Even those who had heard of Umberto did not yet connect him with it. Its sudden appearance, and even more, its wide distribution promoted very puzzled speculation. For though it matured more rapidly in the tropics, specimens in various stages of development were reported from almost any region outside the polar circles and the deserts.

People were surprised, and a little disgusted, to learn that the species was carnivorous, and that the flies and other insects caught in the cups were actually digested by the sticky substance there. We in temperate zones were not ignorant of insectivorous plants, but we were unaccustomed to find them outside special hothouses, and apt to consider them as in some way slightly indecent, or at least improper. But actually alarming was the discovery that the whorl topping a triffid's stem could lash out as a slender stinging weapon ten feet long, capable of discharging enough poison to kill a man if it struck squarely on his unprotected skin.

As soon as this danger was appreciated there followed a nervous smashing and chopping of triffids everywhere until it occurred to someone that all that was necessary to make them harmless was the removal of the actual stinging weapon. At this, the slightly hysterical assault upon the plants declined, with their numbers considerably thinned. A little later it began to be a fashion to have a safely-docked triffid or two about one's garden. It was found that it took about two years for the lost sting to be dangerously replaced, so that an annual pruning assured that they were in a state of safety where they could provide vast amusement for the children.

In temperate countries, where man had succeeded in putting most forms of nature save his own under a reasonable degree of restraint, the status of the triffid was thus made quite clear. But in the tropics, particularly in the dense forest areas, they quickly became a scourge.

The traveller very easily failed to notice one among the normal bushes and undergrowth, and the moment he was in range the venomous sting would slash out. Even the regular inhabitant of such a district found it difficult to detect a motionless triffid cunningly lurking beside a jungle path. They were uncannily sensitive to any movement near them, and it was hard to take them unawares.

Dealing with them became a serious problem in such regions. The most favoured method was to shoot the top off the stem, and the sting with it. The jungle natives took to carrying long, light poles mounted with hooked knives which they used effectively if they could get their blows in first—but not at all if the triffid had a chance to sway forward and increase its range by an unexpected four or five feet. Before long, however, these pike-like devices were mostly superseded by spring-operated guns of various types. Most of them shot spinning discs, cross or small boomerangs of thin steel. As a rule they were inaccurate above about twelve yards, though capable of slicing a triffid stem neatly at twenty-five if they hit it. Their invention pleased both the authorities—who had an almost unanimous distaste for the indiscriminate toting of rifles—and the users who found the missiles of razor-blade steel far cheaper and lighter than cartridges, and admirably adaptable to silent banditry.

Elsewhere immense research into the nature, habits, and constitution of the triffid went on. Earnest experimenters set out to determine in the interests of science how far and for how long it could walk; whether it could be said to have a front, or could perform its march in any direction with equal clumsiness; what proportion of its time it must spend with its roots in the ground; what reactions it showed to the presence of various chemicals in the soil; and a vast quantity of other questions, both useful and useless.

The largest specimen ever observed in the tropics stood nearly ten feet high. No European specimen over eight feet had been seen, and the average was little over seven. They appeared to adapt easily to a wide range of climate and soils. They had, it seemed, no natural enemies—other than man.

But there were a number of not unobvious characteristics which escaped comment for some little time. It was, for instance, quite a while before anyone drew attention to the uncanny accuracy with which they aimed their stings, and that they almost invariably struck for the head. Nor did anyone at first take notice of their habit of lurking near their fallen victims. The reason for that only became clear when it was shown that they fed upon flesh as well as insects. The stinging tendril did not have the muscular power to tear firm flesh, but it had strength enough to pull shreds from a decomposing body and lift them to the cup on its stem.

There was no great interest, either, in the three little leafless sticks at the base of the stem. There was a light notion that they might have something to do with the reproductive system—that system which tends to be a sort of botanical glory-hole for all parts of doubtful purpose until they can be sorted out and more specifically assigned later on. It was assumed, consequently, that their characteristic of suddenly losing their immobility and rattling a rapid tattoo against the main stem was some strange form of triffidian amatory exuberance.

Possibly my uncomfortable distinction of getting myself stung so early in the triffid era had the effect of stimulating my interest, for I seemed to have a sort of link with them from then on. I spent—or "wasted", if you look at me through my father's eyes—a great deal of fascinated time watching them.

One could not blame him for considering this a worthless pursuit, yet, later, the time turned out to have been better employed than either of us suspected, for it was just before I left school that the Arctic and European Fish-Oil Company reconstituted itself, dropping the word "Fish" in the process. The public learned that it and similar companies in other countries were about to farm triffids on a large scale in order to extract valuable oils and juices, and to press highly nutritious oil-cake for stock feeding. Consequently, triffids moved into the realm of big business overnight.

Right away I decided my future. I applied to the Arctic and European where my qualifications got me a job on the production side. My father's disapproval was somewhat qualified by the rate of pay, which was good for my age. But when I spoke enthusiastically of the future he blew doubtfully through his moustache. He had real faith only in a type of work steadied by long tradition, but he let me have my way. "After all, if the thing isn't a success you'll find out young enough to start in on something more solid," he conceded.

There turned out to be no need for that. Before he and my mother were killed together in a holiday air-bus crash five years later they had seen the companies drive all competing oils off the market, and those of us who had been in at the beginning apparently well set for life.

One of the early comers was my friend Walter Lucknor.

There had been some doubt at first about taking Walter on. He knew little of agriculture, less of business, and lacked the qualifications for lab. work. On the other hand, he did know a lot about triffids—he had a kind of inspired knack with them.

What happened to Walter that fatal May years later I do not know—though I can guess. It is a sad thing that he did not escape. He might have been immensely valuable later on. I don't think anybody really understands triffids, or ever will, but Walter came nearer to beginning to understand them than any man I have known. Or should I say that he was given to intuitive feelings about them?

It was a year or two after the job had begun that he first surprised me.

The sun was close to setting. We had knocked off for the day and were looking with a sense of satisfaction at three new fields of nearly fully-grown triffids. In those days we didn't simply corral them as we did later. They were arranged across the fields roughly in rows—at least the steel stakes to which each was tethered by a chain were in rows, though the plants themselves had no sense of tidy regimentation. We reckoned that in another month or so we'd be able to start tapping them for juice. The evening was peaceful, almost the only sounds that broke it were the occasional rattlings of the triffids, little sticks against their stems. Walter regarded them with his head slightly on one side. He removed his pipe.

"They're talkative tonight," he observed.

I took that as anyone else would, metaphorically.

"Maybe it's the weather," I suggested. "I fancy they do it more when it's dry."

He looked sidelong at me, with a smile.

"Do you talk more when it's dry?"

"Why should—?" I began, and then broke off. "You don't really mean you think they're talking?" I said, noticing his expression.

"Well, why not?"

"But it's absurd. Plants talking!".

"So much more absurd than plants walking?" he asked.

I stared at them, and then back at him.

"I never thought—" I began, doubtfully.

"You try thinking of it a bit, and watching them—I'd be interested to hear your conclusions," he said.

It was a curious thing that in all my dealings with triffids such a possibility had never occurred to me. I'd been prejudiced, I suppose, by the love-call theory. But once he had put the idea into my mind, it stuck. I couldn't get away from the feeling that they might indeed be rattling out secret messages to one another.

Up to then I'd fancied I'd watched triffids pretty closely, but when Walter was talking about them I felt that I'd noticed practically nothing. He could, when he was in the mood, talk on about them for hours, advancing theories that were sometimes wild, but sometimes not impossible.

The public had by this time grown out of thinking triffids freakish. They were clumsily amusing, but not greatly interesting. The Company found them interesting, however. It took the view that their existence was a piece of benevolence for everyone—particularly for itself. Walter shared neither view. At times, listening to him, I began to have some misgivings myself.

He had become quite certain that they "talked."

"And that," he argued, "means that somewhere in them is intelligence. It can't be seated in a brain because dissection shows nothing like a brain—but that doesn't prove there isn't something there that does a brain's job.

"And there's certainly intelligence there, of a kind. Have you noticed that when they attack they always go for the unprotected parts? Almost always the head—but sometimes the hands? And another thing: if you look at the statistics of casualties, just take notice of the proportion that has been stung across the eyes, and blinded. It's remarkable—and significant."

"Of what?" I asked.

"Of the fact that they know what is the surest way to put a man out of action—in other words, they know what they're doing. Look at it this way. Granted that they do have intelligence; then that would leave us with only one important superiority—sight. We can see, and they can't. Take away our vision, and the superiority is gone. Worse than that—our position becomes inferior to theirs because they are adapted to a sightless existence, and we are not."

"But even if that were so, they can't *do* things. They can't handle things. There's very little muscular strength in that sting lash," I pointed out.

"True, but what's the good of our ability to handle things if we can't see what to do with them? Anyway, they don't need to handle things—not in the way we do. They can get their nourishment direct from the soil, or from insects and bits of raw meat. They don't have to go through all the complicated business of growing things, distributing them, and usually cooking them as well. In fact, if it were a choice for survival between a triffid and a blind man, I know which I'd put my money on."

"You're assuming equal intelligence," I said.

"Not at all. I don't need to. I should imagine it's likely to be an altogether different type of intelligence, if only because their needs are so much simpler. Look at the complex processes we have to use to get an assimilable extract from a triffid. Now reverse that. What does the triffid have to do? Just sting us, wait a few days, and then begin to assimilate us. The simple, natural course of things."

He would go on like that by the hour until listening to him would have me getting things out of proportion, and I'd find myself thinking of the triffids as though they were some kind of competitor. Walter himself never pretended to think otherwise. He had, he admitted, thought of writing a book on that very aspect of the subject when he had gathered more material.

"Had?" I repeated. "What's stopping you?"

"Just this." He waved his hand to include the farm generally. "It's a vested interest now. It wouldn't pay anyone to put out disturbing thoughts about it. Anyway, we have the triffids controlled well enough so it's an academic point, and scarcely worth raising."

"I never can be quite sure with you," I told him. "I'm never certain how far you are serious, and how far beyond your facts you allow your imagination to lead you. Do you honestly think there is a danger in the things?"

He puffed a bit at his pipe before he answered.

"That's fair enough," he admitted, "because—well, I'm by no means sure myself. But I'm pretty certain of one thing, and that is that there *could* be danger in them. I'd feel a lot nearer giving you a real answer if I could get a line on what it means when they patter. Somehow I don't care for that. There they sit, with everyone thinking no more of them than they might of a pretty odd lot of cabbages, yet half the time they're pattering and clattering away at one another. Why? What is it they patter about? That's what I want to know."

I think Walter rarely gave a hint of his ideas to anyone else, and I kept them confidential, partly because I knew no one who wouldn't be more skeptical than I was myself, and partly because it wouldn't do either of us any good to get a reputation in the firm as crackpots.

For a year or so more we were working fairly close together. But with the opening of new nurseries and the need for studying methods abroad I began to travel a lot. He gave up field work, and went into the research department. It suited him there, doing his own searching as well as the Company's. I used to drop in to see him from time to time. He was for ever making experiments with the triffids, but the results weren't clearing his general ideas as much as he had hoped. He had proved, to his own satisfaction at least, the existence of a well-developed intelligence—and even I had to admit that his results seemed to show something more than instinct. He was still convinced that the pattering of the sticks was a form of communication. For public consumption he had shown that the sticks were something more, and that a triffid deprived of them gradually deteriorated. He had also established that the infertility rate of triffid seeds was something like ninety-five per cent.

"Which," he remarked, "is a damned good thing. If

they all germinated there'd soon be standing room only for triffids on this planet."

With that, too, I agreed. Triffid seed time was quite a sight. The dark green pod just below the cup was glistening and distended, about half as big again as a large apple. When it burst, it did it with a pop that was audible twenty yards away. The white seeds shot into the air like steam, and began drifting away on the lightest of breezes. Looking down on a field of triffids late in August you could well get the idea that some kind of desultory bombardment was in progress.

It was Walter's discovery again that the quality of the extracts was improved if the plants retained their stings. In consequence, the practice of docking was discontinued on farms throughout the trade, and we had to wear protective devices when working among the plants.

At the time of the accident that had landed me in hospital I was actually with Walter. We were examining some specimens which were showing unusual deviations. Both of us were wearing wire-mesh masks. I did not see exactly what happened. All I know is that as I bent forward a sting slashed viciously at my face and smacked against the wire of the mask. Ninety-nine times in a hundred it would not have mattered; that was what the masks were for. But this one came with such force that some of the little poison sacs were burst open, and a few drops from them went into my eyes.

Walter got me back into his lab, and administered the antidote in a few seconds. It was entirely due to his quick work that they had the chance of saving my sight at all. But even so, it had meant over a week in bed, in the dark.

While I lay there I had quite decided that when—and if—I had my sight back I was going to apply for a transfer to another side of the business. And if that did not go through, I'd quit the job altogether.

I had built up a considerable resistance to triffid poison since my first sting in the garden. I could take, and had taken, without very much harm, stings which would have laid an inexperienced man out very cold indeed. But an old saying about a pitcher and a well kept on recurring to me. I was taking my warning.

I spent, I remember, a good many of my enforcedly dark hours deciding what kind of job I would try for if they would not give me that transfer.

Considering what was just around the corner for us all, I could scarcely have found a contemplation more idle.

* * * * * * * * * * * * * * * *

[*The triffids have escaped from the nurseries and are stalking the countryside, either blinding their victims or killing them outright for food.*]

Nine o'clock the next morning saw us already twelve miles or so on our road, and travelling as before in our two lorries. There had been a question whether we should not take a handier vehicle and leave the trucks for the benefit of the Tynsham people, but I was reluctant to abandon mine. I had personally collected the contents, and knew what was in it. Apart from the cases of anti-triffid gear which Michael Beadley had so disapproved, I had given myself slightly wider scope on the last load, and there was a selection of things made with consideration of what might be difficult to find outside a large town; such things as a small lighting set, some pumps, cases of good tools. All these things would be available later for the taking, but there was going to be an interlude when it would be advisable to keep away from towns of any size. The Tynsham people had the means to fetch supplies from towns where there was no sign yet of the disease. A couple of loads would not make a great deal of difference to them either way, so, in the end, we went as we had come.

The weather still held good. On the higher ground there was still little taint in the fresh air, though most villages had become unpleasant. Rarely we saw a still figure lying in a field or by the roadside, but just as in London, the main instinct seemed to have been to hide away in shelter of some kind. Most of the villages showed empty streets, and the countryside around them as deserted as if the whole human race and most of its animals had been spirited away. Until we came to Steeple Honey.

From our road we had a view of the whole of Steeple Honey as we descended the hill. It clustered at the further end of a stone bridge which arched across a small, sparkling river. It was a quiet little place centred round a sleepy-looking church, and stippled off at its edges with white-washed cottages. It did not look as if anything had occurred in a century or more to disturb the quiet life under its thatched roofs. But like other villages it was now without stir or smoke. And then, when we were half-way down the hill, a movement caught my eye.

On the left, at the far end of the bridge one house stood slightly aslant from the road so that it faced obliquely towards us. An inn sign hung from a bracket on its wall, and from the window immediately above that something white was being waved. As we came closer I could see the man who was leaning out and frantically flagging us with a towel. I judged that he must be blind, otherwise he would have come out into the road to intercept us. He was waving too vigorously for a sick man.

I signalled back to Coker, and pulled up as we cleared the bridge. The man at the window dropped his towel. He shouted something which I could not hear above the noise of the engines, and disappeared. We both switched off. It was so quiet that we could hear the clumping of the man's feet on the wooden stairs inside the house. The door opened, and he stepped out, holding both hands before him. Like lightning something whipped out of the hedge on his left, and struck him. He gave a single, high-pitched shout, and dropped where he stood.

I picked up my shotgun, and climbed out of the cab. I circled a little until I could make out the triffid skulking in the shadows of a bush. Then I blew the top off it.

Coker was out of his truck, too, and standing close beside me. He looked at the man on the ground, and then at the shorn triffid.

"It was—no, damn it, it can't have been *waiting* for him?" he said. "It must just have happened . . . It couldn't have *known* he'd come out of that door. . . . I mean, it *couldn't*—could it?"

"Or could it? It was a remarkably neat piece of work," I said.

Coker turned uneasy eyes on me.

"Too damn' neat. You don't really believe . . . ?"

"There's a kind of conspiracy not to believe things about triffids," I said, and added: "There might be more around here."

We looked the adjacent cover over carefully, and drew blank.

"I could do with a drink," suggested Coker.

But for the dust on the counter, the small bar of the inn looked normal. We poured a whiskey each. Coker downed his in one. He turned a worried look on me.

"I didn't like that. Not at all, I didn't. You ought to know a lot more about these bloody things than most people, Bill. It wasn't—I mean, it must just have *happened* to be there, mustn't it?"

"I think—" I began. Then I stopped, listening to the staccato drumming outside. I walked over and opened the window. I let the already trimmed triffid have the other barrel, too; this time just above the bole. The drumming stopped.

"The trouble about triffids," I said, as we poured

another drink, "is chiefly the things we don't know about them." I told him one or two of Walter's theories. He stared.

"You don't seriously suggest that they're 'talking' when they make that rattling noise?"

"I've never made up my mind," I admitted. "I'll go so far as to say I'm sure it's a signal of some sort. But Walter considered it to be real 'talk'—and he did know more about them than anyone else that I know."

I ejected the two spent cartridge cases, and reloaded.

"And he actually mentioned their advantage over a blind man?"

"A number of years ago, that was," I pointed out.

"Still—it's a funny coincidence."

"Impulsive as ever," I said. "Pretty nearly any stroke of fate can be made to look like a funny coincidence if you try hard enough and wait long enough,"

We drank up, and turned to go. Coker glanced out of the window. Then he caught my arm, and pointed. Two triffids had swayed round the corner, and were making for the hedge which had been the hiding-place of the first. I waited until they paused, and then decapitated both of them. We left by the window, which was out of range of any triffid cover, and looked about us carefully as we approached the lorries.

"Another coincidence? Or were they coming to see what had happened to their pal?" asked Coker.

We cleared the village, running on along small, cross-country roads. There seemed to me to be more triffids about now than we had seen on our pervious journey—or was it that I had been made more conscious of them? It might have been that in travelling hitherto chiefly by main roads we had encountered fewer. I knew from experience that they tended to avoid a hard surface, and thought that it perhaps caused them some discomfort in their limb-like roots. Now I began to be convinced that we *were* seeing more of them, and I started to get an idea that they were not entirely indifferent to us—though it was not possible to be sure whether those that we saw approaching across fields from time to time just happened to be coming in our direction.

A more decisive incident occurred when one slashed at me from the hedgerow as I passed. Luckily it was inexpert in its aim at a moving vehicle. It let fly a moment too soon, and left its print in little dots of poison across the windscreen. I was past before it could strike again. But thenceforward, in spite of the warmth I drove with the nearside window closed.

During the past week or more I had given thought to the triffids only when I encountered them. Those I had seen at Josella's home had worried me as had the others that had attacked our group near Hampstead Heath, but most of the time there had been more immediate things to worry about. But, looking back now over our trip, the state of things at Tynsham before Miss Durrant had taken steps to clear it up with shotguns, and the condition of the villages we had passed through, I began to wonder just how big a part the triffids might have been playing in the disappearance of the inhabitants.

In the next village I drove slowly, and looked carefully. In several of the front gardens I could see bodies lying as they had evidently lain for some days—and almost always there was a triffid discernible close by. It looked as if the triffids only ambushed in places where there was soft earth for them to dig their roots into while they waited. One seldom saw a body, and never a triffid in those parts where the house-doors opened straight into the street.

At a guess I would say that what had happened in most of the villages was that the inhabitants emerging for food moved in comparative safety while they were in paved areas, but the moment they left them, or even passed close to a garden wall or fence, they stood in danger of the stings slashing out at them. Some would cry out as they were struck, and when they did not come back those who remained would grow more afraid. Now and then another would be driven out by hunger. A few might be lucky enough to get back, but most would lose themselves and wander on until they dropped, or came within range of a triffid. Those who were left might, perhaps, guess what was happening. Where there was a garden they might have heard the swish of the sting, and known that they faced the alternatives of starvation in the house or the same fate that had overtaken the others who had left it. Many would remain there, living on what food they had while they waited for help that was never going to come. Something like that must have been the predicament of the man in the inn at Steeple Honey.

The likelihood that in the other villages we were passing through there might still be houses in which isolated groups had managed to keep going was not a pleasant thought. It raised again the same kind of question that we had faced in London—the feeling that one should, by all civilized standards, try to find them and do something for them; and the frustrating knowledge of the frittering decline which would overtake any such attempt as it had before.

The same old question. What could one do, with the best will in the world, but prolong the anguish? Placate one's conscience for a while again, just to see the result of the effort wasted once more.

It was not, I had to tell myself firmly, any good at all going into an earthquake area while the buildings were still falling—the rescue and the salvage had to be done when the tremors had stopped. But reason did not make it easy. The old Doctor had been only too right when he stressed the difficulties of mental adaptation. . . .

The triffids were a complication on an unexpected scale. There were, of course, very many nurseries besides our own company's plantations. They raised them for us, for private buyers, or for sale to a number of lesser trades where their derivatives were used, and the majority of them were, for climatic reasons situated in the south. Nevertheless, if what we had already seen was a fair sample of the way they had broken loose and distributed themselves they must have been far more numerous than I had supposed. The prospect of more of them reaching maturity every day and of the docked specimens steadily regrowing their stings was far from reassuring. . . .

With only two more stops, one for food and the other for fuel, we made good time, and ran into Beaminster about half-past four in the afternoon. We had come right into the centre of the town without having seen a sign to suggest the presence of the Beadley party.

At first glimpse the place was as void of life as any other we had seen that day. The main shopping street when we entered it was bare and empty save for a couple of lorries drawn up on one side. I had led the way down it for perhaps twenty yards when a man stepped out from behind one of the lorries, and levelled a rifle. He fired deliberately over my head, and then lowered his aim.

Part Six

Psychological Threat

When the terror in Gothic is produced not through physical threat but through suggestion or some kind of mind-altering process, or when the effect depends on the reader's understanding of the state of mind of the victim, the Gothic is a psychological threat or agency—even though many of the tales so oriented were written long before the terms "psychology" or "psychoanalysis" came into usage. Certain distinctions must be made, however, if only to exclude much that might, through a misunderstanding of the term, be considered psychological. In Lewis' *The Monk,* for example, there is no doubt that Ambrosio possesses a number of psychological aberrations and that his uncontrollable obsessions are not "normal"; and it is also true that Lewis' treatment of the Inquisition anticipates many later investigations about the movement's psychological implications of sadism, torture, and sexual suppression or perversion. Yet these do not make *The Monk* a novel of psychological threat; the dominant threat is still that of human physical force, and the story evokes terror even if the psychological elements are not considered.

The same is true, to greater or lesser extent, in all other approaches to evocation of terror. Descriptions of setting, though affecting the reader's susceptibilities, are not instances of the psychological as a source of threat. In a more inclusive sense, even though all reading may be taken to be a mental or psychological activity, such a consideration is not germane to the present classification of agencies of terror in Gothic literature. In this study, psychological agency refers specifically and only to the use of the psychological as the dominant agency evoking the feeling of terror.

Brown's *Wieland,* for instance, is the story of a man

444

under the evil influence of another, of a man victimized by the brainwashing of a ventriloquist, or, as Brown calls him, "biloquist." It is the psychological manipulation of Wieland which is the agency of terror. Similarly, in James' famous *The Turn of the Screw,* the psychological threat, though subtler, deeper, and far more ambiguous, is still the basis of the story.

Quite different in approach from the foregoing, but still containing a psychological theme, is Saki's delightful though morbid "Sredni Vashtar." The resentments which drive the child into a realm of fantasy and lead to his deifying the ferret are common responses to childhood's frustrations, isolation, and real or imagined wrongs. The implicit and explicit results of this in Saki's tale are, however, far from common, and are strangely reminiscent of the homeopathic magic of primitive societies. And who but Saki could have added that final touch of the matter-of-fact child and his toast, by way of contrast to what has just taken place? The boy's fantasy universe becomes disturbingly real and the adult world singularly ineffective, conventional, and superficial.

It is not really much of a leap from this world of Sredni Vashtar to that of the woman in Gilman's "The Yellow Wall Paper," despite the different emotional states of the protagonists. But Saki's story, in presenting the psychology of a vengeful child, remains within the realm of the rational, whereas Gilman's story goes beyond to deal explicitly with madness, a common Gothic theme. The fear of madness, whatever its sources, is as old as man's history and poses a situation wherein the threat is not external but internal. There is no easy solution, such as driving a holly stake through the evil-doer's heart, no last-minute whisking away of the villain by the Prince of Darkness, no eleventh-hour rescue by the lover, no release even by death itself. The victim is responding to a different world of reality, and he or she, like the reader, cannot be certain any longer of the margin between reality and illusion—or if there is a difference. It is a dire threat, individual man against himself, and represents a kind of final negation of the conventional world of the rational.

from

The Turn of the Screw

by Henry James

[*A governess has come to the English country manor of Bly to take over the duties of the dead Miss Jessel. The new governess gradually suspects that her two young charges, Flora and Miles, are under the evil influence of the dead woman and Peter Quint, another dead servant. Sensing one day that Flora is meeting with Miss Jessel at Bly lake, the governess and Mrs. Grose, the housekeeper, go to the lake to see for themselves.*]

CHAPTER XIX.

We went straight to the lake, as it was called at Bly, and I dare say rightly called, though it may have been a sheet of water less remarkable than my untravelled eyes supposed it. My acquaintance with sheets of water was small, and the pool of Bly, at all events on the few occasions of my consenting, under the protection of my pupils, to affront its surface in the old flat-bottomed boat moored there for our use, had impressed me both with its extent and its agitation. The usual place of embarkation was half a mile from the house, but I had an intimate conviction that, wherever Flora might be, she was not near home. She had not given me the slip for any small adventure, and, since the day of the very great one that I had shared with her by the pond, I had been aware, in our walks, of the quarter to which she most inclined. This was why I had now given to Mrs. Grose's steps so marked a direction—a direction making her, when she perceived it, oppose a resistance that showed me she was freshly mystified. "You're going to the water, Miss?—you think she's *in*—?"

"She may be, though the depth is, I believe, nowhere very great. But what I judge most likely is that she's on the spot from which, the other day, we saw together what I told you."

"When she pretended not to see—?"

"With that astounding self-possession! I've always been sure she wanted to go back alone. And now her brother has managed it for her."

Mrs. Grose still stood where she had stopped. "You suppose they really *talk* of them?"

I could meet this with an assurance! "They say things that, if we heard them, would simply appal us."

"And is she *is* there—?"

"Yes?"

"Then Miss Jessel is?"

"Beyond a doubt. You shall see."

"Oh thank you!" my friend cried, planted so firm that, taking it in, I went straight on without her. By the time I reached the pool, however, she was close behind me, and I knew that, whatever, to her apprehension, might befall me, the exposure of sticking to me struck her as her least danger. She exhaled a moan of relief as we at last came in sight of the greater part of the water without a sight of the child. There was no trace of Flora on that nearer side of the bank where my observation of her had been most startling, and none on the opposite edge, where, save for a margin of some twenty yards, a thick copse came down to the pond. This expanse, oblong in shape, was so narrow compared to its length that, with its ends out of view, it might be taken for a scant river. We looked at the empty stretch, and then I felt the suggestion in my friend's eyes. I knew what she meant and I replied with a negative headshake.

"No, no; wait! She has taken the boat."

My companion stared at the vacant mooring-place and then again across the lake. "Then where is it?"

"Our not seeing it is the strongest of proofs. She has used it to go over, and then has managed to hide it."

"All alone—that child?"

"She's not alone, and at such times she's not a child: she's an old, old woman." I scanned all the visible shore while Mrs. Grose took again, into the queer element I offered her, one of her plunges of submission; then I pointed out the boat might perfectly be in a small refuge formed by one of the recesses of the pool, an indentation masked, for the hither side, by a projection of the bank and by a clump of trees growing close to the water.

"But if the boat's there, where on earth 's *she?*" my colleague anxiously asked.

"That's exactly what we must learn." And I started to walk further.

"By going all the way round?"

"Certainly, far as it is. It will take us but ten minutes, yet it's far enough to have made the child prefer not to walk. She went straight over."

"Laws!" cried my friend again: the chain of my logic was ever too strong for her. It dragged her at my heels even now, and when we had got halfway round—a devious tiresome process, on ground much broken and by a path choked with overgrowth—I paused to give her breath. I sustained her with a grateful arm, assuring her that she might hugely help me; and this started us afresh, so that in the course of but few minutes more we reached a point from which we found the boat to be where I had supposed it. It had been intentionally left as much as possible out of sight and was tied to one of the stakes of a fence that came, just there, down to the brink and that had been an assistance to disembarking. I recognised, as I looked at the pair of short thick oars, quite safely drawn up, the prodigious character of the feat for a little girl; but I had by this time lived too long among wonders and had panted to too many livelier measures. There was a gate in the fence, through which we passed, and that brought us after a trifling interval more into the open. Then "There she is!" we both exclaimed at once.

Flora, a short way off, stood before us on the grass and smiled as if her performance had now become complete. The next thing she did, however, was to stoop straight down and pluck—quite as if it were all she was there for —a big ugly spray of withered fern. I at once felt sure she had just come out of the copse. She waited for us, not herself taking a step, and I was conscious of the rare solemnity with which we presently approached her. She smiled and smiled, and we met; but it was all done in a silence by this time flagrantly ominous. Mrs. Grose was the first to break the spell: she threw herself on her knees and, drawing the child to her breast, clasped in a long embrace the little tender yielding body. While this dumb convulsion lasted I could only watch it—which I did the more intently when I saw Flora's face peep at me over our companion's shoulder. It was serious now—the flicker had left it, but it strengthened the pang with which I at that moment envied Mrs. Grose the simplicity of *her* relation. Still, all this while, nothing more passed between us save that Flora had let her foolish fern again drop to the ground. What she and I had virtually said to each other was that pretexts were useless now. When Mrs. Grose finally got up she kept the child's hand, so that the two were still before me; and the singular reticence of our communion was even more marked in the frank look she addressed me. "I'll be hanged," it said, "if *I'll* speak!"

It was Flora who, gazing all over me in candid wonder, was the first. She was struck with our bareheaded aspect. "Why, where are your things?"

"Where yours are, my dear!" I promptly returned.

She had already got back her gaiety and appeared to take this as an answer quite sufficient. "And where's Miles?" she went on.

There was something in the small valour of it that quite finished me: these three words from her were, in a flash like the glitter of a drawn blade, the jostle of the cup that my hand for weeks and weeks had held high and full to the brim and that now, even before speaking, I felt overflow in a deluge. "I'll tell you if you'll tell *me*—" I heard myself say, then heard the tremor in which it broke.

"Well, what?"

Mrs. Grose's suspense blazed at me, but it was too late now, and I brought the thing out handsomely. "Where, my pet, is Miss Jessel?"

CHAPTER XX.

Just as in the churchyard with Miles, the whole thing was upon us. Much as I had made of the fact that this name had never once, between us, been sounded, the quick smitten glare with which the child's face now received it fairly likened my breach of the silence to the smash of a pane of glass. It added to the interposing cry, as if to stay the blow, that Mrs. Grose at the same instant uttered over my violence—the shriek of a creature scared, or rather wounded, which, in turn, within a few seconds, was completed by a gasp of my own. I seized my colleague's arm. "She's there, she's there!"

Miss Jessel stood before us on the opposite bank exactly as she had stood the other time, and I remember, strangely, as the first feeling now produced in me, my thrill of joy at having brought on a proof. She was there, so I was justified; she was there, so I was neither cruel nor mad. She was there for poor scared Mrs. Grose, but she was there most for Flora; and no moment of my monstrous time was perhaps so extraordinary as that in which I consciously threw out to her—with the sense that, pale and ravenous demon as she was, she would catch and understand it—an inarticulate message of gratitude. She rose erect on the spot my friend and I had lately quitted, and there wasn't in all the long reach of her desire an inch of her evil that fell short. The first vividness of vision and emotion were things of a few seconds, during which Mrs. Grose's dazed blink across to where I pointed struck me as showing that she too at last saw, just as it carried my own eyes precipitately to the child. The revelation then of the manner in which Flora was affected startled me in truth far more than it would have done to find her also merely agitated, for direct dismay was of course not what I had expected. Prepared and on her guard as our pursuit had actually made her, she would repress every betrayal; and I was therefore at once shaken by my first glimpse of the particular one for which I had not allowed. To see her, without a convulsion of her small pink face, not even feign to glance in the direction of the prodigy I announced, but only, instead of that, turn at *me* an expression of hard still gravity, an expression absolutely new and unprecedented and that appeared to read and accuse and judge me—this was a stroke that somehow converted the little girl herself into a figure portentous. I gaped at her coolness even though my certitude of her thoroughly seeing was never greater than at that instant, and then, in the immediate need to defend myself, I called her passionately to witness. "She's there, you little unhappy thing—there, there, *there,* and you know it as well as you know me!" I had said shortly before to Mrs. Grose that she was not at these times a child, but an old, old woman, and my description of her couldn't have been more strikingly confirmed than in the way in which, for all notice of this, she simply showed me, without an expressional concession or admission, a countenance of deeper and deeper, of indeed suddenly quite fixed reprobation. I was by this time—if I can put the whole thing at all together—more appalled at what I may properly call her manner than at anything else, though it was quite simultaneously that I became aware of having Mrs. Grose also, and very formidably, to reckon with. My elder companion, the next moment, at any rate, blotted out everything but her own flushed face and her loud shocked protest, a burst of high disapproval. "What a dreadful turn, to be sure, Miss! Where on earth do you see anything?"

I could only grasp her more quickly yet, for even while she spoke the hideous plain presence stood undimmed and undaunted. It had already lasted a minute, and it lasted while I continued, seizing my colleague, quite thrusting her at it and presenting her to it, to insist with my pointing hand. "You don't see her exactly as *we* see?—you mean to say you don't now—*now?* She's as big as a blazing fire! Only look, dearest woman, *look*—!" She looked, just as I did, and gave me, with her deep groan of negation, repulsion, compassion—the mixture with her pity of her relief at her exemption—a sense, touching to me even then, that she would have backed me up if she had been able. I might well have needed that, for with this hard blow of the proof that her eyes were hopelessly sealed I felt my own situation horribly crumble, I felt—I *saw*—my livid predecessor press, from her position, on my defeat, and I took the measure, more than all, of what I should have from this instant to deal with in the astounding little attitude of Flora. Into this attitude Mrs. Grose immediately and violently entered, breaking, even while there pierced through my sense of ruin a prodigious private triumph, into breathless reassurance.

"She isn't there, little lady, and nobody's there—and you never see nothing, my sweet! How can poor Miss Jessel—when poor Miss Jessel's dead and buried? *We* know, don't we love?"—and she appealed, blundering in, to the child. "It's all a mere mistake and a worry and a joke—and we'll go home as fast as we can!"

Our companion, on this, had responded with a strange quick primness of propriety, and they were again, with Mrs. Grose on her feet, united, as it were, in shocked opposition to me. Flora continued to fix me with her small mask of disaffection, and even at that minute I prayed God to forgive me for seeming to see that, as she stood there holding tight to our friend's dress, her incomparable childish beauty had suddenly failed, had quite vanished. I've said it already—she was literally, she was hideously hard; she had turned common and almost ugly. "I don't know what you mean. I see nobody. I see nothing. I never *have*. I think you're cruel. I don't like you!" Then, after this deliverance, which might have been that of a vulgarly pert little girl in the street, she hugged Mrs. Grose more closely and buried in her skirts the dreadful little face. In this position she launched an almost furious wail. "Take me away, take me away—oh take me away from *her!*"

"From *me?*" I panted.

"From you—from you!" she cried.

Even Mrs. Grose looked across at me dismayed; while I had nothing to do but communicate again with the figure that, on the opposite bank, without a movement, as rigidly still as if catching, beyond the interval, our voices, was as vividly there for my disaster as it was not there for my service. The wretched child had spoken exactly as if she had got from some outside source each of her stabbing little words, and I could therefore, in the full despair of all I had to accept, but sadly shake my head at her. "If I had ever doubted all my doubt would at present have gone. I've been living with the miserable truth, and now it has only too much closed round me. Of course I've lost you: I've interfered, and you've seen, under *her* dictation"—with which I faced, over the pool again, our infernal witness—"the easy and perfect way to meet it. I've done my best, but I've lost you. Good-bye." For Mrs. Grose I had an imperative, an almost frantic "Go, go!" before which, in infinite distress, but mutely possessed of the little girl and clearly convinced, in spite of her blindness, that something awful had occurred and some collapse engulfed us, she retreated, by the way we had come, as fast as she could move.

Of what first happened when I was left alone I had no subsequent memory. I only knew that at the end of, I suppose, a quarter of an hour, an odorous dampness and roughness, chilling and piercing my trouble, had made me understand that I must have thrown myself, on my face, to the ground and given way to a wildness of grief. I must have lain there long and cried and wailed, for when I raised my head the day was almost done. I got up and looked a moment, through the twilight, at the grey pool and its blank haunted edge, and then I took, back to the house, my dreary and difficult course. When I reached the gate in the fence, the boat, to my surprise, was gone, so that I had a fresh reflexion to make on Flora's extraordinary command of the situation. She passed that night, by the most tacit and, I should add, were not the word so grotesque a false note, the happiest of arrangements, with Mrs. Grose. I saw neither of them on my return, but on the other hand I saw, as by an ambiguous compensation, a great deal of Miles.

* * * * * * * * * * * * * * *

CHAPTER XXIII.

[*Flora is sent away so she will no longer be under the influence of Miss Jessel, and the governess turns her at-*

*tention to Miles. Not only is she intent on learning about
the young boy's relationship with Peter Quint, but she
also is determined that the boy will answer questions he
has heretofore managed to avoid.*]

"Oh yes," he said with the brightest superficial eagerness, "you wanted me to tell you something."

"That's it. Out, straight out. What you have on your
mind, you know."

"Ah then is *that* what you've stayed over for?"

He spoke with a gaiety through which I could still
catch the finest little quiver of resentful passion; but I can't
begin to express the effect upon me of an implication of
surrender even so faint. It was as if what I had yearned
for had come at last only to astonish me. "Well, yes—I
may as well make a clean breast of it. It was precisely for
that."

He waited so long that I supposed it for the purpose of
repudiating the assumption on which my action had been
founded; but what he finally said was: "Do you mean
now—here?"

"There couldn't be a better place or time." He looked
round him uneasily, and I had the rare—oh the queer!—
impression of the very first symptom I had seen in him
of the approach of immediate fear. It was as if he were
suddenly afraid of me—which struck me indeed as perhaps
the best thing to make him. Yet in the very pang of the
effort I felt it vain to try sternness, and I heard myself
the next instant so gentle as to be almost grotesque. "You
want so to go out again?"

"Awfully!" He smiled at me heroically, and the touching little bravery of it was enhanced by his actually flush-
ing with pain. He had picked up his hat, which he had
brought in, and stood twirling it in a way that gave me,
even as I was just nearly reaching port, a perverse horror
of what I was doing. To do it in *any* way was an act of
violence, for what did it consist of but the obtrusion of the

idea of grossness and guilt on a small helpless creature who had been for me a revelation of the possibilities of beautiful intercourse? Wasn't it base to create for a being so exquisite a mere alien awkwardness? I suppose I now read into our situation a clearness it couldn't have had at the time, for I seem to see our poor eyes already lighted with some spark of a prevision of the anguish that was to come. So we circled about with terrors and scruples, fighters not daring to close. But it was for each other we feared! That kept us a little longer suspended and un-bruised. "I'll tell you everything," Miles said—"I mean I'll tell you anything you like. You'll stay on with me, and we shall both be all right, and I *will* tell you—I *will*. But not now."

"Why not now?"

My insistence turned him from me and kept him once more at his window in a silence during which, between us, you might have heard a pin drop. Then he was before me again with the air of a person for whom, outside, some one who had frankly to be reckoned with was waiting. "I have to see Luke."

I had not yet reduced him to quite so vulgar a lie, and I felt proportionately ashamed. But horrible as it was, his lies made up my truth. I achieved thoughtfully a few loops of my knitting. "Well then go to Luke, and I'll wait for what you promise. Only in return for that satisfy, before you leave me, one very much smaller request."

He looked as if he felt he had succeeded enough to be able still a little to bargain. "Very much smaller—?"

"Yes, a mere fraction of the whole. Tell me"—oh my work preoccupied me, and I was off-hand!—"if, yesterday afternoon from the table in the hall, you took, you know, my letter."

CHAPTER XXIV.

My grasp of how he received this suffered for a minute

from something that I can describe only as a fierce split of my attention—a stroke that at first, as I sprang straight up, reduced me to the mere blind movement of getting hold of him, drawing him close and, while I just fell for support against the nearest piece of furniture, instinctively keeping him with his back to the window. The appearance was full upon us that I had already had to deal with here: Peter Quint had come into view like a sentinel before a prison. Then next thing I saw was that, from outside, he had reached the window, and then I knew that, close to the glass and glaring in through it, he offered once more to the room his white face of damnation. It represents but grossly what took place within me at the sight to say that on the second my decision was made; yet I believe that no woman so overwhelmed ever in so short a time recovered her command of the *act*. It came to me in the very horror of the immediate presence that the act would be, seeing and facing what I saw and faced, to keep the boy himself unaware. The inspiration—I can call it by no other name —was that I felt how voluntarily, how transcendently, I *might*. It was like fighting with a demon for a human soul, and when I had fairly so appraised it I saw how the human soul—held out, in the tremor of my hands, at arms' length—had a perfect dew of sweat on a lovely childish forehead. The face that was close to mine was as white as the face against the glass, and out of it presently came a sound, not low or weak, but as if from much further away, that I drank like a waft of fragrance.

"Yes—I took it."

At this, with a moan of joy, I enfolded, I drew him close; and while I held him to my breast, where I could feel in the sudden fever of his little body the tremendous pulse of his little heart, I kept my eyes on the thing at the window and saw it move and shift its posture. I have likened it to a sentinel, but its slow wheel, for a moment, was rather the prowl of a baffled beast. My present quickened courage, however, was such that, not too much to let it through, I had to shade, as it were, my flame. Meanwhile the glare of the face was again at the window, the scoundrel fixed as if to watch and wait. It was the very confidence that I might now defy him, as well as the positive certitude, by this time, of the child's unconsciousness, that made me go on. "What did you take it for?"

"To see what you said about me."

"You opened the letter?"

"I opened it."

My eyes were now, as I held him off a little again, on Miles's own face, in which the collapse of mockery showed me how complete was the ravage of uneasiness. What was prodigious was that at last, by my success, his sense was sealed and his communication stopped: he knew that he was in presence, but knew not of what, and knew still less that I also was and that I did know. And what did this strain of trouble matter when my eyes went back to the window only to see that the air was clear again and—by my personal triumph—the influence quenched? There was nothing there. I felt that the cause was mine and that I should surely get *all*. "And you found nothing!"—I let my elation out.

He gave the most mournful, thoughtful little headshake. "Nothing."

"Nothing, nothing!" I almost shouted in my joy.

"Nothing, nothing," he sadly repeated.

I kissed his forehead; it was drenched. "So what have you done with it?"

"I've burnt it."

"Burnt it?" It was now or never. "Is that what you did at school?"

Oh what this brought up! "At school?"

"Did you take letters?—or other things?"

"Other things?" He appeared now to be thinking of something far off and that reached him only through the pressure of his anxiety. Yet it did reach him. "Did I *steal?*"

I felt myself redden to the roots of my hair as well as wonder if it were more strange to put to a gentleman such a question or to see him take it with allowances that gave the very distance of his fall in the world. "Was it for that you mightn't go back?"

The only thing he felt was rather a dreary little surprise. "Did you know I mightn't go back?"

"I know everything."

He gave me at this the longest and strangest look. "Everything?"

"Everything. Therefore *did* you—?" But I couldn't say it again.

Miles could, very simply. "No I didn't steal."

My face must have shown him I believed him utterly; yet my hands—but it was for pure tenderness—shook him as if to ask him why, if it was all for nothing, he had condemned me to months of torment. "What then did you do?"

He looked in vague pain all round the top of the room and drew his breath, two or three times over, as if with difficulty. He might have been standing at the bottom of the sea and raising his eyes to some faint green twilight. "Well—I said things."

"Only that?"

"They thought it was enough!"

"To turn you out for?"

Never, truly, had a person "turned out" shown so little to explain it as this little person! He appeared to weigh my question, but in a manner quite detached and almost helpless. "Well, I suppose I oughtn't."

"But to whom did you say them?"

He evidently tried to remember, but it dropped—he had lost it. "I don't know!"

He almost smiled at me in the desolation of his surrender, which was indeed practically, by this time, so complete that I ought to have left it there. But I was infatuated —I was blind with victory, though even then the very effect that was to have brought him so much nearer was already that of added separation. "Was it to every one?" I asked.

"No; it was only to——" But he gave a sick little head-shake. "I don't remember their names."

"Were they then so many?"

"No—only a few. Those I liked."

Those he liked? I seemed to float not into clearness, but into a darker obscure, and within a minute there had come to me out of my very pity the appalling alarm of his being perhaps innocent. It was for the instant confounding and bottomless, for if he *were* innocent what then on earth was I? Paralysed, while it lasted, by the mere brush of the question, I let him go a little, so that, with a deep-drawn sigh, he turned away from me again; which, as he faced toward the clear window, I suffered, feeling that I had nothing now there to keep him from. "And did they repeat what you said?" I went on after a moment.

He was soon at some distance from me, still breathing hard and again with the air, though now without anger for it, of being confined against his will. Once more, as he had done before, he looked up at the dim day as if, of what had hitherto sustained him, nothing was left but an unspeakable anxiety. "Oh yes," he nevertheless replied—"they must have repeated them. To those *they* liked," he added.

There was somehow less of it than I had expected; but I turned it over. "And these things came round—?"

"To the masters? Oh yes!" he answered very simply. "But I didn't know they'd tell."

"The masters? They didn't—they've never told. That's why I ask you."

He turned to me again his little beautiful fevered face. "Yes, it was too bad."

"Too bad?"

"What I suppose I sometimes said. To write home."

I can't name the exquisite pathos of the contradiction

given to such a speech by such a speaker; I only know that the next instant I heard myself throw off with homely force: "Stuff and nonsense!" But the next after that I must have sounded stern enough. "What *were* these things?"

My sternness was all for his judge, his executioner; yet it made him avert himself again, and that movement made *me,* with a single bound and an irrepressible cry, spring straight upon him. For there again, against the glass, as if to blight his confession and stay his answer, was the hideous author of our woe—the white face of damnation. I felt a sick swim at the drop of my victory and all the return of my battle, so that the wildness of my veritable leap only served as a great betrayal. I saw him, from the midst of my act, meet it with a divination, and on the perception that even now he only guessed, and that the window was still to his own eyes free, I let the impulse flame up to convert the climax of his dismay into the very proof of his liberation. "No more, no more, no more!" I shrieked to my visitant as I tried to press him against me.

"Is she *here?*" Miles panted as he caught with his sealed eyes in the direction of my words. Then as his strange "she" staggered me and, with a gasp, I echoed it, "Miss Jessel, Miss Jessel!" he with sudden fury gave me back.

I seized, stupefied, his supposition—some sequel to what we had done to Flora, but this made me only want to show him that it was better still than that. "It's not Miss Jessel! But it's at the window—straight before us. It's *there*—the coward horror, there for the last time!"

At this, after a second in which his head made the movement of a baffled dog's on a scent and then gave a frantic little shake for air and light, he was at me in a white rage, bewildered, glaring vainly over the place and missing wholly, though it now, to my sense, filled the room like the taste of poison, the wide overwhelming presence. "It's *he?*"

I was so determined to have all my proof that I flashed

into ice to challenge him. "Whom do you mean by 'he'?"

"Peter Quint—you devil!" His face gave again, round the room, its convulsed supplication. *"Where?"*

They are in my ears still, his supreme surrender of the name and his tribute to my devotion. "What does he matter now, my own?—what will he *ever* matter? *I* have you," I launched at the beast, "but he has lost you for ever!" Then for the demonstration of my work, "There, *there!*" I said to Miles.

But he had already jerked straight round, stared, glared again, and seen but the quiet day. With the stroke of the loss I was so proud of he uttered the cry of a creature hurled over an abyss, and the grasp with which I recovered him might have been that of catching him in his fall. I caught him, yes, I held him—it may be imagined with what a passion; but at the end of a minute I began to feel what it truly was that I held. We were alone with the quiet day, and his little heart, dispossessed, had stopped.

from

𝔚𝔦𝔢𝔩𝔞𝔫𝔡

𝔟𝔶 𝔒𝔥𝔞𝔯𝔩𝔢𝔰 𝔅𝔯𝔬𝔠𝔨𝔡𝔢𝔫 𝔅𝔯𝔬𝔴𝔫

[*Theodore Wieland, gripped with a religious mania akin to madness, is duped into thinking that the voice of God instructs him to kill his wife and children. Actually the voice is that of Carwin, a skilled ventriloquist. Wieland murders his family and is brought to trial. The following manuscript tells of these terrible events.*]

CHAPTER XIX.

Theodore Wieland, the prisoner at the bar, was now called upon for his defence. He looked around him for some time in silence, and with a mild countenance. At length he spoke:

"It is strange; I am known to my judges and my auditors. Who is there present a stranger to the character of Wieland? who knows him not as a husband—as a father—as a friend? yet here am I arraigned as a criminal. I am charged with diabolical malice; I am accused of the murder of my wife and children!

"It is true, they were slain by me; they all perished by

464

my hand. The task of vindication is ignoble. What is it that I am called to vindicate? and before whom?

"You know that they are dead, and that they were killed by me. What more would you have? Would you extort from me a statement of my motives? Have you failed to discover them already? You charge me with malice; but your eyes are not shut; your reason is still vigorous; your memory has not forsaken you. You know whom it is that you thus charge. The habits of his life are known to you; his treatment of his wife and his off-spring is known to you; the soundness of his integrity, and the unchangeableness of his principles, are familiar to your apprehension; yet you persist in this charge! You lead me hither manacled as a felon; you deem me worthy of a vile and tormenting death!

"Who are they whom I have devoted to death? My wife—the little ones, that drew their being from me—that creature who, as she surpassed them in excellence, claimed a larger affection than those whom natural affinities bound to my heart. Think ye that malice could have urged me to this deed? Hide your audacious fronts from the scrutiny of heaven. Take refuge in some cavern unvisited by human eyes. Ye may deplore your wickedness or folly, but ye cannot expiate it.

"Think not that I speak for your sakes. Hug to your hearts this detestable infatuation. Deem me still a murderer, and drag me to untimely death. I make not an effort to dispel your illusion: I utter not a word to cure you of your sanguinary folly: but there are probably some in this assembly who have come from far: for their sakes, whose distance has disabled them from knowing me, I will tell what I have done, and why.

"It is needless to say that God is the object of my supreme passion. I have cherished, in his presence, a single and upright heart. I have thirsted for the knowledge of his will. I have burnt with ardour to approve my faith and my obedience.

"My days have been spent in searching for the revelation of that will; but my days have been mournful, because my search failed. I solicited direction: I turned on every side where glimmerings of light could be discovered. I have not been wholly uninformed; but my knowledge has always stopped short of certainty. Dissatisfaction has insinuated itself into all my thoughts. My purposes have been pure; my wishes indefatigable; but not till lately were these purposes thoroughly accomplished, and these wishes fully gratified.

"I thank thee, my father, for thy bounty; that thou didst not ask a less sacrifice than this; that thou placedst me in a condition to testify my submission to thy will! What have I withheld which it was thy pleasure to exact? Now may I, with dauntless and erect eye, claim my reward, since I have given thee the treasure of my soul.

"I was at my own house: it was late in the evening: my sister had gone to the city, but proposed to return. It was in expectation of her return that my wife and I delayed going to bed beyond the usual hour; the rest of the family, however, were retired.

"My mind was contemplative and calm; not wholly devoid of apprehension on account of my sister's safety. Recent events, not easily explained, had suggested the existence of some danger; but this danger was without a distinct form in our imagination, and scarcely ruffled our tranquility.

"Time passed, and my sister did not arrive; her house is at some distance from mine, and though her arrangements had been made with a view to residing with us, it was possible that, through forgetfulness, or the occurrence of unforeseen emergencies, she had returned to her own dwelling.

"Hence it was conceived proper that I should ascertain the truth by going thither. I went. On my way my mind was full of these ideas which related to my intellectual condition. In the torrent of fervid conceptions, I lost sight of my purpose. Some times I stood still; some times I wandered from my path, and experienced some difficulty, on recovering from my fit of musing, to regain it.

"The series of my thoughts is easily traced. At first every vein beat with raptures known only to the man whose parental and conjugal love is without limits, and the cup of whose desires, immense as it is, overflows with gratification. I know not why emotions that were perpetual visitants should now have recurred with unusual energy. The transition was not new from sensations of joy to a consciousness of gratitude. The author of my being was likewise the dispenser of every gift with which that being was embellished. The service to which a benefactor like this was entitled, could not be circumscribed. My social sentiments were indebted to their alliance with devotion for all their value. All passions are base, all joys feeble, all energies malignant, which are not drawn from this source.

"For a time, my contemplations soared above earth and its inhabitants. I stretched forth my hands; I lifted my eyes, and exclaimed, O! that I might be admitted to thy presence; that mine were the supreme delight of knowing thy will, and of performing it! The blissful privilege of direct communication with thee, and of listening to the audible enunciation of thy pleasure!

"What task would I not undertake, what privation would I not cheerfully endure, to testify my love of thee? Alas! thou hidest thyself from my view: glimpses only of thy excellence and beauty are afforded me. Would that a momentary emanation from thy glory would visit me! that some unambiguous token of thy presence would salute my senses!

"In this mood, I entered the house of my sister. It was vacant. Scarcely had I regained recollection of the purpose that brought me hither. Thoughts of a different tendency had such absolute possession of my mind, that the relations of time and space were almost obliterated from my understanding. These wanderings, however, were restrained, and I ascended to her chamber.

"I had no light, and might have known by external observation, that the house was without any inhabitant. With this, however, I was not satisfied. I entered the room, and the object of my search not appearing, I prepared to return.

"The darkness required some caution in descending the stair. I stretched my hand to seize the balustrade by which I might regulate my steps. How shall I describe the lustre, which, at that moment, burst upon my vision!

"I was dazzled. My organs were bereaved of their activity. My eye-lids were half-closed, and my hands withdrawn from the balustrade. A nameless fear chilled my veins, and I stood motionless. This irradiation did not retire or lessen. It seemed as if some powerful effulgence covered me like a mantle.

"I opened my eyes and found all about me luminous and glowing. It was the element of heaven that flowed around. Nothing but a fiery stream was at first visible; but, anon, a shrill voice from behind called upon me to attend.

"I turned: It is forbidden to describe what I saw: Words, indeed, would be wanting to the task. The lineaments of that being, whose veil was now lifted, and whose visage beamed upon my sight, no hues of pencil or of language can pourtray.

"As it spoke, the accents thrilled to my heart. 'Thy prayers are heard. In proof of thy faith, render me thy wife. This is the victim I chuse. Call her hither, and here let her fall.'—The sound, and visage, and light vanished at once.

"What demand was this? The blood of Catharine was to be shed! My wife was to perish by my hand! I sought opportunity to attest my virtue. Little did I expect that a proof like this would have been demanded.

"My wife! I exclaimed: O God! substitute some other

victim. Make me not the butcher of my wife. My own blood is cheap. This will I pour out before thee with a willing heart; but spare, I beseech thee, this precious life, or commission some other than her husband to perform the bloody deed.

"In vain. The conditions were prescribed; the decree had gone forth, and nothing remained but to execute it. I rushed out of the house and across the intermediate fields, and stopped not till I entered my own parlour.

"My wife had remained here during my absence, in anxious expectation of my return with some tidings of her sister. I had none to communicate. For a time, I was breathless with my speed: This, and the tremors that shook my frame, and the wildness of my looks, alarmed her. She immediately suspected some disaster to have happened to her friend, and her own speech was as much overpowered by emotion as mine.

"She was silent, but her looks manifested her impatience to hear what I had to communicate. I spoke, but with so much precipitation as scarcely to be understood; catching her, at the same time, by the arm, and forcibly pulling her from her seat.

" 'Come along with me: fly: waste not a moment: time will be lost, and the deed will be omitted. Tarry not; question not; but fly with me!'

"This deportment added afresh to her alarms. Her eyes pursued mine, and she said, 'What is the matter? For God's sake what is the matter? Where would you have me go?'

"My eyes were fixed upon her countenance while she spoke. I thought upon her virtues; I viewed her as the mother of my babes; as my wife: I recalled the purpose for which I thus urged her attendance. My heart faltered, and I saw that I must rouse to this work all my faculties. The danger of the least delay was imminent.

"I looked away from her, and again exerting my force,

drew her towards the door—'You must go with me—indeed you must.'

"In her fright she half-resisted my efforts, and again exclaimed, 'Good heaven! what is it you mean? Where go? What has happened? Have you found Clara?'

" 'Follow me, and you will see,' I answered, still urging her reluctant steps forward.

" 'What phrenzy has seized you? Something must needs have happened. Is she sick? Have you found her?'

" 'Come and see. Follow me, and know for yourself.'

"Still she expostulated and besought me to explain this mysterious behaviour. I could not trust myself to answer her; to look at her; but grasping her arm, I drew her after me. She hesitated, rather through confusion of mind than from unwillingness to accompany me. This confusion gradually abated, and she moved forward, but with irresolute footsteps, and continual exclamations of wonder and terror. Her interrogations of 'what was the matter?' and 'whither was I going?' were ceaseless and vehement.

"It was the scope of my efforts not to think; to keep up a conflict and uproar in my mind in which all order and distinctness should be lost; to escape from the sensations produced by her voice. I was, therefore, silent. I strove to abridge this interval by my haste, and to waste all my attention in furious gesticulations.

"In this state of mind we reached my sister's door. She looked at the windows and saw that all was desolate—'Why come we here? There is no body here. I will not go in.'

"Still I was dumb; but opening the door, I drew her into the entry. This was the allotted scene: here she was to fall. I let go her hand, and pressing my palms against my forehead, made one mighty effort to work up my soul to the deed.

"In vain; it would not be; my courage was appalled;

my arms nerveless: I muttered prayers that my strength might be aided from above. They availed nothing.

"Horror diffused itself over me. This conviction of my cowardice, my rebellion, fastened upon me, and I stood rigid and cold as marble. From this state I was somewhat relieved by my wife's voice, who renewed her supplications to be told why we came hither, and what was the fate of my sister.

"What could I answer? My words were broken and inarticulate. Her fears naturally acquired force from the observation of these symptoms; but these fears were misplaced. The only inference she deduced from my conduct was, that some terrible mishap had befallen Clara.

"She wrung her hands, and exclaimed in an agony, "O tell me, where is she? What has become of her? Is she sick? Dead? Is she in her chamber? O let me go thither and know the worst!"

"This proposal set my thoughts once more in motion. Perhaps what my rebellious heart refused to perform here, I might obtain strength enough to execute elsewhere.

"'Come then,' said I, 'let us go.'

"'I will, but not in the dark. We must first procure a light.'

"'Fly and procure it; but I charge you, linger not. I will await your return.'

"While she was gone, I strode along the entry. The fellness of a gloomy hurricane but faintly resembled the discord that reigned in my mind. To omit this sacrifice must not be; yet my sinews had refused to perform it. No alternative was offered. To rebel against the mandate was impossible; but obedience would render me the executioner of my wife. My will was strong, but my limbs refused their office.

"She returned with a light; I led the way to the chamber; she looked round her; she lifted the curtain of the bed; she saw nothing.

"At length, she fixed inquiring eyes upon me. The light now enabled her to discover in my visage what darkness had hitherto concealed. Her cares were now transferred from my sister to myself, and she said in a tremulous voice, 'Wieland! you are not well: What ails you? Can I do nothing for you?'

"That accents and looks so winning should disarm me of my resolution, was to be expected. My thoughts were thrown anew into anarchy. I spread my hand before my eyes that I might not see her, and answered only by groans. She took my other hand between hers, and pressing it to my heart, spoke with that voice which had ever swayed my will, and wafted away sorrow.

" 'My friend! my soul's friend! tell me thy cause of grief. Do I not merit to partake with thee in thy cares? Am I not thy wife?'

"This was too much. I broke from her embrace, and retired to a corner of the room. In this pause, courage was once more infused into me. I resolved to execute my duty. She followed me, and renewed her passionate entreaties to know the cause of my distress.

"I raised my head and regarded her with stedfast looks. I muttered something about death, and the injunctions of my duty. At these words she shrunk back, and looked at me with a new expression of anguish. After a pause, she clasped her hands, and exclaimed—

" 'O Wieland! Wieland! God grant that I am mistaken; but surely something is wrong. I see it: it is too plain; thou art undone—lost to me and to thyself.' At the same time she gazed on my features with intensest anxiety, in hope that different symptoms would take place. I replied to her with vehemence—

" 'Undone! No; my duty is known, and I thank my God that my cowardice is now vanquished, and I have power to fulfil it. Catharine! I pity the weakness of thy nature: I pity thee, but must not spare. Thy life is claimed from my hands: thou must die!'

"Fear was now added to her grief. 'What mean you? Why talk you of death? Bethink yourself, Wieland: bethink yourself, and this fit will pass. O why came I hither! Why did you drag me hither?'

" 'I brought thee hither to fulfil a divine command. I am appointed thy destroyer, and destroy thee I must.' Saying this I seized her wrists. She shrieked aloud, and endeavoured to free herself from my grasp; but her efforts were in vain.

" 'Surely, surely Wieland, thou dost not mean it. Am I not thy wife? and wouldst thou kill me? Thou wilt not; and yet—I see—thou art Wieland no longer! A fury resistless and horrible possesses thee—Spare me—spare—help—help——'

"Till her breath was stopped she shrieked for help—for mercy. When she could speak no longer, her gestures, her looks appealed to my compassion. My accursed hand was irresolute and tremulous. I meant thy death to be sudden, thy struggles to be brief. Alas! my heart was infirm; my resolves mutable. Thrice I slackened my grasp, and life kept its hold, though in the midst of pangs. Her eye-balls started from their sockets. Grimness and distortion took place of all that used to bewitch me into transport, and subdue me into reverence.

"I was commissioned to kill thee, but not to torment thee with the foresight of thy death; not to multiply thy fears, and prolong thy agonies. Haggard, and pale, and lifeless, at length thou ceasedst to contend with thy destiny.

"This was a moment of triumph. Thus had I successfully subdued the stubbornness of human passions: the victim which had been demanded was given: the deed was done past recal.

"I lifted the corpse in my arms and laid it on the bed. I gazed upon it with delight. Such was the elation of my thoughts, that I even broke into laughter. I clapped my hands and exclaimed, 'It is done! My sacred duty is fulfilled! To that I have sacrificed, O my God! thy last and best gift, my wife!'

"For a while I thus soared above frailty. I imagined I had set myself forever beyond the reach of selfishness; but my imaginations were false. This rapture quickly subsided. I looked again at my wife. My joyous ebullitions vanished, and I asked myself who it was whom I saw. Methought it could not be Catharine. It could not be the woman who had lodged for years in my heart; who had slept nightly, in my bosom; who had borne in her womb, who had fostered at her breast, the beings who called me father; whom I had watched with delight, and cherished with a fondness ever new and perpetually growing: it could not be the same.

"Where was her bloom! These deadly and blood-suffused orbs but ill resemble the azure and exstatic tenderness of her eyes. The lucid stream that meandered over that bosom, the flow of love that was wont to sit upon that cheek, are much unlike these livid stains and this hideous deformity. Alas! these were the traces of agony; the gripe of the assassin had been here!

"I will not dwell upon my lapse into desperate and outrageous sorrow. The breath of heaven that sustained me was withdrawn, and I sunk into *mere man*. I leaped from the floor: I dashed my head against the wall: I uttered screams of horror: I panted after torment and pain. Eternal fire, and the bickerings of hell, compared with what I felt, were music and a bed of roses.

"I thank my God that this degeneracy was transient, that he designed once more to raise me aloft. I thought upon what I had done as a sacrifice to duty, and *was calm*. My wife was dead; but I reflected, that though this source of human consolation was closed, yet others were still open. If the transports of an husband were no more, the feelings of a father had still scope for exercise. When remembrance of their mother should excite too keen a pang, I would look upon them, and *be comforted*.

"While I revolved these ideas, new warmth flowed in upon my heart—I was wrong. These feelings were the growth of selfishness. Of this I was not aware, and to dispel the mist that obscured my perceptions, a new effulgence and a new mandate were necessary.

"From these thoughts I was recalled by a ray that was shot into the room. A voice spake like that which I had before heard—'Thou hast done well; but all is not done—the sacrifice is incomplete—thy children must be offered—they must perish with their mother!——' "

Sredni Vashtar

by Saki

Conradin was ten years old, and the doctor had pronounced his professional opinion that the boy would not
live another five years. The doctor was silky and effete, and
counted for little, but his opinion was endorsed by Mrs.
De Ropp, who counted for nearly everything. Mrs. De
Ropp was Conradin's cousin and guardian, and in his
eyes she represented those three-fifths of the world that
are necessary and disagreeable and real; the other two-
fifths, in perpetual antagonism to the foregoing, were
summed up in himself and his imagination. One of these
days Conradin supposed he would succumb to the master-
ing pressure of wearisome necessary things—such as ill-
nesses and coddling restrictions and drawn-out dulness.
Without his imagination, which was rampant under the
spur of loneliness, he would have succumbed long ago.

Mrs. De Ropp would never, in her honestest moments,
have confessed to herself that she disliked Conradin,
though she might have been dimly aware that thwarting
him "for his good" was a duty which she did not find
particularly irksome. Conradin hated her with a desperate

sincerity which he was perfectly able to mask. Such few pleasures as he could contrive for himself gained an added relish from the likelihood that they would be displeasing to his guardian, and from the realm of his imagination she was locked out—an unclean thing, which should find no entrance.

In the dull, cheerless garden, overlooked by so many windows that were ready to open with a message not to do this or that, or a reminder that medicines were due, he found little attraction. The few fruit-trees that it contained were set jealously apart from his plucking, as though they were rare specimens of their kind blooming in an arid waste; it would probably have been difficult to find a market-gardener who would have offered ten shillings for their entire yearly produce. In a forgotten corner, however, almost hidden behind a dismal shrubbery, was a disused tool-shed of respectable proportions, and within its walls Conradin found a haven, something that took on the varying aspects of a playroom and a cathedral. He had peopled it with a legion of familiar phantoms, evoked partly from fragments of history and partly from his own brain, but it also boasted two inmates of flesh and blood. In one corner lived a ragged-plumaged Houdan hen, on which the boy lavished an affection that had scarcely another outlet. Further back in the gloom stood a large hutch, divided into two compartments, one of which was fronted with close iron bars. This was the abode of a large polecat-ferret, which a friendly butcher-boy had once smuggled, cage and all, into its present quarters, in exchange for a long-secreted hoard of small silver. Conradin was dreadfully afraid of the lithe, sharp-fanged beast, but it was his most treasured possession. Its very presence in the tool-shed was a secret and fearful joy, to be kept scrupulously from the knowledge of the Woman, as he privately dubbed his cousin. And one day, out of Heaven knows what material, he spun the beast a wonderful name, and from that moment it grew into a god and a religion.

The Woman indulged in religion once a week at a church near by, and took Conradin with her, but to him the church service was an alien rite in the House of Rimmon. Every Thursday, in the dim and musty silence of the toolshed, he worshipped with mystic and elaborate ceremonial before the wooden hutch where dwelt Sredni Vashtar, the great ferret. Red flowers in their season and scarlet berries in the winter-time were offered at his shrine, for he was a god who laid some special stress on the fierce impatient side of things, as opposed to the Woman's religion, which, as far as Conradin could observe, went to great lengths in the contrary direction. And on great festivals powdered nutmeg was strewn in front of his hutch, an important feature of the offering being that nutmeg had to be stolen. These festivals were of irregular occurrence, and were chiefly appointed to celebrate some passing event. On one occasion, when Mrs. De Ropp suffered from acute toothache for three days, Conradin kept up the festival during the entire three days, and almost succeeded in persuading himself that Sredni Vashtar was personally responsible for the toothache. If the malady had lasted for another day the supply of nutmeg would have given out.

The Houdan hen was never drawn into the cult of Sredni Vashtar. Conradin had long ago settled that she was an Anabaptist. He did not pretend to have the remotest knowledge as to what an Anabaptist was, but he privately hoped that it was dashing and not very respectable. Mrs. De Ropp was the ground plan on which he based and detested all respectability.

After a while Conradin's absorption in the tool-shed began to attract the notice of his guardian. "It is not good for him to be pottering down there in all weathers," she promptly decided, and at breakfast one morning she announced that the Houdan hen had been sold and taken away overnight. With her short-sighted eyes she peered at Conradin, waiting for an outbreak of rage and sorrow, which she was ready to rebuke with a flow of excellent precepts and reasoning. But Conradin said nothing: there was nothing to be said. Something perhaps in his white set face gave her a momentary qualm, for at tea that afternoon there was toast on the table, a delicacy which she usually banned on the ground that it was bad for him; also because the making of it "gave trouble," a deadly offence in the middle-class feminine eye.

"I thought you liked toast," she exclaimed, with an injured air, observing that he did not touch it.

"Sometimes," said Conradin.

In the shed that evening there was an innovation in the worship of the hutch-god. Conradin had been wont to chant his praises, tonight he asked a boon.

"Do one thing for me, Sredni Vashtar."

The thing was not specified. As Sredni Vashtar was a god he must be supposed to know. And choking back a sob as he looked at that other empty corner, Conradin went back to the world he so hated.

And every night, in the welcome darkness of his bedroom, and every evening in the dusk of the tool-shed, Conradin's bitter litany went up: "Do one thing for me, Sredni Vashtar."

Mrs. De Ropp noticed that the visits to the shed did not cease, and one day she made a further journey of inspection.

"What are you keeping in that locked hutch?" she asked. "I believe it's guinea-pigs. I'll have them all cleared away."

Conradin shut his lips tight, but the Woman ransacked his bedroom till she found the carefully hidden key, and forthwith marched down to the shed to complete her discovery. It was a cold afternoon, and Conradin had been bidden to keep to the house. From the furthest window of the dining-room the door of the shed could just be seen beyond the corner of the shrubbery, and there Conradin stationed himself. He saw the Woman enter, and then he imagined her opening the door of the sacred hutch and peering down with her short-sighted eyes into the thick straw bed where his god lay hidden. Perhaps she would prod at the straw in her clumsy impatience. And Conradin fervently breathed his prayer for the last time. But he knew as he prayed that he did not believe. He knew that the Woman would come out presently with that pursed smile he loathed so well on her face, and that in an hour or two the gardener would carry away his wonderful god, a god no longer, but a simple brown ferret in a hutch. And he knew that the Woman would triumph always as she triumphed now, and that he would grow ever more sickly under her pestering and domineering and superior wisdom, till one day nothing would matter much more with him, and the doctor would be proved right. And in the sting and misery of his defeat, he began to chant loudly and defiantly the hymn of his threatened idol:

Sredni Vashtar went forth,
His thoughts were red thoughts and his teeth were white.
His enemies called for peace, but he brought them death.
Sredni Vashtar the Beautiful.

An then of a sudden he stopped his chanting and drew closer to the window-pane. The door of the shed still stood ajar as it had been left, and the minutes were slipping by. They were long minutes, but they slipped by nevertheless. He watched the starlings running and flying in little parties across the lawn; he counted them over and over again, with one eye always on that swinging door. A sour-faced maid came in to lay the table for tea, and still Conradin stood and waited and watched. Hope had crept by inches into his heart, and now a look of triumph began to blaze in his eyes that had only known the wistful patience of defeat. Under his breath, with a furtive exultation, he began once again the pæan of victory and devastation. And presently his eyes were rewarded: out through that doorway came a long, low, yellow-and-brown beast, with eyes a-blink at the waning daylight, and dark wet stains around the fur of jaws and throat. Conradin dropped on his knees. The great polecat-ferret made its way down to a small brook at the foot of the garden, drank for a moment, then crossed a little plank bridge and was lost to sight in the bushes. Such was the passing of Sredni Vashtar.

"Tea is ready," said the sour-faced maid; "where is the mistress?"

"She went down to the shed some time ago," said Conradin.

And while the maid went to summon her mistress to tea, Conrad fished a toasting-fork out of the sideboard drawer and proceeded to toast himself a piece of bread. And during the toasting of and the buttering of it with much butter and the slow enjoyment of eating it, Conradin listened to the noises and silences which fell in quick spasms beyond the dining-room door. The loud foolish screaming of the maid, the answering chorus of wondering ejaculations from the kitchen region, the scuttering footsteps and hurried embassies for outside help, and then, after a lull, the scared sobbings and the shuffling tread of those who bore a heavy burden into the house.

"Whoever will break it to the poor child? I couldn't for the life of me!" exclaimed a shrill voice. And while they debated the matter among themselves, Conradin made himself another piece of toast.

The Yellow Wall Paper

by Charlotte Perkins Gilman

It is very seldom that mere ordinary people like John and myself secure ancestral halls for the summer.

A colonial mansion, a hereditary estate, I would say a haunted house, and reach the height of romantic felicity —but that would be asking too much of fate!

Still I will proudly declare that there is something queer about it.

Else, why should it be let so cheaply? And why have stood so long untenanted?

John laughs at me, of course, but one expects that in marriage.

John is practical in the extreme. He has no patience with faith, an intense horror of superstition, and he scoffs openly at any talk of things not to be felt and seen and put down in figures.

John is a physician, and *perhaps*—(I would not say it to a living soul, of course, but this is dead paper and a great relief to my mind)—*perhaps* that is one reason I do not get well faster.

You see, he does not believe I am sick! And what can one do?

If a physician of high standing, and one's own husband, assures friends and relatives that there is really nothing the matter with one but temporary nervous depression—a slight hysterical tendency—what is one to do?

My brother is also a physician, and also of high standing, and he says the same thing.

So I take phosphates or phosphites—whichever it is —and tonics, and journeys, and air, and exercise, and am absolutely forbidden to "work" until I am well again.

Personally, I disagree with their ideas.

Personally, I believe that congenial work, with excitement and change, would do me good.

But what is one to do?

I did write for a while in spite of them; but it *does* exhaust me a good deal—having to be so sly about it, or else meet with heavy opposition.

I sometimes fancy that in my condition if I had less opposition and more society and stimulus—but John says the very worst thing I can do is to think about my condition, and I confess it always makes me feel bad.

So I will let it alone and talk about the house.

The most beautiful place! It is quite alone, standing well back from the road, quite three miles from the village. It makes me think of English places that you read about, for there are hedges and walls and gates that lock, and lots of separate little houses for the gardeners and people.

There is a *delicious* garden! I never saw such a garden —large and shady, full of box-bordered paths, and lined with long grape-covered arbors with seats under them.

There were two greenhouses, too, but they are all broken now.

There was some legal trouble, I believe, something about the heirs and co-heirs; anyhow, the place has been empty for years.

That spoils my ghostliness, I am afraid, but I don't care

—there is something strange about the house—I can feel it.

I even said so to John one moonlight evening, but he said what I felt was a draught, and shut the window.

I get unreasonably angry with John sometimes. I'm sure I never used to be so sensitive. I think it is due to this nervous condition.

But John says if I feel so I shall neglect proper self-control; so I take pains to control myself—before him, at least—and that makes me very tired.

I don't like our room a bit. I wanted one downstairs that opened on the piazza and had roses all over the window, and such pretty old-fashioned chintz hangings! But John would not hear of it.

He said there was only one window and not room for two beds, and no near room for him if he took another.

He is very careful and loving, and hardly lets me stir without special direction.

I have a schedule prescription for each hour in the day; he takes all care from me, and so I feel basely ungrateful not to value it more.

He said we came here solely on my account, that I was to have perfect rest and all the air I could get. "Your exercise depends on your strength, my dear," said he, "and your food somewhat on your appetite; but air you can absorb all the time." So we took the nursery at the top of the house.

It is a big, airy room, the whole floor nearly, with windows that look all ways, and air and sunshine galore. It was nursery first and then playroom and gymnasium, I should judge; for the windows are barred for little children, and there are rings and things in the walls.

The paint and paper look as if a boys' school had used it. It is stripped off—the paper—in great patches all around the head of my bed, about as far as I can reach, and in a great place on the other side of the room low down. I never saw a worse paper in my life.

One of those sprawling flamboyant patterns committing every artistic sin.

It is dull enough to confuse the eye in following, pronounced enough constantly to irritate and provoke study, and when you follow the lame uncertain curves for a little distance they suddenly commit suicide—plunge off at outrageous angles, destroy themselves in unheard-of contradictions.

The color is repellent, almost revolting; a smouldering unclean yellow, strangely faded by the slow-turning sunlight.

It is a dull yet lurid orange in some places, a sickly sulphur tint in others.

No wonder the children hated it! I should hate it myself if I had to live in this room long.

There comes John, and I must put this away—he hates to have me write a word.

* * * * * * * * * * * * * * * *

We have been here two weeks, and I haven't felt like writing before, since the first day.

I am sitting by the window now, up in this atrocious nursery, and there is nothing to hinder my writing as much as I please, save lack of strength.

John is away all day, and even some nights when his cases are serious.

I am glad my case is not serious!

But these nervous troubles are dreadfully depressing.

John does not know how much I really suffer. He knows there is no *reason* to suffer, and that satisfies him.

Of course it is only nervousness. It does weigh on me so not to do my duty in any way!

I meant to be such a help to John, such a real rest and comfort, and here I am a comparative burden already!

Nobody would believe what an effort it is to do what little I am able—to dress and entertain, and order things.

It is fortunate Mary is so good with the baby. Such a dear baby!

And yet I *cannot* be with him, it makes me so nervous.

I suppose John never was nervous in his life. He laughs at me so about this wall paper!

At first he meant to repaper the room, but afterwards he said that I was letting it get the better of me, and that nothing was worse for a nervous patient than to give way to such fancies.

He said that after the wall paper was changed it would be the heavy bedstead, and then the barred windows, and then that gate at the head of the stairs, and so on.

"You know the place is doing you good," he said, "and really, dear, I don't care to renovate the house just for a three months' rental."

"Then do let us go downstairs," I said, "there are such pretty rooms there."

Then he took me in his arms and called me a blessed little goose, and said he would go down cellar, if I wished, and have it whitewashed into the bargain.

But he is right enough about the beds and windows and things.

It is as airy and comfortable a room as any one need wish, and, of course, I would not be so silly as to make him uncomfortable just for a whim.

I'm really getting quite fond of the big room, all but that horrid paper.

Out of one window I can see the garden, those mysterious deep-shaded arbors, the riotous old-fashioned flowers, and bushes and gnarly trees.

Out of another I get a lovely view of the bay and a little private wharf belonging to the estate. There is a beautiful shaded lane that runs down there from the house. I always fancy I see people walking in these numerous paths and arbors, but John has cautioned me not to give way to fancy in the least. He says that with my imaginative power and habit of story-making, a nervous weakness like mine is sure to lead to all manner of excited fancies, and that I ought to use my will and good sense to check the tendency. So I try.

I think sometimes that if I were only well enough to write a little it would relieve the press of ideas and rest me.

But I find I get pretty tired when I try.

It is so discouraging not to have any advice and companionship about my work. When I get really well, John says we will ask Cousin Henry and Julia down for a long visit; but he says he would as soon put fireworks in my pillowcase as to let me have those stimulating people about now.

I wish I could get well faster.

But I must not think about that. This paper looks to me as if it *knew* what vicious influence it had!

There is a recurrent spot where the pattern lolls like a broken neck and two bulbous eyes stare at you upside down.

I get positively angry with the impertinence of it and the everlastingness. Up and down and sideways they crawl, and those absurd, unblinking eyes are everywhere. There is one place where two breadths didn't match, and the eyes go all up and down the line, one a little higher than the other.

I never saw so much expression in an inanimate thing before, and we all know how much expression they have! I used to lie awake as a child and get more entertainment and terror out of blank walls and plain furniture than most children could find in a toy-store.

I remember what a kindly wink the knobs of our big, old bureau used to have, and there was one chair that always seemed like a strong friend.

I used to feel that if any of the other things looked too fierce I could always hop into that chair and be safe.

The furniture in this room is not worse than inharmonious, however, for we had to bring it all from downstairs. I suppose when this was used as a playroom they had to take the nursery things out, and no wonder! I never saw such ravages as the children have made here.

The wall paper, as I said before, is torn off in spots, and it sticketh closer than a brother—they must have had perseverance as well as hatred.

Then the floor is scratched and gouged and splintered, the plaster itself is dug out here and there, and this great heavy bed, which is all we found in the room, looks as if it had been through the wars.

But I don't mind a bit—only the paper.

There comes John's sister. Such a dear girl as she is, and so careful of me! I must not let her find me writing.

She is a perfect and enthusiastic housekeeper, and hopes for no better profession. I verily believe she thinks it is the writing which made me sick!

But I can write when she is out, and see her a long way off from these windows.

There is one that commands the road, a lovely shaded winding road, and one that just looks off over the country. A lovely country, too, full of great elms and velvet meadows.

This wall paper has a kind of sub-pattern in a different shade, a particularly irritating one, for you can only see it in certain lights, and not clearly then.

But in the places where it isn't faded and where the sun is just so—I can see a strange, provoking, formless sort of figure, that seems to skulk about behind that silly and conspicuous front design.

There's sister on the stairs!

*   *   *   *   *   *   *   *   *   *   *   *   *   *   *   *

Well, the Fourth of July is over! The people are all gone and I am tired out. John thought it might do me good to see a little company, so we just had mother and Nellie and the children down for a week.

Of course I didn't do a thing. Jennie sees to everything now.

But it tired me all the same.

John says if I don't pick up faster he shall send me to Weir Mitchell in the fall.

But I don't want to go there at all. I had a friend who was in his hands once, and she says he is just like John and my brother, only more so!

Besides, it is such an undertaking to go so far.

I don't feel as if it was worth while to turn my hand over for anything, and I'm getting dreadfully fretful and querulous.

I cry at nothing, and cry most of the time.

Of course I don't when John is here, or anybody else, but when I am alone.

And I am alone a good deal just now. John is kept in town very often by serious cases, and Jennie is good and lets me alone when I want her to.

So I walk a little in the garden or down that lovely lane, sit on the porch under the roses, and lie down up here a good deal.

I'm getting really fond of the room in spite of the wall paper. Perhaps *because* of the wall paper.

It dwells in my mind so!

I lie here on this great immovable bed—it is nailed down, I believe—and follow that pattern about by the hour. It is as good as gymnastics, I assure you. I start, we'll say, at the bottom, down in the corner over there where it has not been touched, and I determine for the thousandth time that I *will* follow that pointless pattern to some sort of conclusion.

I know a little of the principle of design, and I know this thing was not arranged on any laws of radiation, or alternation, or repetition, or symmetry, or anything else that I ever heard of.

It is repeated, of course, by the breadths, but not otherwise.

Looked at in one way each breadth stands alone, the bloated curves and flourishes—a kind of "debased Romanesque" with delirium tremens—go waddling up and down in isolated columns of fatuity.

But, on the other hand, they connect diagonally, and the sprawling outlines run off in great slanting waves of optic horror, like a lot of wallowing sea-weeds in full chase.

The whole thing goes horizontally, too, at least it seems so, and I exhaust myself trying to distinguish the order of its going in that direction.

They have used a horizontal breadth for a frieze, and that adds wonderfully to the confusion.

There is one end of the room where it is almost intact, and there, when the cross-lights fade and the low sun shines directly upon it, I can almost fancy radiation after all,—the interminable grotesques seem to form around a common centre and rush off in headlong plunges of equal distraction.

It makes me tired to follow it. I will take a nap, I guess.

*   *   *   *   *   *   *   *   *   *   *   *   *   *   *   *

I don't know why I should write this.

I don't want to.

I don't feel able.

And I know John would think it absurd. But I *must* say what I feel and think in some way—it is such a relief!

But the effort is getting to be greater than the relief.

Half the time now I am awfully lazy, and lie down ever so much.

John says I mustn't lose my strength, and has me take cod liver oil and lots of tonics and things, to say nothing of ale and wine and rare meat.

Dear John! He loves me very dearly, and hates to have me sick. I tried to have a real earnest reasonable talk with him the other day, and tell him how I wish he would let me go and make a visit to Cousin Henry and Julia.

But he said I wasn't able to go, nor able to stand it after I got there; and I did not make out a very good case for myself, for I was crying before I had finished.

It is getting to be a great effort for me to think straight. Just this nervous weakness, I suppose.

And dear John gathered me up in his arms, and just carried me upstairs and laid me on the bed, and sat by me and read to me till it tired my head.

He said I was his darling and his comfort and all he had, and that I must take care of myself for his sake, and keep well.

He says no one but myself can help me out of it, that I must use my will and self-control and not let any silly fancies run away with me.

There's one comfort, the baby is well and happy, and does not have to occupy this nursery with the horrid wall paper.

If we had not used it, that blessed child would have! What a fortunate escape! Why, I wouldn't have a child of mine, an impressionable little thing, live in such a room for worlds.

I never thought of it before, but it is lucky that John kept me here, after all. I can stand it so much easier than a baby, you see.

Of course I never mention it to them any more—I am too wise—but I keep watch for it all the same.

There are things in that paper that nobody knows but me, or ever will.

Behind that outside pattern the dim shapes get clearer every day.

It is always the same shape, only very numerous.

And it is like a woman stooping down and creeping about behind that pattern. I don't like it a bit. I wonder —I begin to think—I wish John would take me away from here!

* * * * * * * * * * * * * * *

It is hard to talk with John about my case, because he is so wise, and because he loves me so.

But I tried it last night.

It was moonlight. The moon shines in all around just as the sun does.

I hate to see it sometimes, it creeps so slowly, and always comes in by one window or another.

John was asleep and I hated to waken him, so I kept still and watched the moonlight on that undulating wall paper till I felt creepy.

The faint figure behind seemed to shake the pattern, just as if she wanted to get out.

I got up softly and went to feel and see if the paper *did* move, and when I came back John was awake.

"What is it, little girl?" he said. "Don't go walking about like that—you'll get cold."

I thought it was a good time to talk, so I told him that I really was not gaining here, and that I wished he would take me away.

"Why, darling!" said he, "our lease will be up in three weeks, and I can't see how to leave before.

"The repairs are not done at home, and I cannot possibly leave town just now. Of course if you were in any danger, I could and would, but you really are better, dear, whether you can see it or not. I am a doctor, dear, and I know. You are gaining flesh and color, your appetite is better. I feel really much easier about you."

"I don't weigh a bit more," said I, "nor as much; and my appetite may be better in the evening when you are here, but it is worse in the morning when you are away!"

"Bless her little heart!" said he with a big hug, "she shall be as sick as she pleases! But now let's improve the shining hours by going to sleep, and talk about it in the morning!"

"And you won't go away?" I asked gloomily.

"Why, how can I, dear? It is only three weeks more and then we will take a nice little trip of a few days while

Jennie is getting the house ready. Really, dear, you are better!"

"Better in body perhaps—" I began, and stopped short, for he sat up straight and looked at me with such a stern, reproachful look that I could not say another word.

"My darling," said he, "I beg of you, for my sake and for our child's sake, as well as for your own, that you will never for one instant let that idea enter your mind! There is nothing so dangerous, so fascinating, to a temperament like yours. It is a false and foolish fancy. Can you not trust me as a physician when I tell you so?"

So of course I said no more on that score, and we went to sleep before long. He thought I was asleep first, but I wasn't, and lay there for hours trying to decide whether that front pattern and the back pattern really did move together or separately.

On a pattern like this, by daylight, there is a lack of sequence, a defiance of law, that is a constant irritant to a normal mind.

The color is hideous enough, and unreliable enough, and infuriating enough, but the pattern is torturing.

You think you have mastered it, but just as you get well under way in following, it turns a back somersault and there you are. It slaps you in the face, knocks you down, and tramples upon you. It is like a bad dream.

The outside pattern is a florid arabesque, reminding one of a fungus. If you can imagine a toadstool in joints, an interminable string of toadstools, budding and sprouting in endless convolutions—why, that is something like it.

That is, sometimes!

There is one marked peculiarity about this paper, a thing nobody seems to notice but myself, and that is that it changes as the light changes.

When the sun shoots in through the east window—I always watch for that first, long, straight ray—it changes so quickly that I never can quite believe it.

That is why I watch it always.

By moonlight—the moon shines in all night when there is a moon—I wouldn't know it was the same paper.

At night in any kind of light, in twilight, candlelight, lamplight, and worst of all by moonlight, it becomes bars! The outside pattern I mean, and the woman behind it is as plain as can be.

I didn't realize for a long time what the thing was that showed behind, that dim sub-pattern, but now I am quite sure it is a woman.

By daylight she is subdued, quiet. I fancy it is the pattern that keeps her so still. It is so puzzling. It keeps me quiet by the hour.

I lie down ever so much now. John says it is good for me, and to sleep all I can.

Indeed, he started the habit by making me lie down for an hour after each meal.

It is a very bad habit, I am convinced, for, you see, I don't sleep.

And that cultivates deceit, for I don't tell them I'm awake—O, no!

The fact is, I am getting a little afraid of John.

He seems very queer sometimes, and even Jennie has an inexplicable look.

It strikes me occasionally, just as a scientific hypothesis, that perhaps it is the paper!

I have watched John when he did not know I was looking, and come into the room suddenly on the most innocent excuses, and I've caught him several times *looking at the paper!* And Jennie too. I caught Jennie with her hand on it once.

She didn't know I was in the room, and when I asked her in a quiet, a very quiet voice, with the most restrained manner possible, what she was doing with the paper—she turned around as if she had been caught stealing, and looked quite angry—asked me why I should frighten her so!

Then she said that the paper stained everything it touched, that she had found yellow smooches on all my clothes and John's, and she wished we would be more careful!

Did not that sound innocent? But I know she was studying that pattern, and I am determined that nobody shall find it out but myself!

* * * * * * * * * * * * * * *

Life is very much more exciting now than it used to be. You see I have something more to expect, to look forward to, to watch. I really do eat better, and am more quiet than I was.

John is so pleased to see me improve! He laughed a little the other day, and said I seemed to be flourishing in spite of my wall paper.

I turned it off with a laugh. I had no intention of telling him it was *because* of the wall paper—he would make fun of me. He might even want to take me away.

I don't want to leave now until I have found it out. There is a week more, and I think that will be enough.

* * * * * * * * * * * * * * *

I'm feeling ever so much better! I don't sleep much at night, for it is so interesting to watch developments; but I sleep a good deal in the daytime.

In the daytime it is tiresome and perplexing.

There are always new shoots on the fungus, and new shades of yellow all over it. I cannot keep count of them, though I have tried conscientiously.

It is the strangest yellow, that wall paper! It makes me think of all the yellow things I ever saw—not beautiful ones like buttercups, but old foul, bad yellow things.

But there is something else about that paper—the smell! I noticed it the moment we came into the room, but with so much air and sun it was not bad. Now we have had a week of fog and rain, and whether the windows are open or not, the smell is here.

It creeps all over the house.

I find it hovering in the dining-room, skulking in the parlor, hiding in the hall, lying in wait for me on the stairs.

It gets into my hair.

Even when I go to ride, if I turn my head suddenly and surprise it—there is that smell!

Such a peculiar odor, too! I have spent hours in trying to analyze it, to find what it smelled like.

It is not bad—at first, and very gentle, but quite the subtlest, most enduring odor I ever met.

In this damp weather it is awful, I wake up in the night and find it hanging over me.

It used to disturb me at first. I thought seriously of burning the house—to reach the smell.

But now I am used to it. The only thing I can think of that it is like is the *color* of the paper! A yellow smell.

There is a very funny mark on this wall, low down, near the mopboard. A streak that runs round the room. It goes behind every piece of furniture, except the bed, a long, straight, even *smooch,* as if it had been rubbed over and over.

I wonder how it was done and who did it, and what they did it for. Round and round and round—round and round—it makes me dizzy!

I really have discovered something at last.

Through watching so much at night, when it changes so, I have finally found out.

The front pattern *does* move—and no wonder! The woman behind shakes it!

Sometimes I think there are a great many women behind, and sometimes only one, and she crawls around fast, and her crawling shakes it all over.

Then in the very bright spots she keeps still, and in the very shady spots she just takes hold of the bars and shakes them hard.

And she is all the time trying to climb through. But nobody could climb through that pattern—it strangles so; I think that is why it has so many heads.

They get through, and then the pattern strangles them off and turns them upside down, and makes their eyes white!

If those heads were covered or taken off it would not be half so bad.

I think that woman gets out in the daytime!

And I'll tell you why—privately—I've seen her!

I can see her out of every one of my windows!

It is the same woman, I know, for she is always creeping, and most women do not creep by daylight.

I see her in that long shaded lane, creeping up and down. I see her in those dark grape arbors, creeping all around the garden.

I see her on that long road under the trees, creeping along, and when a carriage comes she hides under the blackberry vines.

I don't blame her a bit. It must be very humiliating to be caught creeping by daylight!

I always lock the door when I creep by daylight. I can't do it at night, for I know John would suspect something at once.

And John is so queer now, I don't want to irritate him. I wish he would take another room! Besides, I don't want anybody to get that woman out at night but myself.

I often wonder if I could see her out of all the windows at once.

But turn as fast as I can, I can only see out of one at one time.

And though I always see her, she *may* be able to creep faster than I can turn!

I have watched her sometimes away off in the open country, creeping as fast as a cloud shadow in a high wind.

* * * * * * * * * * * * * * * *

If only that top pattern could be gotten off from the under one! I mean to try it, little by little.

I have found out another funny thing, but I shan't tell it this time! It does not do to trust people too much.

There are only two more days to get this paper off, and I believe John is beginning to notice. I don't like the look in his eyes.

And I heard him ask Jennie a lot of professional questions about me. She had a very good report to give.

She said I slept a good deal in the daytime.

John knows I don't sleep very well at night, for all I'm so quiet!

He asked me all sorts of questions, too, and pretended to be very loving and kind.

As if I couldn't see through him!

Still, I don't wonder he acts so, sleeping under this paper for three months.

It only interests me, but I feel sure John and Jennie are secretly affected by it.

* * * * * * * * * * * * * * * *

Hurrah! This is the last day, but it is enough. John to stay in town over night, and won't be out until this evening.

Jennie wanted to sleep with me—the sly thing! but I told her I should undoubtedly rest better for a night all alone.

That was clever, for really I wasn't alone a bit! As soon as it was moonlight and that poor thing began to crawl and shake the pattern, I got up and ran to help her.

I pulled and she shook, I shook and she pulled, and before morning we had peeled off yards of that paper.

A strip about as high as my head and half around the room.

And then when the sun came and that awful pattern began to laugh at me, I declared I would finish it to-day!

We go away to-morrow, and they are moving all my furniture down again to leave things as they were before.

Jennie looked at the wall in amazement, but I told her merrily that I did it out of pure spite at the vicious thing.

She laughed and said she wouldn't mind doing it herself, but I must not get tired.

How she betrayed herself that time!

But I am here, and no person touches this paper but me—not *alive!*

She tried to get me out of the room—it was too patent! But I said it was so quiet and empty and clean now that I believed I would lie down again and sleep all I could; and not to wake me even for dinner—I would call when I woke.

So now she is gone, and the servants are gone, and the things are gone, and there is nothing left but that great bedstead nailed down, with the canvas mattress we found on it.

We shall sleep downstairs to-night, and take the boat home to-morrow.

I quite enjoy the room, now it is bare again.

How those children did tear about here!

This bedstead is fairly gnawed!

But I must get to work.

I have locked the door and thrown the key down into the front path.

I don't want to go out, and I don't want to have anybody come in, till John comes.

I want to astonish him.

I've got a rope up here that even Jennie did not find. If

that woman does get out, and tries to get away, I can tie her!

But I forgot I could not reach far without anything to stand on!

This bed will *not* move!

I tried to lift and push it until I was lame, and then I got so angry I bit off a little piece at the corner—but it hurt my teeth.

Then I peeled off all the paper I could reach standing on the floor. It sticks horribly and the pattern just enjoys it! All those strangled heads and bulbous eyes and waddling fungus growths just shriek with derision!

I am getting angry enough to do something desperate. To jump out of the window would be admirable exercise, but the bars are too strong even to try.

Besides I wouldn't do it. Of course not. I know well enough that a step like that is improper and might be misconstrued.

I don't like to *look* out of the windows even—there are so many of those creeping women, and they creep so fast.

I wonder if they all come out of that wall paper as I did?

But I am securely fastened now by my well-hidden rope—you don't get *me* out in the road there!

I suppose I shall have to get back behind the pattern when it comes night, and that is hard!

It is so pleasant to be out in this great room and creep around as I please!

I don't want to go outside. I won't, even if Jennie asks me to.

For outside you have to creep on the ground, and everything is green instead of yellow.

But here I can creep smoothly on the floor, and my shoulder just fits in that long smooch around the wall, so I cannot lose my way.

Why, there's John at the door!

It is no use, young man, you can't open it!

How he does call and pound!

Now he's crying for an axe.

It would be a shame to break down that beautiful door!

"John, dear!" said I in the gentlest voice, "the key is down by the front steps, under a plantain leaf!"

That silenced him for a few moments.

Then he said, very quietly indeed, "Open the door, my darling!"

"I can't," said I. "The key is down by the front door under a plantain leaf!"

And then I said it again, several times, very gently and slowly, and said it so often that he had to go and see, and he got it of course, and came in. He stopped short by the door.

"What is the matter?" he cried. "For God's sake, what are you doing!"

I kept on creeping just the same, but I looked at him over my shoulder.

"I've got out at last," said I, "in spite of you and Jane. And I've pulled off most of the paper, so you can't put me back!"

Now why should that man have fainted? But he did, and right across my path by the wall, so that I had to creep over him every time!

Part Seven

Unknown Threat

The totally unknown agency at work in Gothic literature, such as the mysterious death force in Cram's "The Dead Valley," is generally comprehended only by its effect on the victim. As mentioned previously, the unknown agency is distinct from the supernatural agency in that there is no explanation whatsoever for the former force. It is so completely beyond man's comprehension that he can know nothing about it, including in some cases its purpose, if any—except that this unknown agency is usually associated with death and/or evil.

The unknown threat gives an additional dimension of terror, precisely because it is not identified with any external object or person, nor is it related to a mental aberration on the part of the victim. It may, as in "The Willows," leave some physical trace of its presence, or it may, as in "The Dead Valley," reveal itself by nothing more than chill and fog—warning signs only to the intuitive. But there are no reasons given for the presence of these evil forces nor are there any explanations of their origins. The Swede in "The Willows" knows only that the force is from another world of experience.

In most cases in Gothic literature, the threat arises from some sort of cause—greed, lust, revenge, desire for power, and even, as in vampirism, the urge for survival. The victim may be a random sacrifice, or he may be deliberately selected by the agent in question, but if there is a reason for the selection—an association between the agent and the victim—it creates a type of rational motivation or situation with which the reader can more readily empathize and cope. In "What Was It?" O'Brien creates an initially eerie situation with an unknown threat, but once he gives physical dimension to the "thing," when the plaster cast reveals a quasi-human form, the reader can begin to consider the "thing" in rational terms, perhaps even sympathize with its need for food. With an absolutely unknown agency, on the contrary, this possibility of putting the agency into a rational context does not exist. The reader must endure the eerie and frustrating knowledge of the victim—and, by extension, the reader himself—surrounded by threats against which human defenses are powerless. There is no way to measure the danger, no way to form battle plans for survival. And though the abstraction involved may lessen the immediate impact in this approach to the Gothic, in the long view it may prove the ultimate in terror.

from

The Willows

by Algernon Blackwood

[*The narrator and his Swedish companion are canoeing down the Danube and have reached the desolate marshlands between Vienna and Budapest when they decide to make camp for the night on one of the hundreds of sandy islands overgrown with willow shrubs. In flood and helped by high-velocity winds, the river is slowly washing away the island.*

During the night, while the Swede sleeps peacefully, the restless narrator becomes aware of vague, gigantic presences which, screened by the willows, seem to be threatening the two voyagers. Later he feels a "something" pressing down on him.

In the morning the narrator takes care not to mention his experiences of the previous night, and he remains silent even after they discover that one of the paddles is missing, the other has been weakened to the point of uselessness, and there is a long rent in the bottom of the canoe. The day is spent repairing the damaged boat. Gradually the terrible winds subside, and by suppertime it is quiet.]

The pot had just began to bubble when I heard his voice calling to me from the bank, where he had wandered away without my noticing. I ran up.

"Come and listen," he said, "and see what you make of it." He held his hand cupwise to his ear, as so often before.

"*Now* do you hear anything?" he asked, watching me curiously.

We stood there, listening attentively together. At first I heard only the deep note of the water and the hissings rising from its turbulent surface. The willows, for once, were motionless and silent. Then a sound began to reach my ears faintly, a peculiar sound—something like the humming of a distant gong. It seemed to come across to us in the darkness from the waste of swamps and willows opposite. It was repeated at regular intervals, but it was certainly neither the sound of a bell nor the hooting of a distant steamer. I can liken it to nothing so much as to the sound of an immense gong, suspended far up in the sky, repeating incessantly its muffled metallic note, soft and musical, as it was repeatedly struck. My heart quickened as I listened.

"I've heard it all day," said my companion. "While you slept this afternoon it came all round the island. I hunted it down, but could never get near enough to see—to localise it correctly. Sometimes it was overhead, and sometimes it seemed under the water. Once or twice, too, I could have sworn it was not outside at all, but *within myself*—you know—the way a sound in the fourth dimension is supposed to come."

I was too much puzzled to pay much attention to his words. I listened carefully, striving to associate it with any known familiar sound I could think of, but without success. It changed in direction, too, coming nearer, and then sinking utterly away into remote distance. I cannot say that it was ominous in quality, because to me it seemed distinctly musical, yet I must admit it set going a distressing feeling that made me wish I had never heard it.

"The wind blowing in those sand-funnels," I said, determined to find an explanation, "or the bushes rubbing together after the storm perhaps."

"It comes off the whole swamp," my friend answered. "It comes from everywhere at once." He ignored my explanations. "It comes from the willow bushes somehow. . . ."

"But now the wind has dropped," I objected. "The willows can hardly make a noise by themselves, can they?"

His answer frightened me, first because I had dreaded it, and, secondly, because I knew intuitively it was true.

"It is *because* the wind has dropped we now hear it. It was drowned before. It is the cry, I believe, of the . . ."

I dashed back to my fire, warned by a sound of bubbling that the stew was in danger, but determined at the same time to escape from further conversation. I was resolute, if possible, to avoid the exchanging of views. I dreaded, too, that he would begin again about the gods, or the elemental forces, or something else disquieting, and I wanted to keep myself well in hand for what might happen later. There was another night to be faced before we escaped from this distressing place, and there was no knowing yet what it might bring forth.

"Come and cut up bread for the pot," I called to him, vigorously stirring the appetising mixture. That stew-pot held sanity for us both, and the thought made me laugh.

He came over slowly and took the provision sack from the tree, fumbling in its mysterious depths, and then emptying the entire contents upon the ground-sheet at his feet.

"Hurry up!" I cried; "it's boiling."

The Swede burst out into a roar of laughter that startled me. It was forced laughter, not artificial exactly, but mirthless.

"There's nothing here!" he shouted, holding his sides. "Bread, I mean."

"It's gone. There is no bread. They've taken it!"

I dropped the long spoon and ran up. Everything the sack had contained lay upon the groundsheet, but there was no loaf.

The whole dead weight of my growing fear fell upon me and shook me. Then I burst out laughing too. It was the only thing to do: and the sound of my own laughter also made me understand his. The strain of physical pressure caused it—this explosion of unnatural laughter in both of us; it was an effort of repressed forces to seek relief; it was a temporary safety valve. And with both of us it ceased quite suddenly.

"How criminally stupid of me!" I cried, still determined to be consistent and find an explanation. "I clean forgot to buy a loaf at Pressburg. That chattering woman put everything out of my head, and I must have left it lying on the counter or . . ."

"The oatmeal, too, is much less than it was this morning," the Swede interrupted.

Why in the world need he draw attention to it? I thought angrily.

"There's enough for tomorrow," I said, stirring vigorously, "and we can get lots more at Komorn or Gran. In twenty-four hours we shall be miles from here."

"I hope so—to God," he muttered, putting the things back into the sack, "unless we're claimed first as victims for the sacrifice," he added with a foolish laugh. He dragged the sack into the tent, for safety's sake, I suppose, and I heard him mumbling on to himself.

* * * * * * * * * * * * * * * *

Some of these sentences, moreover, were confoundedly disquieting to me, coming as they did to corroborate much that I felt myself: corroboration, too—which made it so much more convincing—from a totally different point of view. He composed such curious sentences, and hurled them at me in such an inconsequential sort of way, as though his main line of thought was secret to himself, and these fragments were the bits he found it impossible to digest. He got rid of them by uttering them. Speech relieved him. It was like being sick.

"There are things about us, I'm sure, that make for disorder, disintegration, destruction, *our* destruction," he said once, while the fire blazed between us. "We've strayed out of a safe line somewhere."

And another time, when the gong sounds had come nearer, ringing much louder than before, and directly over our heads, he said, as though talking to himself:

"I don't think a phonograph would show any record of that. The sound doesn't come to me by the ears at all. The vibrations reach me in another manner altogether, and seem to be within me, which is precisely how a fourth-dimensional sound might be supposed to make itself heard."

I purposely made no reply to this, but I sat up a little closer to the fire and peered about me into the darkness. The clouds were massed all over the sky and no trace of moonlight came through. Very still, too, everything was, so that the river and the frogs had things all their own way.

"It has that about it," he went on, "which is utterly out of common experience. It is *unknown*. Only one thing describes it really: it is a non-human sound; I mean a sound outside humanity."

Having rid himself of this undigestible morsel, he lay quiet for a time; but he had so admirably expressed my own feeling that it was a relief to have the thought out, and to have confined it by the limitation of words from dangerous wandering to and fro in the mind.

The solitude of that Danube camping-place, can I ever

forget it? The feeling of being utterly alone on an empty planet! My thoughts ran incessantly upon cities and the haunts of men. I would have given my soul, as the saying is, for the "feel" of those Bavarian villages we had passed through by the score; for the normal, human common-places: peasants drinking beer, tables beneath the trees, hot sunshine, and a ruined castle on the rocks behind the red-roofed church. Even the tourists would have been welcome.

Yet what I felt of dread was no ordinary ghostly fear. It was infinitely greater, stranger, and seemed to arise from some dim ancestral sense of terror more profoundly disturbing than anything I had ever known or dreamed of. We had "strayed", as the Swede put it, into some region or some set of conditions where the risks were great, yet unintelligible to us; where the frontiers of some unknown world lay close about us. It was a spot held by the dwellers in some outer space, a sort of peep-hole whence they could spy upon the earth, themselves unseen, a point where the veil between had worn a little thin. As the final result of too long a sojourn here, we should be carried over the border and deprived of what we called "our lives", yet by mental, not physical, processes. In that sense, as he said, we should be the victims of our adventure—a sacrifice.

It took us in different fashion, each according to the measure of his sensitiveness and powers of resistance. I translated it vaguely into a personification of the mightily disturbed elements, investing them with the horror of a deliberate and malefic purpose, resentful of our audacious intrusion into their breeding-place; whereas my friend threw it into the unoriginal form at first of a trespass on some ancient shrine, some place where the old gods still held sway, where the emotional forces of former worshippers still clung, and the ancestral portion of him yielded to the old pagan spell.

At any rate, here was a place unpolluted by men, kept clean by the winds from coarsening human influences, a place where spiritual agencies were within reach and aggressive. Never, before or since, have I been so attacked by indescribable suggestions of a "beyond region", of another scheme of life, another evolution not parallel to the human. And in the end our minds would succumb under the weight of the awful spell, and we should be drawn across the frontier into *their* world.

Small things testified to this amazing influence of the place, and now in the silence round the fire they allowed themselves to be noted by the mind. The very atmosphere had proved itself a magnifying medium to distort every indication: the otter rolling in the current, the hurrying boatman making signs, the shifting willows, one and all had been robbed of its natural character, and revealed in something of its other aspect—as it existed across the border in that other region. And this changed aspect I felt was new not merely to me, but to the race. The whole experience whose verge we touched was unknown to humanity at all. It was a new order of experience, and in the true sense of the word *unearthly*.

"It's the deliberate, calculating purpose that reduces one's courage to zero," the Swede said suddenly, as if he had been actually following my thoughts. "Otherwise imagination might count for much. But the paddle, canoe, the lessening of food . . ."

"Haven't I explained all that once?" I interrupted viciously.

"You have," he answered dryly; "you have indeed."

He made other remarks too, as usual, about what he called the "plain determination to provide a victim"; but, having now arranged my thoughts better, I recognised that this was simply the cry of his frightened soul against the knowledge that he was being attacked in a vital part, and that he would be somehow taken or destroyed. The situation called for a courage and calmness of reasoning that neither of us could compass, and I have never before been so clearly conscious of two persons in me—the one that explained everything, and the other that laughed at such foolish explanations, yet was horribly afraid.

Meanwhile, in the pitchy night the fire died down and the wood pile grew small. Neither of us moved to replenish the stock, and the darkness consequently came up very close to our faces. A few feet beyond the circle of firelight it was inky black. Occasionally a stray puff of wind set the willows shivering about us, but apart from this not very welcome sound a deep and depressing silence reigned, broken only by the gurgling of the river and the humming in the air overhead.

We both missed, I think, the shouting company of the winds.

At length, at a moment when a stray puff prolonged itself as though the wind were about to rise again, I reached the point for me of saturation, the point where it was absolutely necessary to find relief in plain speech, or else to betray myself by some hysterical extravagance that must have been far worse in its effect upon both of us. I kicked the fire into a blaze, and turned to my companion abruptly. He looked up with a start.

"I can't disguise it any longer," I said; "I don't like this place, and the darkness, and the noises, and the awful feelings I get. There's something here that beats me utterly. I'm in a blue funk, and that's the plain truth. If the other shore was—different, I swear I'd be inclined to swim for it!"

The Swede's face turned very white beneath the deep tan of sun and wind. He stared straight at me and answered quietly, but his voice betrayed his huge excitement by its unnatural calmness. For the moment, at any rate, he was the strong man of the two. He was more phlegmatic for one thing.

"It's not a physical condition we can escape from by

running away," he replied, in the tone of a doctor diagnosing some grave disease; "we must sit tight and wait. There are forces close here that could kill a herd of elephants in a second as easily as you or I could squash a fly. Our only chance is to keep perfectly still. Our insignificance perhaps may save us."

I put a dozen questions into my expression of face, but found no words. It was precisely like listening to an accurate description of a disease whose symptoms had puzzled me.

"I mean that so far, although aware of our disturbing presence, they have not *found* us—not 'located' us, as the Americans say," he went on. "They're blundering about like men hunting for a leak of gas. The paddle and canoe and provisions prove that. I think they *feel* us, but cannot actually see us. We must keep our minds quiet—it's our minds they feel. We must control our thoughts, or it's all up with us."

"Death you mean?" I stammered, icy with the horror of his suggestion.

"Worse—by far," he said. "Death, according to one's belief, means either annihilation or release from the limitations of the senses, but it involves no change of character. *You* don't suddenly alter just because the body's gone. But this means a radical alteration, a complete change, a horrible loss of oneself by substitution—far worse than death, and not even annihilation. We happen to have camped in a spot where their region touches ours, where the veil between has worn thin"—horrors! he was using my own phrase, my actual words—"so that they are aware of our being in their neighbourhood."

"But *who* are aware?" I asked.

I forgot the shaking of the willows in the windless calm, the humming overhead, everything except that I was waiting for an answer that I dreaded more than I can possibly explain.

He lowered his voice at once to reply, leaning forward a little over the fire, an indefinable change in his face that made me avoid his eyes and look down upon the ground.

"All my life," he said, "I have been strangely, vividly conscious of another region—not far removed from our own world in one sense, yet wholly different in kind—where great things go on unceasingly, where immense and terrible personalities hurry by, intent on vast purposes compared to which earthly affairs, the rise and fall of nations, the destinies of empires, the fate of armies and continents, are all as dust in the balance; vast purposes, I mean, that deal directly with the soul, and not indirectly with mere expressions of the soul. . . ."

"I suggest just now . . ." I began, seeking to stop him, feeling as though I was face to face with a madman. But he instantly overbore me with his torrent that *had* to come.

"You think," he said, "it is the spirits of the elements, and I thought perhaps it was the old gods. But I tell you now it is—*neither*. These would be comprehensible entities, for they have relations with men, depending upon them for worship or sacrifice, whereas these beings who are now about us have absolutely nothing to do with mankind, and it is mere chance that their space happens just at this spot to touch our own."

The mere conception, which his words somehow made so convincing, as I listened to them there in the dark stillness of that lonely island, set me shaking a little all over. I found it impossible to control my movements.

"And what do you propose?" I began again.

"A sacrifice, a victim, might save us by distracting them until we could get away," he went on, "just as the wolves stop to devour the dogs and give the sleigh another start. But—I see no chance of any other victim now."

I stared blankly at him. The gleam in his eyes was dreadful. Presently he continued.

"It's the willows, of course. The willows *mask* the others, but the others are feeling about for us. If we let our minds betray our fear, we're lost, lost utterly," He looked at me with an expression so calm, so determined, so sincere, that I no longer had any doubts as to his sanity. He was as sane as any man ever was. "If we can hold out through the night," he added, "we may get off in the daylight unnoticed, or rather, *undiscovered.*"

"But you really think a sacrifice would . . ."

That gong-like humming came down very close over our heads as I spoke, but it was my friend's scared face that really stopped my mouth.

"Hush!" he whispered, holding up his hand. "Do not mention them more than you can help. Do not refer to them *by name*. To name is to reveal: it is the inevitable clue, and our only hope lies in ignoring them, in order that they may ignore us."

"Even in thought?" He was extraordinarily agitated.

"Especially in thought. Our thoughts make spirals in their world. We must keep them *out of our minds* at all costs if possible."

I raked the fire together to prevent the darkness having everything its own way. I never longed for the sun as I longed for it then in the awful blackness of that summer night.

"Were you awake all last night?" he went on suddenly.

"I slept badly a little after dawn," I replied evasively, trying to follow his instructions, which I knew instinctively were true, "but the wind, of course . . ."

"I know. But the wind won't account for all the noises."

"Then you heard it too?"

"The multiplying countless little footsteps I heard," he said, adding, after a moment's hesitation, "and that other sound. . . ."

"You mean above the tent, and the pressing down upon us of something tremendous, gigantic?"

He nodded significantly.

"It was like the beginning of a sort of inner suffocation?" I said.

"Partly, yes. It seemed to me that the weight of the atmosphere had been altered—had increased enormously, so that we should be crushed."

"And *that*," I went on, determined to have it all out, pointing upwards where the gong-like note hummed ceaselessly, rising and falling like wind. "What do you make of that?"

"It's *their* sound," he whispered gravely. "It's the sound of their world, the humming in their region. The division here is so thin that it leaks through somehow. But, if you listen carefully, you'll find it's not above so much as around us. It's the willows themselves humming, because here the willows have been made symbols of the forces that are against us."

I could not follow exactly what he meant by this, yet the thought and idea in my mind were beyond question the thought and idea in his. I realised what he realised, only with less power of analysis than his. It was on the tip of my tongue to tell him about my hallucination of the ascending figures and the moving bushes, when he suddenly thrust his face again close into mine across the firelight and began to speak in a very earnest whisper. He amazed me by his calmness and pluck, his apparent control of the situation. This man I had for years deemed unimaginative, stolid!

"Now listen," he said. "The only thing for us to do is to go on as though nothing had happened, follow our usual habits, go to bed, and so forth; pretend we feel nothing and notice nothing. It is a question wholly of the mind, and the less we think about them the better our chance of escape. Above all, don't *think,* for what you think happens!"

"All right," I managed to reply, simply breathless with his words and the strangeness of it all; "all right, I'll try, but tell me one thing more first. Tell me what you make of those hollows in the ground all about us, those sand-funnels?"

"No!" he cried, forgetting to whisper in his excitement. "I dare not; simply dare not, put the thought into words. If you have not guessed, I am glad. Don't try to. *They* have put it into my mind; try your hardest to prevent their putting it into yours."

He sank his voice again to a whisper before he finished, and I did not press him to explain. There was already just about as much horror in me as I could hold. The conversation came to an end, and we smoked our pipes busily in silence.

Then something happened, something unimportant apparently, as the way is when the nerves are in a very great state of tension, and this small thing for a brief space gave me an entirely different point of view. I chanced to look down at my sand-shoe—the sort we used for the canoe—and something to do with the hole at the toe suddenly recalled to me the London shop where I had bought them, the difficulty the man had in fitting me, and other details of the uninteresting but practical operation. At once, in its train, followed a wholesome view of the modern sceptical world I was accustomed to move in at home. I thought of roast beef and ale, motor-cars, policemen, brass bands, and a dozen other things that proclaimed the soul of ordinariness or utility. The effect was immediate and astonishing even to myself. Psychologically, I suppose, it was simply a sudden and violent reaction after the strain of living in an atmosphere of things that to the normal consciousness must seem impossible and incredible. But, whatever the cause, it momentarily lifted the spell from my heart, and left me for the short space of a minute feeling free and utterly unafraid. I looked up at my friend opposite.

"You damned old pagan!" I cried, laughing aloud in his face. "You imaginative idiot! You superstitious idolator! You . . ."

I stopped in the middle, seized anew by the old horror. I tried to smother the sound of my voice as something sacrilegious. The Swede, of course, heard it too—that strange cry overhead in the darkness—and that sudden drop in the air as though something had come nearer.

He turned ashen white under the tan. He stood bolt upright in front of the fire, stiff as a rod, staring at me.

"After that," he said in a sort of helpless, frantic way, "we must go! We can't stay now; we must strike camp this very instant and go on—down the river."

He was talking, I saw, quite wildly, his words dictated by abject terror—the terror he had resisted so long, but which had caught him at last.

"In the dark?" I exclaimed, shaking with fear after my hysterical outburst, but still realising our position better than he did. "Sheer madness! The river's in flood, and we've only got a single paddle. Besides, we only go deeper into their country! There's nothing ahead for fifty miles but willows, willows, willows!"

He sat down again in a state of semi-collapse. The positions, by one of those kaleidoscopic changes nature loves, were suddenly reversed, and the control of our forces passed into my hands. His mind at last had reached the point where it was beginning to weaken.

"What on earth possessed you to do such a thing?" he whispered, with the awe of genuine terror in his voice and face.

I crossed round to his side of the fire. I took both his hands in mine, kneeling down beside him and looking straight into his frightened eyes.

"We'll make one more blaze," I said firmly, "and then turn in for the night. At sunrise we'll be off full speed for Komorn. Now, pull yourself together a bit, and remember your own advice about *not thinking fear*!"

He said no more, and I saw that he would agree and obey. In some measure, too, it was a sort of relief to get up and make an excursion into the darkness for more wood. We kept close together, almost touching, groping among the bushes and along the bank. The humming overhead never ceased, but seemed to me to grow louder as we increased our distance from the fire. It was shivery work!

We were grubbing away in the middle of a thickish clump of willows where some driftwood from a former flood had caught high among the branches, when my body was seized in a grip that made me half drop upon the sand. It was the Swede. He had fallen against me, and was clutching me for support. I heard his breath coming and going in short gasps.

"Look! By my soul!" he whispered, and for the first time in my experience I knew what it was to hear tears of terror in a human voice. He was pointing to the fire, some fifty feet away. I followed the direction of his finger, and I swear my heart missed a beat.

There, in front of the dim glow, *something was moving*.

I saw it through a veil that hung before my eyes like the gauze drop-curtain used at the back of a theatre—hazily a little. It was neither a human figure nor an animal. To me it gave the strange impression of being as large as several animals grouped together, like horses, two or three, moving slowly. The Swede, too, got a similar result, though expressing it differently, for he thought it was shaped and sized like a clump of willow bushes, rounded at the top, and moving all over upon its surface—"coiling upon itself like smoke," he said afterwards.

"I watched it settle downwards through the bushes," he sobbed at me. "Look, by God! It's coming this way! Oh, oh!"—he gave a kind of whistling cry. *"They've found us."*

I gave one terrified glance, which just enabled me to see

that the shadowy form was swinging towards us through the bushes, and then I collapsed backwards with a crash into the branches. These failed, of course, to support my weight so that with the Swede on the top of me we fell in a struggling heap upon the sand. I really hardly knew what was happening. I was conscious only of a sort of enveloping sensation of icy fear that plucked the nerves out of their fleshly covering, twisted them this way and that, and replaced them quivering. My eyes were tightly shut; something in my throat choked me: a feeling that my consciousness was expanding, extending out into space, swiftly gave way to another feeling that I was losing it altogether, and about to die.

An acute spasm of pain passed through me, and I was aware that the Swede had hold of me in such a way that he hurt me abominably. It was the way he caught at me in falling.

But it was this pain, he declared afterwards, that saved me: it caused me to *forget them* and think of something else at the very instant when they were about to find me. It concealed my mind from them at the moment of discovery, yet just in time to evade their terrible seizing of me. He himself, he says actually swooned at the same moment, and that was what saved him.

I only know that at a later time, how long or short is impossible to say, I found myself scrambling up out of the slippery network of willow branches, and saw my companion standing in front of me holding out a hand to assist me. I stared at him in a dazed way, rubbing the arm he had twisted for me. Nothing came to me to say, somehow.

"I lost consciousness for a moment or two," I heard him say. "That's what saved me. It made me stop thinking about them."

"You nearly broke my arm in two," I said, uttering my only connected thought at the moment. A numbness came over me.

"That's what saved *you!*" he replied. "Between us, we've managed to set them off on a false tack somewhere. The humming has ceased. It's gone—for the moment at any rate!"

A wave of hysterical laughter seized me again, and this time spread to my friend too—great healing gusts of shaking laughter that brought a tremendous sense of relief in their train. We made our way back to the fire and put the wood on so that it blazed at once. Then we saw the tent had fallen over and lay in a tangled heap upon the ground.

We picked it up, and during the process tripped more than once and caught our feet in sand.

"It's those sand-funnels," exclaimed the Swede, when the tent was up again and the firelight lit up the ground for several yards about us. "And look at the size of them!"

All around the tent and about the fireplace where we had seen the moving shadows there were deep funnel-shaped hollows in the sand, exactly similar to the ones we had already found all over the island, only far bigger and deeper, beautifully formed and wide enough in some instances to admit the whole of my foot and leg.

Neither of us said a word. We both knew that sleep was the safest thing we could do, and to bed we went accordingly without further delay, having first thrown sand on the fire and taken the provision sack and the paddle inside the tent with us. The canoe, too, we propped in such a way at the end of the tent that our feet touched it, and the least motion would disturb and wake us.

In case of emergency, too, we again went to bed in our clothes, ready for a sudden start.

V.

It was my firm intention to lie awake all night and watch, but the exhaustion of nerves and body decreed otherwise, and sleep after a while came over me with a welcome blanket of oblivion. The fact that my companion also slept quickened its approach. At first he fidgeted and constantly sat up, asking me if I "heard this" or "heard that". He tossed about on his cork mattress, and said the tent was moving and the river had risen over the point of the island; but each time I went out to look I returned with the report that all was well, and finally he grew calmer and lay still. Then at length his breathing became regular and I heard unmistakable sounds of snoring—the first and only time in my life when snoring has been a welcome and calming influence.

This, I remember, was the last thought in my mind before dozing off.

A difficulty in breathing woke me, and I found the blanket over my face. But something else besides the blanket was pressing upon me, and my first thought was that my companion had rolled off his mattress on to my own in his sleep. I called to him and sat up, and at the same moment it came to me that the tent was *surrounded*. That sound of multitudinous soft pattering was again audible outside, filling the night with horror.

I called again to him, louder than before. He did not answer, but I missed the sound of his snoring, and also noticed that the flap of the tent door was down. This was the unpardonable sin. I crawled out in the darkness to hook it back securely, and it was then for the first time I realised positively that the Swede was not there. He had gone.

I dashed out in a mad run, seized by a dreadful agitation, and the moment I was out I plunged into sort of a torrent of humming that surrounded me completely and came out of every quarter of the heavens at once. It was that same familiar humming—gone mad! A swarm of great invisible bees might have been about me in the air. The sound seemed to thicken the very atmosphere, and I felt that my lungs worked with difficulty.

But my friend was in danger, and I could not hesitate.

The dawn was just about to break, and a faint whitish light spread upwards over the clouds from a thin strip of clear horizon. No wind stirred. I could just make out the bushes and river beyond, and the pale sandy patches. In my excitement I ran frantically to and fro about the island, calling him by name, shouting at the top of my voice the first words that came into my head. But the willows smothered my voice, and the humming muffled it, so that the sound only travelled a few feet round me. I plunged among the bushes, tripping headlong, tumbling over roots, and scraping my face as I tore this way and that among the preventing branches.

Then, quite unexpectedly, I came out upon the island's point and saw a dark figure outlined between the water and the sky. It was the Swede. And already he had one foot in the river! A moment more and he would have taken the plunge.

I threw myself upon him, flinging my arms about his waist and dragging him shorewards with all my strength. Of course he struggled furiously, making a noise all the time just like that cursed humming, and using the most outlandish phrases in his anger about "going *inside* to Them", and "taking the way of the water and the wind", and God only knows what more besides, that I tried in vain to recall afterwards, but which turned me sick with horror and amazement as I listened. But in the end I managed to get him into the comparative safety of the tent, and flung him breathless and cursing upon the mattress, where I held him until the fit had passed.

I think the suddenness with which it all went and he grew calm, coinciding as it did with the equally abrupt cessation of the humming and pattering outside—I think this was almost the strangest part of the whole business perhaps. For he just opened his eyes and turned his tired face up to me so that the dawn threw a pale light upon it through the doorway, and said, for all the world just like a frightened child:

"My life, old man—it's my life I owe you. But it's all

over now anyhow. They've found a victim in our place!"

Then he dropped back upon his blankets and went to sleep literally under my eyes. He simply collapsed, and began to snore again as healthily as though nothing had happened and he had never tried to offer his own life as a sacrifice by drowning. And when the sunlight woke him three hours later—hours of ceaseless vigil for me—it became so clear to me that he remembered absolutely nothing of what he had attempted to do, that I deemed it wise to hold my peace and ask no dangerous questions.

He woke naturally and easily, as I have said, when the sun was already high in a windless hot sky, and he at once got up and set about the preparation of the fire for breakfast. I followed him anxiously at bathing, but he did not attempt to plunge in, merely dipping his head and making some remark about the extra coldness of the water.

"River's falling at last," he said, "and I'm glad of it."

"The humming has stopped too," I said.

He looked up at me quietly with his normal expression. Evidently he remembered everything except his own attempt at suicide.

"Everything has stopped," he said, "because . . ."

He hesitated. But I knew some reference to that remark he had made just before he fainted was in his mind, and I was determined to know it.

"Because 'They've found another victim'?" I said, forcing a little laugh.

"Exactly," he answered, "exactly! I feel as positive of it as though—as though—I feel quite safe again, I mean," he finished.

He began to look curiously about him. The sunlight lay in hot patches on the sand. There was no wind. The willows were motionless. He slowly rose to his feet.

"Come," he said; "I think if we look, we shall find it."

He started off in a run, and I followed him. He kept to the banks, poking with a stick among the sandy bays and caves and little back-waters, myself always close on his heels.

"Ah!" he exclaimed presently, "ah!"

The tone of his voice somehow brought back to me a vivid sense of the horror of the last twenty-four hours, and I hurried up to join him. He was pointing with his stick at a large black object that lay half in the water and half on the sand. It appeared to be caught by some twisted willow roots so that the river could not sweep it away. A few hours before the spot must have been under water.

"See," he said quietly, "the victim that made our escape possible!"

And when I peered across his shoulder I saw that his stick rested on the body of a man. He turned it over. It was the corpse of a peasant, and the face was hidden in the sand. Clearly the man had been drowned but a few hours before, and his body must have been swept down upon our island somewhere about the hour of the dawn— *at the very time the fit had passed.*

"We must give it a decent burial, you know."

"I suppose so," I replied. I shuddered a little in spite of myself, for there was something about the appearance of that poor drowned man that turned me cold.

The Swede glanced up sharply at me, an undecipherable expression on his face, and began clambering down the bank. I followed him more leisurely. The current, I noticed, had torn away much of the clothing from the body, so that the neck and part of the chest lay bare.

Half-way down the bank my companion suddenly stopped and held up his hand in warning; but either my foot slipped or I had gained too much momentum to bring myself quickly to a halt, for I bumped into him and sent him forward with a sort of leap to save himself. We tumbled together on to the hard sand so that our feet splashed into the water. And, before anything could be done, we collided a little heavily against the corpse.

The Swede uttered a sharp cry. And I sprang back as if I had been shot.

At the moment we touched the body there rose from its surface the loud sound of humming—the sound of several hummings—which passed with a vast commotion as of winged things in the air about us and disappeared upwards into the sky, growing fainter and fainter till they finally ceased in the distance. It was exactly as though we had disturbed some living yet invisible creatures at work.

My companion clutched me, and I think I clutched him, but before either of us had time properly to recover from the unexpected shock, we saw that a movement of the current was turning the corpse round so that it became released from the grip of the willow roots. A moment later it had turned completely over, the dead face uppermost, staring at the sky. It lay on the edge of the main stream. In another moment it would be swept away.

The Swede started to save it, shouting again something I did not catch about a "proper burial"—and then abruptly dropped upon his knees on the sand and covered his eyes with his hands. I was beside him in an instant.

I saw what he had seen.

For just as the body swung round to the current the face and the exposed chest turned full towards us, and showed plainly how the skin and flesh were indented with small hollows, beautifully formed, and exactly similar in shape and kind to the sand-funnels that we had found all over the island.

"Their mark!" I heard my companion mutter under his breath. "Their awful mark!"

And when I turned my eyes again from his ghastly face to the river, the current had done its work, and the body had been swept away into midstream and was already beyond our reach and almost out of sight, turning over and over on the waves like an otter.

from

The Horla

by Guy de Maupassant

Mar. 8. What a lovely day! I have spent all the morning lying on the grass in front of my house, under the enormous plantain tree which covers and shades and shelters the whole of it. I like this part of the country; I am fond of living here because I am attached to it by deep roots, the profound and delicate roots which attach a man to the soil on which his ancestors were born and died, to their traditions, their usages, their food, the local expressions, the peculiar language of the peasants, the smell of the soil, the hamlets, and to the atmosphere itself.

I love the house in which I grew up. From my windows I can see the Seine, which flows by the side of my garden, on the other side of the road, almost through my grounds, the great and wide Seine, which goes to Rouen and Havre, and which is covered with boats passing to and fro.

On the left, down yonder, lies Rouen, populous Rouen with its blue roofs massing under pointed Gothic towers. Innumerable are they, delicate or broad, dominated by the spire of the cathedral, full of bells which sound through the blue air on fine mornings, sending their sweet and distant iron clang to me, their metallic sounds, now stronger and now weaker, according as the wind is strong or light.

What a delicious morning it was! About eleven o'clock, a long line of boats drawn by a steam-tug, as big as a fly, and which scarcely puffed while emitting its thick smoke, passed my gate.

After two English schooners, whose red flags fluttered toward the sky, there came a magnificent Brazilian three-master; it was perfectly white and wonderfully clean and shining. I saluted it, I hardly know why, except that the sight of the vessel gave me great pleasure.

May 12. I have had a slight feverish attack for the last few days, and I feel ill, or rather I feel low-spirited.

Whence come those mysterious influences which change our happiness into discouragement, and our self-confidence into diffidence? One might almost say that the air, the invisible air, is full of unknowable Forces, whose mysterious presence we have to endure. I wake up in the best of spirits, with an inclination to sing in my heart. Why? I go down by the side of the water, and suddenly, after walking a short distance, I return home wretched, as if some misfortune were awaiting me there. Why? Is it a cold shiver which, passing over my skin, has upset my nerves and given me a fit of low spirits? Is it the form of the clouds, or the tints of the sky, or the colors of the surrounding objects which are so changeable, which have troubled my thoughts as they passed before my eyes? Who can tell? Everything that surrounds us, everything that we see without looking at it, everything that we touch without knowing it, everything that we handle without feeling it, everything that we meet without clearly distinguishing it, has a rapid, surprising, and inexplicable effect upon us and upon our organs, and through them on our ideas and on our being itself.

How profound that mystery of the Invisible is! We

cannot fathom it with our miserable senses: our eyes are unable to perceive what is either too small or too great, too near to or too far from us; we can see neither the inhabitants of a star nor of a drop of water; our ears deceive us, for they transmit to us the vibrations of the air in sonorous notes. Our senses are fairies who work the miracle of changing that movement into noise, and by that metamorphosis give birth to music, which makes the mute agitation of nature a harmony. So with our sense of smell, which is weaker than that of a dog, and so with our sense of taste, which can scarcely distinguish the age of a wine!

Oh! If we only had other organs which could work other miracles in our favor, what a number of fresh things we might discover around us!

May 16. I am ill, decidedly! I was so well last month! I am feverish, horribly feverish, or rather I am in a state of feverish enervation, which makes my mind suffer as much as my body. I have without ceasing the horrible sensation of some danger threatening me, the apprehension of some coming misfortune or of approaching death, a presentiment which is, no doubt, an attack of some illness still unnamed, which germinates in the flesh and in the blood.

May 18. I have just come from consulting my medical man, for I can no longer get my sleep. He found that my pulse was high, my eyes dilated, my nerves highly strung, but no alarming symptoms. I must have a course of shower baths and of bromide of potassium.

May 25. No change! My state is really very peculiar. As the evening comes on, an incomprehensible feeling of disquietude seizes me, just as if night concealed some terrible menace toward me. I dine quickly, and then try to read, but I do not understand the words, and can scarcely distinguish the letters. Then I walk up and down my drawing-room, oppressed by a feeling of confused and irresistible fear, a fear of sleep and a fear of my bed.

About ten o'clock I go up to my room. As soon as I have entered I lock and bolt the door. I am frightened—of what? Up till the present time I have been frightened of nothing. I open my cupboards, and look under my bed; I listen—I listen—to what? How strange it is that a simple feeling of discomfort, of impeded or heightened circulation, perhaps the irritation of a nervous center, a slight congestion, a small disturbance in the imperfect and delicate functions of our living machinery, can turn the most light-hearted of men into a melancholy one, and make a coward of the bravest? Then, I go to bed, and I wait for sleep as a man might wait for the executioner. I wait for its coming with dread, and my heart beats and my legs tremble, while my whole body shivers beneath the warmth of the bedclothes, until the moment when I suddenly fall asleep, as a man throws himself into a pool of stagnant water in order to drown. I do not feel this perfidious sleep coming over me as I used to, but a sleep which is close to me and watching me, which is going to seize me by the head, to close my eyes and annihilate me.

I sleep—a long time—two or three hours perhaps—then a dream—no—a nightmare lays hold of me. I feel that I am in bed asleep—I feel it and I know it—and I feel also that somebody is coming close to me, is looking at me, touching me, is getting onto my bed, is kneeling on my chest, is taking my neck between his hands and squeezing it—squeezing it with all his might in order to strangle me.

I struggle, bound by that terrible powerlessness which paralyzes us in our dreams; I try to cry out—but I cannot; I want to move—I cannot; I try, with the most violent efforts and out of breath, to turn over and throw off this being which is crushing and suffocating me—I cannot!

And then suddenly I wake up, shaken and bathed in perspiration; I light a candle and find that I am alone, and after that crisis, which occurs every night, I at length fall asleep and slumber tranquilly till morning.

June 2. My state has grown worse. What is the matter with me? The bromide does me no good, and the shower-baths have no effect whatever. Sometimes, in order to tire myself out, though I am fatigued enough already, I go for a walk in the forest of Roumare. I used to think at first that the fresh light and soft air, impregnated with the odor of herbs and leaves, would instill new life into my veins and impart fresh energy to my heart. One day I turned into a broad ride in the wood, and then I diverged toward La Bouille, through a narrow path, between two rows of exceedingly tall trees, which placed a thick, green, almost black roof between the sky and me.

A sudden shiver ran through me, not a cold shiver, but a shiver of agony, and so I hastened my steps, uneasy at being alone in the wood, frightened stupidly and without reason, at the profound solitude. Suddenly it seemed as if I were being followed, that somebody was walking at my heels, close, quite close to me, near enough to touch me.

I turned round suddenly, but I was alone. I saw nothing behind me except the straight, broad ride, empty and bordered by high trees, horribly empty; on the other side also it extended until it was lost in the distance, and looked just the same—terrible.

I closed my eyes. Why? And then I began to turn round on one heel very quickly, just like a top. I nearly fell down, and opened my eyes; the trees were dancing round me and the earth heaved; I was obliged to sit down. Then, ah! I no longer remembered how I had come! What a strange idea! What a strange, strange idea! I did not the least know. I started off to the right, and got back into the avenue which had led me into the middle of the forest.

June 3. I have had a terrible night. I shall go away

for a few weeks, for no doubt a journey will set me up again.

July 2. I have come back, quite cured, and have had a most delightful trip into the bargain. I have been to Mont Saint-Michel, which I had not seen before.

* * * * * * * * * * * * * * *

July 3. I have slept badly; certainly there is some feverish influence here, for my coachman is suffering in the same way as I am. When I went back home yesterday, I noticed his singular paleness, and I asked him: "What is the matter with you, Jean?"

"The matter is that I never get any rest, and my nights devour my days. Since your departure, Monsieur, there has been a spell over me."

However, the other servants are all well, but I am very frightened of having another attack, myself.

July 4. I am decidedly taken again; for my old nightmares have returned. Last night I felt somebody leaning on me who was sucking my life from between my lips with his mouth. Yes, he was sucking it out of my neck as a leech would have done. Then he got up, satiated, and I woke up, so beaten, crushed, and annihilated that I could not move. If this continues for a few days, I shall certainly go away again.

July 5. Have I lost my reason? What has happened? What I saw last night is so strange that my head wanders when I think of it!

As I do now every evening, I had locked my door; then, being thirsty, I drank half a glass of water, and I accidentally noticed that the water-bottle was full up to the cut-glass stopper.

Then I went to bed and fell into one of my terrible sleeps, from which I was aroused in about two hours by a still more terrible shock.

Picture to yourself a sleeping man who is being

murdered, who wakes up with a knife in his chest, a gurgling in his throat, is covered with blood, can no longer breathe, is going to die and does not understand anything at all about it—there you have it.

Having recovered my senses, I was thirsty again, so I lighted a candle and went to the table on which my water-bottle was. I lifted it up and tilted it over my glass, but nothing came out. It was empty! It was completely empty! At first I could not understand it at all; then suddenly I was seized by such a terrible feeling that I had to sit down, or rather fall into a chair! Then I sprang up with a bound to look about me; then I sat down again, overcome by astonishment and fear, in front of the transparent crystal bottle! I looked at it with fixed eyes, trying to solve the puzzle, and my hands trembled! Somebody had drunk the water, but who? I? I without any doubt. It could surely only be I? In that case I was a somnambulist—was living, without knowing it, that double, mysterious life which makes us doubt whether there are not two beings in us—whether a strange, un-knowable, and invisible being does not, during our moments of mental and physical torpor, animate the inert body, forcing it to a more willing obedience than it yields to ourselves.

Oh! Who will understand my horrible agony? Who will understand the emotion of a man sound in mind, wide awake, full of sense, who looks in horror at the disappearance of a little water while he was asleep, through the glass of a water-bottle! And I remained sitting until it was daylight, without venturing to go to bed again.

July 6. I am going mad. Again all the contents of my water-bottle have been drunk during the night; or rather I have drunk it!

But is it I? Is it I? Who could it be? Who? Oh! God! Am I going mad? Who will save me?

July 10. I have just been through some surprising ordeals. Undoubtedly I must be mad! And yet!

On July 6, before going to bed, I put some wine, milk, water, bread, and strawberries on my table. Somebody drank—I drank—all the water and a little of the milk, but neither the wine, nor the bread, nor the strawberries were touched.

On the seventh of July I renewed the same experiment, with the same results, and on July 8 I left out the water and the milk and nothing was touched.

Lastly, on July 9 I put only water and milk on my table, taking care to wrap up the bottles in white muslin and to tie down the stoppers. Then I rubbed my lips, my beard, and my hands with pencil lead, and went to bed.

Deep slumber seized me, soon followed by a terrible awakening. I had not moved, and my sheets were not marked. I rushed to the table. The muslin round the bottles remained intact; I undid the string, trembling with fear. All the water had been drunk, and so had the milk! Ah! Great God! I must start for Paris immediately.

July 12. Paris. I must have lost my head during the last few days! I must be the plaything of my enervated imagination, unless I am really a somnambulist, or I have been brought under the power of one of those influences—hypnotic suggestion, for example—which are known to exist, but have hitherto been inexplicable. In any case, my mental state bordered on madness, and twenty-four hours of Paris sufficed to restore me to my equilibrium.

Yesterday after doing some business and paying some visits, which instilled fresh and invigorating mental air into me, I wound up my evening at the Théâtre Français. A drama by Alexander Dumas the Younger was being acted, and his brilliant and powerful play completed my cure. Certainly solitude is dangerous for active minds. We need men around us who can think and can talk. When we are alone for a long time, we people space with phantoms.

I returned along the boulevards to my hotel in excellent spirits. Amid the jostling of the crowd I thought, not without irony, of my terrors and surmises of the previous week, because I believed, yes, I believed, that an invisible being lived beneath my roof. How weak our mind is; how quickly it is terrified and unbalanced as soon as we are confronted with a small, incomprehensible fact. Instead of dismissing the problem with: "We do not understand because we cannot find the cause," we immediately imagine terrible mysteries and supernatural powers.

* * * * * * * * * * * * * * * *

July 30. I came back to my own house yesterday. Everything is going well.

August 2. Nothing fresh; it is splendid weather, and I spend my days in watching the Seine flow past.

August 4. Quarrels among my servants. They declare that the glasses are broken in the cupboards at night. The footman accuses the cook, she accuses the needle-woman, and the latter accuses the other two. Who is the culprit? It would take a clever person to tell.

August 6. This time, I am not mad. I have seen—I have seen—I have seen!—I can doubt no longer—*I have seen it!*

I was walking at two o'clock among my rose-trees, in the full sunlight—in the walk bordered by autumn roses which are beginning to fall. As I stopped to look at a Géant de Bataille, which had three splendid blooms, I distinctly saw the stalk of one of the roses bend close to me, as if an invisible hand had bent it, and then break, as if that hand had picked it! Then the flower raised itself, following the curve which a hand would have described in carrying toward a mouth, and remained suspended in the transparent air, alone and motionless, a terrible red spot, three yards from my eyes. In desperation I rushed at it to take it! I found nothing; it disappeared. Then I was seized with furious rage against myself, for it is not wholesome for a reasonable and serious man to have such hallucinations.

But was it a hallucination? I turned to look for the stalk, and I found it immediately under the bush, freshly broken, between the two other roses which remained on the branch. I returned home, then, with a much disturbed mind; for I am certain now, certain as I am of the alternation of day and night, that there exists close to me an invisible being who lives on milk and on water, who can touch objects, take them and change their places; who is, consequently, endowed with a material nature, although imperceptible to sense, and who lives as I do, under my roof—

August 7. I slept tranquilly. He drank the water out of my decanter, but did not disturb my sleep.

I ask myself whether I am mad. As I was walking just now in the sun by the riverside, doubts as to my own sanity arose in me; not vague doubts such as I have had hitherto, but precise and absolute doubts. I have seen mad people, and I have known some who were quite intelligent, lucid, even clear-sighted in every concern of life, except on one point. They could speak clearly, readily, profoundly on everything; till their thoughts were caught in the breakers of their delusions and went to pieces there, were dispersed and swamped in that furious and terrible sea of fogs and squalls which is called *madness*.

I certainly should think that I was mad, absolutely mad, if I were not conscious that I knew my state, if I could not fathom it and analyze it with the most complete lucidity. I should, in fact, be a reasonable man laboring under a hallucination. Some unknown disturbance must have been excited in my brain, one of those disturbances which physiologists of the present day try to note and to fix precisely, and that disturbance must have caused a profound gulf in my mind and in the order and logic of my ideas. Similar phenomena occur in dreams, and lead us through the most unlikely phantasmagoria, without causing us any surprise, because our verifying apparatus and our sense of control have gone to sleep, while our imaginative faculty wakes and works. Was it not possible that one of the imperceptible keys of the cerebral finger-board had been paralyzed in me? Some men lose the recollection of proper names, or of verbs, or of numbers, or merely of dates, in consequence of an accident. The localization of all the avenues of thought has been accomplished nowadays; what, then, would there be surprising in the fact that my faculty of controlling the unreality of certain hallucinations should be destroyed for the time being?

I thought of all this as I walked by the side of the water. The sun was shining brightly on the river and made earth delightful, while it filled me with love for life, for the swallows, whose swift agility is always delightful in my eyes, for the plants by the riverside, whose rustling is a pleasure to my ears.

By degrees, however, an inexplicable feeling of discomfort seized me. It seemed to me as if some unknown force were numbing and stopping me, were preventing me from going further and were calling me back. I felt that painful wish to return which comes on you when you have left a beloved invalid at home, and are seized by a presentiment that he is worse.

I, therefore, returned despite myself, feeling certain that I should find some bad news awaiting me, a letter or a telegram. There was nothing, however, and I was surprised and uneasy, more so than if I had had another fantastic vision.

August 8. I spent a terrible evening, yesterday. He does not show himself any more, but I feel that He is near me, watching me, looking at me, penetrating me, dominating me, and more terrible to me when He hides himself thus than if He were to manifest his constant and invisible presence by supernatural phenomena. However, I slept.

August 9. Nothing, but I am afraid.

August 10. Nothing; but what will happen tomorrow?

August 11. Still nothing. I cannot stop at home with this fear hanging over me and these thoughts in my mind; I shall go away.

August 12. Ten o'clock at night. All day long I have been trying to get away, and have not been able. I contemplated a simple and easy act of liberty, a carriage ride to Rouen—and I have not been able to do it. What is the reason?

August 13. When one is attacked by certain maladies, the springs of our physical being seem broken, our energies destroyed, our muscles relaxed, our bones to be as soft as our flesh, and our blood as liquid as water. I am experiencing the same in my moral being, in a strange and distressing manner. I have no longer any strength, any courage, any self-control, nor even any power to set my own will in motion. I have no power left to *will* anything, but some one does it for me and I obey.

August 14. I am lost! Somebody possesses my soul and governs it! Somebody orders all my acts, all my movements, all my thoughts. I am no longer master of myself, nothing except an enslaved and terrified spectator of the things which I do. I wish to go out; I cannot. *He* does not wish to; and so I remain, trembling and distracted in the armchair in which he keeps me sitting. I merely wish to get up and to rouse myself, so as to think that I am still master of myself: I cannot! I am riveted to my chair, and my chair adheres to the floor in such a manner that no force of mine can move us.

Then suddenly, I must, I *must* go to the foot of my garden to pick some strawberries and eat them—and I go there, I pick the strawberries and I eat them! Oh! my God! my God! Is there a God? If there be one, deliver me! save me! succor me! Pardon! Pity! Mercy! Save me! Oh! what sufferings! what torture! what horror!

August 15. . . . But who is He, this invisible being that rules me, this unknowable being, this rover of a supernatural race?

Invisible beings exist, then! How is it, then, that since the beginning of the world they have never manifested themselves in such a manner as they do to me? I have never read anything that resembles what goes on in my house. Oh! If I could only leave it, if I could only go away and flee, and never return, I should be saved; but I cannot.

August 16. I managed to escape today for two hours, like a prisoner who finds the door of his dungeon accidentally open. I suddenly felt that I was free and that He was far away, and so I gave orders to put the horses in as quickly as possible, and I drove to Rouen. Oh! how delightful to be able to say to my coachman: "Go to Rouen!"

I made him pull up before the library, and I begged them to lend me Dr. Herrmann Herestauss's treatise on the unknown inhabitants of the ancient and modern world.

Then, as I was getting into my carriage, I intended to say: "To the railway station!" but instead of this I shouted—I did not speak, but I shouted—in such a loud voice that all the passers-by turned round: "Home!" and I fell back onto the cushion of my carriage, overcome by mental agony. He had found me out and regained possession of me.

August 17. Oh! What a night! what a night! And yet it seems to me that I ought to rejoice. I read until one o'clock in the morning! Herestauss, Doctor of Philosophy and Theogony, wrote the history and the manifestation of all those invisible beings which hover around man, or of whom he dreams. He describes their origin, their domains, their power; but none of them resembles the one which haunts me. One might say that man, ever since he has thought, has had a foreboding and a fear of a new being, stronger than himself, his successor in this world, and that, feeling him near, and not being able to foretell the nature of the unseen one, he has, in his terror, created the whole race of hidden beings, vague phantoms born of fear.

Having, therefore, read until one o'clock in the morning, I went and sat down at the open window, in order to cool my forehead and my thoughts in the calm night air. It was very pleasant and warm! How I should have enjoyed such a night formerly!

There was no moon, but the stars darted out their rays in the dark heavens. Who inhabits those worlds? What forms, what living beings, what animals are there yonder? Do those who are thinkers in those distant worlds know more than we do? What can they do more than we? What do they see which we do not? Will not one of them, some day or other, traversing space, appear on our earth to conquer it, just as formerly the Norsemen crossed the sea in order to subjugate nations feebler than themselves?

We are so weak, so powerless, so ignorant, so small— we who live on this particle of mud which revolves in liquid air.

I fell asleep, dreaming thus in the cool night air, and then, having slept for about three quarters of an hour, I opened my eyes without moving, awakened by an indescribably confused and strange sensation. At first I saw nothing, and then suddenly it appeared to me as if a page of the book, which had remained open on my table, turned over of its own accord. Not a breath of air had come in at my window, and I was surprised and waited. In about four minutes, I saw, I saw—yes I saw with my own eyes—another page lift itself up and fall down on the others, as if a finger had turned it over. My armchair was empty, appeared empty, but I knew that He was there. He, and sitting in my place, and that He

542   *GHOSTS, CASTLES, AND VICTIMS*

was reading. With a furious bound, the bound of an enraged wild beast that wishes to disembowel its tamer, I crossed my room to seize Him, to strangle Him, to kill Him! But before I could reach it, my chair fell over as if somebody had run away from me. My table rocked, my lamp fell and went out, and my window closed as if some thief had been surprised and had fled out into the night, shutting it behind him.

So He had run away; He had been afraid; He, afraid of me!

So tomorrow, or later—some day or other, I should be able to hold him in my clutches and crush him against the ground! Do not dogs occasionally bite and strangle their masters?

August 18. I have been thinking the whole day long. Oh! yes, I will obey Him, follow His impulses, fulfill all His wishes, show myself humble, submissive, a coward. He is the stronger; but an hour will come.

August 19. I know, I know, I know all! I have just read the following in the *Revue du Monde Scientifique:* "A curious piece of news comes to us from Rio de Janeiro. Madness, an epidemic of madness, which may be compared to that contagious madness which attacked the people of Europe in the Middle Ages, is at this moment raging in the Province of San-Paulo. The frightened inhabitants are leaving their houses, deserting their villages, abandoning their land, saying that they are pursued, possessed, governed like human cattle by invisible, though tangible beings, by a species of vampire, which feeds on their life while they are asleep, and which, besides, drinks water and milk without appearing to touch any other nourishment.

"Professor Don Pedro Henriques, accompanied by several medical savants, has gone to the Province of San-Paulo, in order to study the origin and the manifestations of this surprising madness on the spot, and to propose such measures to the Emperor as may appear to him to be most fitted to restore the mad population to reason."

Ah! Ah! I remember now that fine Brazilian three master which passed in front of my windows as it was going up the Seine, on the eighth of last May! I thought it looked so pretty, so white and bright! That Being was on board of her, coming from there, where its race sprang from. And it saw me! It saw my house, which was also white, and He sprang from the ship on to the land. Oh! Good heavens.

Now I know, I can divine. The reign of man is over, and He has come. He whom disquieted priests exorcised, whom sorcerers evoked on dark nights, without seeing Him appear, He to whom the imaginations of the transient masters of the world lent all the monstrous or graceful forms of gnomes, spirits, genii, fairies, and familiar spirits. After the coarse conceptions of primitive fear, men more enlightened gave him a truer form. Mesmer divined him, and ten years ago physicians accurately discovered the nature of His power, even before He exercised it Himself. They played with that weapon of their new Lord, the sway of a mysterious will over the human soul, which had become enslaved. They called it mesmerism, hypnotism, suggestion, I know not what. I have seen them diverting themselves like rash children with this horrible power! Woe to us! Woe to man! He has come, the—the—what does He call Himself—the—I fancy that He is shouting out His name to me and I do not hear Him—the—yes—He is shouting it out—I am listening—I cannot—repeat—it—Horla—I have heard—the Horla —it is He—the Horla—He has come!—

Ah! the vulture has eaten the pigeon, the wolf has eaten the lamb; the lion has devoured the sharp-horned buffalo; man has killed the lion with an arrow, with a spear, with gunpowder; but the Horla will make of man what man has made of the horse and of the ox: His chattel, His slave, and His food, by the mere power of His will. Woe to us!

But, nevertheless, sometimes the animal rebels and kills the man who has subjugated it. I should also like— I shall be able to—but I must know Him, touch Him, see Him! Learned men say that eyes of animals, as they differ from ours, do not distinguish as ours do. And my eye cannot distinguish this newcomer who is oppressing me.

Why? Oh! Now I remember the words of the monk at Mont Saint-Michel: "Can we see the hundred-thousandth part of what exists? Listen; there is the wind which is the strongest force in nature; it knocks men down, blows down buildings, uproots trees, raises the sea into mountains of water, destroys cliffs, and casts great ships onto the breakers; it kills, it whistles, it sighs, it roars—have you ever seen it, and can you see it? It exists for all that, however!"

And I went on thinking: my eyes are so weak, so imperfect, that they do not even distinguish hard bodies, if they are as transparent as glass! If a glass without quicksilver behind it were to bar my way, I should run into it, just like a bird which has flown into a room breaks its head against the windowpanes. A thousand things, moreover, deceive a man and lead him astray. How then is it surprising that he cannot perceive a new body which is penetrated and pervaded by the light?

A new being! Why not? It was assuredly bound to come! Why should we be the last? We do not distinguish it, like all the others created before us? The reason is, that its nature is more delicate, its body finer and more finished than ours. Our make-up is so weak, so awkwardly conceived; our body is encumbered with organs that are always tired, always being strained like locks that are too complicated; it lives like a plant and like an animal nourishing itself with difficulty on air, herbs, and flesh; it is a brute machine which is a prey to maladies, to malformations, to decay; it is broken-winded, badly regulated, simple and eccentric, ingeniously yet badly made, a coarse and yet a delicate mechanism, in brief, the outline of a being which might become intelligent and great.

There are only a few—so few—stages of development in this world, from the oyster up to man. Why should there not be one more, when once that period is accomplished which separates the successive products one from the other?

Why not one more? Why not, also, other trees with immense, splendid flowers, perfuming whole regions? Why not other elements besides fire, air, earth, and water? There are four, only four, nursing fathers of various beings! What a pity! Why should not there be forty, four hundred, four thousand! How poor everything is, how mean and wretched—grudgingly given, poorly invented, clumsily made! Ah! the elephant and the hippopotamus, what power! And the camel, what suppleness!

But the butterfly, you will say, a flying flower! I dream of one that should be as large as a hundred worlds, with wings whose shape, beauty, colors, and motion I cannot even express. But I see it—it flutters from star to star, refreshing them and perfuming them with the light and harmonious breath of its flight! And the people up there gaze at it as it passes in an ecstasy of delight!

What is the matter with me? It is He, the Horla who haunts me, and who makes me think of these foolish things! He is within me, He is becoming my soul; I shall kill Him!

August 20. I shall kill Him. I have seen Him! Yesterday I sat down at my table and pretended to write very assiduously. I knew quite well that He would come prowling round me, quite close to me, so close that I might perhaps be able to touch Him, to seize Him. And then—then I should have the strength of desperation; I should have my hands, my knees, my chest, my forehead, my teeth to strangle Him, to crush Him, to bite Him, to tear Him to pieces. And I watched for Him with all my overexcited nerves.

I had lighted my two lamps and the eight wax candles on my mantlepiece, as if, by this light I should discover Him.

My bed, my old oak bed with its columns, was opposite to me; on my right was the fireplace; on my left the door, which was carefully closed, after I had left it open for some time, in order to attract Him; behind me was a very high wardrobe with a looking-glass in it, which served me to dress by every day, and in which I was in the habit of inspecting myself from head to foot every time I passed it.

So I pretended to be writing in order to deceive Him, for He also was watching me, and suddenly I felt, I was certain, that He was reading over my shoulder, that He was there, almost touching my ear.

I got up so quickly, with my hands extended, that I almost fell. Horror! It was as bright as at midday, but I did not see myself in the glass! It was empty, clear, profound, full of light! But my figure was not reflected in it —and I, I was opposite to it! I saw the large, clear glass from top to bottom, and I looked at it with unsteady eyes. I did not dare advance; I did not venture to make a movement; feeling certain, nevertheless, that He was there, but that He would escape me again, He whose imperceptible body had absorbed my reflection.

How frightened I was! And then suddenly I began to see myself through a mist in the depths of the looking-glass, in a mist as it were, or through a veil of water; and it seemed to me as if this water were flowing slowly from left to right, and making my figure clearer every moment. It was like the end of an eclipse. Whatever hid me did not appear to possess any clearly defined outlines, but was a sort of opaque transparency, which gradually grew clearer.

At last I was able to distinguish myself completely, as I do every day when I look at myself.

I had seen Him! And the horror of it remained with me, and makes me shudder even now.

August 21. How could I kill Him, since I could not get hold of Him? Poison? But he would see me mix it with the water; and then, would our poisons have any effect on His impalpable body? No—no—no doubt about the matter. Then?—then?

August 22. I sent for a blacksmith from Rouen and ordered iron shutters of him for my room, such as some private hotels in Paris have on the ground floor, for fear of thieves and he is going to make me a similar door as well. I have made myself out a coward, but I do not care about that!

September 10. Rouen, Hotel Continental. It is done; it is done—but is He dead? My mind is thoroughly upset by what I have seen.

Well then, yesterday, the locksmith having put on the iron shutters and door, I left everything open until midnight, although it was getting cold.

Suddenly I felt that He was there, and joy, mad joy took possession of me. I got up softly, and I walked to the right and left for some time, so that He might not guess anything; then I took off my boots and put on my slippers carelessly; then I fastened the iron shutters and going back to the door quickly I double-locked it with a padlock, putting the key into my pocket.

Suddenly I noticed that He was moving restlessly round me, that in His turn He was frightened and was ordering me to let Him out. I nearly yielded, though I did not quite, but putting my back to the door, I half opened it, just enough to allow me to go out backward, and as I am very tall, my head touched the lintel. I was sure that He had not been able to escape, and I shut Him up quite alone, quite alone. What happiness! I had Him fast. Then I ran downstairs into the drawing room which was under my bedroom. I took the two lamps and poured all the oil onto the carpet, the furniture, everywhere; then I set fire to it and made my escape, after having carefully double-locked the door.

I went and hid myself at the bottom of the garden in a clump of laurel bushes. How long it was! how long it was! Everything was dark, silent, motionless, not a breath of air and not a star, but heavy banks of clouds which one could not see, but which weighted, oh! so heavily on my soul.

I looked at my house and waited. How long it was! I already began to think that the fire had gone out of its own accord, or that He had extinguished it, when one of the lower windows gave way under the violence of the flames, and a long, soft, caressing sheet of red flame mounted up the white wall, and kissed it as high as the roof. The light fell on to the trees, the branches, and the leaves, and a shiver of fear pervaded them also! The birds awoke; a dog began to howl, and it seemed to me as if the day were breaking! Almost immediately two other windows flew into fragments, and I saw that the whole of the lower part of my house was nothing but a terrible furnace. But a cry, a horrible, shrill, heart-rending cry, a woman's cry sounded through the night, and two garret windows were opened! I had forgotten the servants! I saw the terror-struck faces, and the frantic waving of their arms!

Then, overwhelmed with horror, I ran off to the village, shouting: "Help! help! fire! fire!" Meeting some people who were already coming on to the scene, I went back with them to see!

By this time the house was nothing but a horrible and magnificent funeral pile, a monstrous pyre which lit up the whole country, a pyre where men were burning, and where He was burning also, He, He, my prisoner, that new Being, the new Master, the Horla!

Suddenly the whole roof fell in between the walls, and a volcano of flames darted up to the sky. Through all the windows which opened on to that furnace, I saw the flames darting, and I reflected that He was there, in that kiln, dead.

Dead? Perhaps? His body? Was not his body, which was transparent, indestructible by such means as would kill ours?

If He were not dead? Perhaps time alone has power over that Invisible and Redoubtable Being. Why this transparent, unrecognizable body, this body belonging to a spirit, if it also had to fear ills, infirmities, and premature destruction?

Premature destruction? All human terror springs from that! After man the Horla. After him who can die every day, at any hour, at any moment, by any accident, He came, He who was only to die at his own proper hour and minute, because He had touched the limits of his existence!

No—no—there is no doubt about it—He is not dead. Then—then—I suppose I must kill *myself!*

The Dead Valley

by Ralph Adams Cram

I have a friend, Olof Ehrensvärd, a Swede by birth, who yet, by reason of a strange and melancholy mischance of his early boyhood, has thrown his lot with that of the New World. It is a curious story of a headstrong boy and a proud and relentless family: the details do not matter here, but they are sufficient to weave a web of romance around the tall yellow-bearded man with the sad eyes and the voice that gives itself perfectly to plaintive little Swedish songs remembered out of childhood. In the winter evenings we play chess together, he and I, and after some close fierce battle has been fought to a finish—usually with my own defeat—we fill our pipes again, and Ehrensvärd tells me stories of the far, half-remembered days in the fatherland, before he went to sea: stories that grow very strange and incredible as the night deepens and the fire falls together, but stories that, nevertheless, I fully believe.

One of them made a strong impression on me, so I set it down here, only regretting that I cannot reproduce the curiously perfect English and the delicate accent which to me increased the fascination of the tale. Yet, as best I can remember it, here it is.

"I never told you how Nils and I went over the hills to Hallsberg, and how we found the Dead Valley, did I? Well, this is the way it happened. I must have been about twelve years old, and Nils Sjöberg, whose father's estate joined ours, was a few months younger. We were inseparable just at that time, and whatever we did, we did together.

"Once a week it was market day in Engelholm, and Nils and I went always there to see the strange sights that the market gathered from all the surrounding country. One day we quite lost our hearts, for an old man from across the Elfborg had brought a little dog to sell, that seemed to us the most beautiful dog in all the world. He was a round, woolly puppy, so funny that Nils and I sat down on the ground and laughed at him, until he came and played with us in so jolly a way that we felt that there was only one really desirable thing in life, and that was the little dog of the old man from across the hills. But alas! we had not half money enough wherewith to buy him, so we were forced to beg the old man not to sell him before the next market day, promising that we would bring the money for him then. He gave us his word, and we ran home very fast and implored our mothers to give us money for the little dog.

"We got the money, but we could not wait for the next market day. Suppose the puppy should be sold! The thought frightened us so that we begged and implored that we might be allowed to go over the hills to Hallsberg where the old man lived, and get the little dog ourselves, and at last they told us we might go. By starting early in the morning we should reach Hallsberg by three o'clock, and it was arranged that we should stay there that night with Nils's aunt, and, leaving by noon the next day, be home again by sunset.

"Soon after sunrise we were on our way, after having

received minute instructions as to just what we should do in all possible and impossible circumstances, and finally a repeated injunction that we should start for home at the same hour the next day, so that we might get safely back before nightfall.

"For us, it was magnificent sport, and we started off with our rifles, full of the sense of our very great importance: yet the journey was simple enough, along a good road, across the big hills we knew so well, for Nils and I had shot over half the territory this side of the dividing ridge of the Elfborg. Back of Engelholm lay a long valley, from which rose the low mountains, and we had to cross this, and then follow the road along the side of the hills for three or four miles, before a narrow path branched off to the left, leading up through the pass.

"Nothing occurred of interest on the way over, and we reached Hallsberg in due season, found to our inexpressible joy that the little dog was not sold, secured him, and so went to the house of Nils's aunt to spend the night.

"Why we did not leave early on the following day, I can't quite remember; at all events, I know we stopped at a shooting range just outside of the town, where most attractive paste-board pigs were sliding slowly through painted foliage, serving so as beautiful marks. The result was that we did not get fairly started for home until afternoon, and as we found ourselves at last pushing up the side of the mountain with the sun dangerously near their summits, I think we were a little scared at the prospect of the examination and possible punishment that awaited us when we got home at midnight.

"Therefore we hurried as fast as possible up the mountain side, while the blue dusk closed in about us, and the light died in the purple sky. At first we had talked hilariously, and the little dog had leaped ahead of us with the utmost joy. Latterly, however, a curious oppression came on us; we did not speak or even whistle, while the dog fell behind, following us with hesitation in every muscle.

"We had passed through the foothills and the low spurs of the mountains, and were almost at the top of the main range, when life seemed to go out of everything, leaving the world dead, so suddenly silent the forest became, so stagnant the air. Instinctively we halted to listen.

"Perfect silence,—the crushing silence of deep forests at night; and more, for always, even in the most impenetrable fastness of the wooded mountains, is the multitudinous murmur of little lives, awakened by the darkness, exaggerated and intensified by the stillness of the air and the great dark: but here and now the silence seemed unbroken even by the turn of a leaf, the movement of a twig, the note of night bird or insect. I could hear the blood beat through my veins; and the crushing of the grass under our feet as we advanced with hesitating steps sounded like the falling of trees.

"And the air was stagnant,—dead. The atmosphere seemed to lie upon the body like the weight of sea on a diver who has ventured too far into its awful depths. What we usually call silence seems so only in relation to the din of ordinary experience. This was silence in the absolute, and it crushed the mind while it intensified the senses, bringing down the awful weight of inextinguishable fear.

"I know that Nils and I stared towards each other in abject terror, listening to our quick, heavy breathing, that sounded to our acute senses like the fitful rush of waters. And the poor little dog we were leading justified our terror. The black oppression seemed to crush him even as it did us. He lay close on the ground, moaning feebly, and dragging himself painfully and slowly closer to Nils's feet. I think this exhibition of utter animal fear was the last touch, and must inevitably have blasted our reason— mine anyway; but just then, as we stood quaking on the bounds of madness, came a sound, so awful, so ghastly, so horrible, that it seemed to rouse us from the dead spell that was on us.

"In the depth of the silence came a cry, beginning as a low, sorrowful moan, rising to a tremulous shriek, culminating in a yell that seemed to tear the night in sunder and rend the world as by a cataclysm. So fearful was it that I could not believe it had actual existence: it passed previous experience, the powers of belief, and for a moment I thought it the result of my own animal terror, an hallucination born of tottering reason.

"A glance at Nils dispelled this thought in a flash. In the pale light of the high stars he was the embodiment of all possible human fear, quaking with an ague, his jaw fallen, his tongue out, his eyes protruding like those of a hanged man. Without a word we fled, the panic of fear giving us strength, and together, the little dog caught close in Nils's arms, we sped down the side of the cursed mountains,—anywhere, goal was of no account: we had but one impulse—to get away from that place.

"So under the black trees and the far white stars that flashed through the still leaves overhead, we leaped down the mountain side, regardless of path or landmark, straight through the tangled underbrush, across mountain streams, through fens and copses, anywhere, so only that our course was downward.

"How long we ran thus, I have no idea, but by and by the forest fell behind, and we found ourselves among the foothills, and fell exhausted on the dry short grass, panting like tired dogs.

"It was lighter here in the open, and presently we looked around to see where we were, and how we were to strike out in order to find the path that would lead us home. We looked in vain for a familiar sign. Behind us rose the great wall of black forest on the flank of the mountain: before us lay the undulating mounds of low foot-hills, unbroken by trees or rocks, and beyond, only the fall of black sky bright with multitudinous stars that turned its velvet depth to a luminous gray.

"As I remember, we did not speak to each other once: the terror was too heavy on us for that, but by and by we rose simultaneously and started out across the hills.

"Still the same silence, the same dead, motionless air— air that was at once sultry and chilling: a heavy heat struck through with an icy chill that felt almost like the burning of frozen steel. Still carrying the helpless dog, Nils pressed on through the hills, and I followed close behind. At last, in front of us, rose a slope of moor touching the white stars. We climbed it wearily, reached the top, and found ourselves gazing down into a great, smooth valley, filled half way to the brim with—what?

"As far as the eye could see stretched a level plain of ashy white, faintly phosphorescent, a sea of velvet fog that lay like motionless water, or rather like a floor of alabaster, so dense did it appear, so seemingly capable of sustaining weight. If it were possible, I think that sea of dead white mist struck even greater terror into my soul than the heavy silence or the deadly cry—so ominous was it, so utterly unreal, so phantasmal, so impossible, as it lay there like a dead ocean under the steady stars. Yet through that mist *we must go!* there seemed no other way home, and, shattered with abject fear, mad with the one desire to get back, we started down the slope to where the sea of milky mist ceased, sharp and distinct around the stems of the rough grass.

"I put one foot into the ghostly fog. A chill as of death struck through me, stopping my heart, and I threw myself backward on the slope. At that instant came again the shriek, close, close, right in our ears, in ourselves, and far out across that damnable sea I saw the cold fog lift like a water-spout and toss itself high in writhing convolutions towards the sky. The stars began to grow dim as thick vapor swept across them, and in the growing dark I saw a great, watery moon lift itself slowly above the palpitating sea, vast and vague in the gathering mist.

"This was enough: we turned and fled along the margin of the white sea that throbbed now with fitful motion below us, rising, rising slowly and steadily, driving us higher and higher up the side of the foothills.

"It was a race for life; that we knew. How we kept it up I cannot understand, but we did, and at last we saw the white sea fall behind us as we staggered up the end of the valley, and then down into a region that we knew, and so into the old path. The last thing I remember was hearing a strange voice, that of Nils, but horribly changed, brokenly 'The dog is dead!' and then the whole world turned around twice, slowly and resistlessly, and consciousness went out with a crash.

"It was some three weeks later, as I remember, that I awoke in my own room, and found my mother sitting beside the bed. I could not think very well at first, but as I slowly grew strong again, vague flashes of recollection began to come to me, and little by little the whole sequence of events of that awful night in the Dead Valley came back. All that I could gain from what was told me was that three weeks before I had been found in my own bed, raging sick, and that my illness grew fast into brain fever. I tried to speak of the dread things that had happened to me, but I saw at once that no one looked on them save as the hauntings of a dying frenzy, and so I closed my mouth and kept my own counsel.

"I must see Nils however, and so I asked for him. My mother told me that he also had been ill with a strange fever, but that he was now quite well again. Presently they brought him in, and when we were alone I began to speak to him of the night on the mountain. I shall never forget the shock that struck me down on my pillow when the boy denied everything: denied having gone with me, ever having heard the cry, having seen the valley, or feeling the deadly chill of the ghostly fog. Nothing would shake his determined ignorance, and in spite of myself I was forced to admit that his denials came from no policy of concealment, but from blank oblivion.

"My weakened brain was in a turmoil. Was it all but the floating phantasm of delirium? Or had the horror of the real thing blotted Nils's mind into blankness so far as the events of the night in the Dead Valley were concerned? The latter explanation seemed the only one, else how explain the sudden illness which in a night had struck us both down? I said nothing more, either to Nils or to my own people, but waited, with a growing determination that, once well again, I would find that valley if it really existed.

"It was some weeks before I was really well enough to go, but finally, late in September, I chose a bright, warm, still day, the last smile of the dying summer, and started early in the morning along the path that led to Hallsberg. I was sure I knew where the trail struck off to the right, down which we had come from the valley of dead water, for a great tree grew by the Hallsberg path at the point where, with a sense of salvation, we had found the home road. Presently I saw it to the right, a little distance ahead.

"I think the bright sunlight and the clear air had worked as a tonic to me, for by the time I came to the foot of the great pine, I had quite lost faith in the verity of the vision that haunted me, believing at last that it was indeed but the nightmare of madness. Nevertheless, I turned sharply to the right, at the base of the tree, into a narrow path that led through a dense thicket. As I did so I tripped over something. A swarm of flies sung into the air around me, and looking down I saw the matted fleece, with the poor little bones thrusting through, of the dog we had bought in Hallsberg.

"Then my courage went out with a puff, and I knew that it all was true, and that now I was frightened. Pride and the desire for adventure urged me on, however, and

I pressed into the close thicket that barred my way. The path was hardly visible: merely the worn road of some small beasts, for, though it showed in the crisp grass, the bushes above grew thick and hardly penetrable. The land rose slowly, and rising grew clearer, until at last I came out on a great slope of hill, unbroken by trees or shrubs, very like my memory of that rise of land we had topped in order that we might find the dead valley and the icy fog. I looked at the sun; it was bright and clear, and all around insects were humming in the autumn air, and birds were darting to and fro. Surely there was no danger, not until nightfall at least; so I began to whistle, and with a rush mounted the last crest of brown hill.

"There lay the Dead Valley! A great oval basin, almost as smooth and regular as though made by man. On all sides the grass crept over the brink of the encircling hills, dusty green on the crests, then fading into ashy brown, and so to a deadly white, this last color forming a thin ring, running in a long line around the slope. And then? Nothing. Bare, brown, hard earth, glittering with grains of alkali, but otherwise dead and barren. Not a tuft of grass, not a stick of brushwood, not even a stone, but only the vast expanse of beaten clay.

"In the midst of the basin, perhaps a mile and a half away, the level expanse was broken by a great dead tree, rising leafless and gaunt into the air. Without a moment's hesitation I started down into the valley and made for this goal. Every particle of fear seemed to have left me, and even the valley itself did not look so very terrifying. At all events, I was driven by an overwhelming curiosity, and there seemed to be but one thing in the world to do,—to get to that Tree! As I trudged along over the hard earth, I noticed that the multitudinous voices of birds and insects had died away. No bee or butterfly hovered through the air, no insects leaped or crept over the dull earth. The very air itself was stagnant.

"As I drew near the skeleton tree, I noticed the glint

of sunlight on a kind of white mound around its roots, and I wondered curiously. It was not until I had come close that I saw its nature.

"All around the roots and barkless trunk was heaped a wilderness of little bones. Tiny skulls of rodents and of birds, thousands of them, rising about the dead tree and streaming off for several yards in all directions, until the dreadful pile ended in isolated skulls and scattered skeletons. Here and there a larger bone appeared,—the thigh of a sheep, the hoofs of a horse, and to one side, grinning slowly, a human skull.

"I stood quite still, staring with all my eyes, when suddenly the dense silence was broken by a faint, forlorn cry high over my head. I looked up and saw a great falcon turning and sailing downward just over the tree. In a moment more she fell motionless on the bleaching bones.

"Horror struck me, and I rushed for home, my brain whirling, a strange numbness growing in me. I ran steadily, on and on. At last I glanced up. Where was the rise of hill? I looked around wildly. Close before me was the dead tree with its pile of bones. I had circled it round and round, and the valley wall was still a mile and a half away.

"I stood dazed and frozen. The sun was sinking, red and dull, towards the line of hills. In the east the dark was growing fast. Was there still time? *Time!* It was not *that* I wanted, it was *will!* My feet seemed clogged as in a nightmare. I could hardly drag them over the barren earth. And then I felt the slow chill creeping through me. I looked down. Out of the earth a thin mist was rising, collecting in little pools that grew ever larger until they joined here and there, their currents swirling slowly like thin blue smoke. The western hills halved the copper sun. When it was dark I should hear that shriek again, and then I should die. I knew that, and with every remaining atom of will I staggered towards the red west through the writhing mist that crept clammily around my ankles, retarding my steps.

"And as I fought my way off from the Tree, the horror grew, until at last I thought I was going to die. The silence pursued me like dumb ghosts, the still air held my breath, the hellish fog caught at my feet like cold hands.

"But I won! though not a moment too soon. As I crawled on my hands and knees up the brown slope, I heard, far away and high in the air, the cry that already had almost bereft me of reason. It was faint and vague, but unmistakable in its horrible intensity. I glanced behind. The fog was dense and pallid, heaving undulously up the brown slope. The sky was gold under the setting sun, but below was the ashy gray of death. I stood for a moment on the brink of this sea of hell, and then leaped down the slope. The sunset opened before me, the night closed behind, and as I crawled home weak and tired, darkness shut down on the Dead Valley."

From Beyond

by H. P. Lovecraft

Horrible beyond conception was the change which had taken place in my best friend, Crawford Tillinghast. I had not seen him since that day, two months and a half before, when he told me toward what goal his physical and meta-physical researches were leading; when he had answered my awed and almost frightened remonstrances by driving me from his laboratory and his house in a burst of fanatical rage, I had known that he now remained mostly shut in the attic laboratory with that accursed electrical machine, eating little and excluding even the servants, but I had not thought that a brief period of ten weeks could so alter and disfigure any human creature. It is not pleasant to see a stout man suddenly grown thin, and it is even worse when the baggy skin becomes yellowed or greyed, the eyes sunken, circled, and uncannily glowing, the fore-head veined and corrugated, and the hands tremulous and twitching. And if added to this there be a repellent un-kemptness, a wild disorder of dress, a bushiness of dark hair white at the roots, and an unchecked growth of white beard on a face once clean-shaven, the cumulative effect is quite shocking. But such was the aspect of Crawford

Tillinghast on the night his half coherent message brought me to his door after my weeks of exile; such was the spectre that trembled as it admitted me, candle in hand, and glanced furtively over its shoulder as if fearful of unseen things in the ancient, lonely house set back from Benevolent Street.

That Crawford Tillinghast should ever have studied science and philosophy was a mistake. These things should be left to the frigid and impersonal investigator for they offer two equally tragic alternatives to the man of feeling and action; despair, if he fail in his quest, and terrors unutterable and unimaginable if he succeed. Tillinghast had once been the prey of failure, solitary and melancholy; but now I knew, with nauseating fears of my own, that he was the prey of success. I had indeed warned him ten weeks before, when he burst forth with his tale of what he felt himself about to discover. He had been flushed and excited then, talking in a high and unnatural, though always pedantic, voice.

"What do we know," he had said, "of the world and the universe about us? Our means of receiving impressions are absurdly few, and our notions of surrounding objects infinitely narrow. We see things only as we are constructed to see them, and can gain no idea of their absolute nature. With five feeble senses we pretend to comprehend the boundlessly complex cosmos, yet other beings with a wider, stronger, or different range of senses might not only see very differently the things we see, but might see and study whole worlds of matter, energy, and life which lie close at hand yet can never be detected with the senses we have. I have always believed that such strange, inaccessible worlds exist at our very elbows, *and now I believe I have found a way to break down the barriers*. I am not joking. Within twenty-four hours that machine near the table will generate waves acting on unrecognized sense-organs that exist in us as atrophied or rudimentary vestiges. Those waves will open up to us many vistas unknown to man, and several unknown to anything we consider organic life. We shall see that at which dogs howl in the dark, and that at which cats prick up their ears after midnight. We shall see these things, and other things which no breathing creature has yet seen. We shall overleap time, space, and dimensions, and without bodily motion peer to the bottom of creation."

When Tillinghast said these things I remonstrated, for I knew him well enough to be frightened rather than amused; but he was a fanatic, and drove me from the house. Now he was no less a fanatic, but his desire to speak had conquered his resentment, and he had written me imperatively in a hand I could scarcely recognize. As I entered the abode of the friend so suddenly metamorphosed to a shivering gargoyle, I became infected with the terror which seemed stalking in all the shadows. The words and beliefs expressed ten weeks before seemed bodied forth in the darkness beyond the small circle of candle light, and I sickened at the hollow, altered voice of my host. I wished the servants were about, and did not like it when he said they had all left three days previously. It seemed strange that old Gregory, at least, should desert his master without telling as tried a friend as I. It was he who had given me all the information I had of Tillinghast after I was repulsed in rage.

Yet I soon subordinated all my fears to my growing curiosity and fascination. Just what Crawford Tillinghast now wished of me I could only guess, but that he had some stupendous secret or discovery to impart, I could not doubt. Before I had protested at his unnatural pryings into the unthinkable; now that he had evidently succeeded to some degree I almost shared his spirit, terrible though the cost of victory appeared. Up through the dark emptiness of the house I followed the bobbing candle in the hand of this shaking parody on man. The electricity seemed to be turned off, and when I asked my guide he said it was for a definite reason.

"It would be too much. . . . I would not dare," he continued to mutter. I especially noted his new habit of muttering, for it was not like him to talk to himself. We entered the laboratory in the attic, and I observed that detestable electrical machine, glowing with a sickly, sinister violet luminosity. It was connected with a powerful chemical battery, but seemed to be receiving no current; for I recalled that in its experimental stage it had sputtered and purred when in action. In reply to my question Tillinghast mumbled that this permanent glow was not electrical in any sense that I could understand.

He now seated me near the machine, so that it was on my right, and turned a switch somewhere below the crowning cluster of glass bulbs. The usual sputtering began, turned to a whine, and terminated in a drone so soft as to suggest a return to silence. Meanwhile the luminosity increased, waned again, then assumed a pale, outré colour or blend of colours which I could neither place nor describe. Tillinghast had been watching me, and noted my puzzled expression.

"Do you know what that is?" he whispered, *"that is ultra-violet."* He chuckled oddly at my surprise. "You thought ultra-violet was invisible, and so it is—but you can see that and many other invisible things *now*.

"Listen to me! The waves from that thing are waking a thousand sleeping senses in us; senses which we inherit from aeons of evolution from the state of detached electrons to the state of organic humanity. I have seen the *truth,* and I intend to show it to you. Do you wonder how it will seem? I will tell you." Here Tillinghast seated himself directly opposite me, blowing out his candle and staring hideously into my eyes. "Your existing sense-organs—ears first, I think—will pick up many of the impressions, for they are closely connected with the dormant organs. Then there will be others. You have heard of the pineal gland? I laugh at the shallow endocrinologist, fellow-dupe and fellow-parvenu of the Freudian. That gland is the great sense organ of organs—*I have found out*. It is like sight in the end, and transmits visual pictures to the brain. If you are normal, that is the way you ought to get most of it . . . I mean get most of the evidence *from beyond!*"

I looked about the immense attic room with the sloping south wall, dimly lit by rays which the every-day eye cannot see. The far corners were all shadows, and the whole place took on a hazy unreality which obscured its nature and invited the imagination to symbolism and phantasm. During the interval that Tillinghast was silent I fancied myself in some vast incredible temple of long-dead gods; some vague edifice of innumerable black stone columns reaching up from a floor of damp slabs to a cloudy height beyond the range of my vision. The picture was very vivid for a while, but gradually gave way to a more horrible conception; that of utter, absolute solitude in infinite, sightless, soundless space. There seemed to be a void, and nothing more, and I felt a childish fear which prompted me to draw from my hip pocket the revolver I always carried after dark since the night I was held up in East Providence. Then, from the farthermost regions of remoteness, the *sound* softly glided into existence. It was infinitely faint, subtly vibrant, and unmistakably musical, but held a quality of surpassing wildness which made its impact feel like a delicate torture of my whole body. I felt sensations like those one feels when accidentally scratching ground glass. Simultaneously there developed something like a cold draught, which apparently swept past me from the direction of the distant sound. As I waited breathlessly I perceived that both sound and wind were increasing; the effect being to give me an odd notion of myself as tied to a pair of rails in the path of a gigantic approaching locomotive. I began to speak to Tillinghast, and as I did so all the unusual impressions abruptly vanished. I saw only the man, the glowing machines, and the dim apartment. Tillinghast was grinning repulsively at the revolver which I had almost unconsciously drawn, but from his expression I was sure he had seen and heard as much as I, if not a great deal more. I whispered what I had experienced and he bade me to remain as quiet and receptive as possible.

"Don't move," he cautioned, "for in these rays *we are able to be seen as well as to see.* I told you the servants left, but I didn't tell you *how.* It was that thick-witted house-keeper—she turned on the lights down-stairs after I had warned her not to, and the wires picked up sympathetic vibrations. It must have been frightful—I could hear the screams up here in spite of all I was seeing and hearing from another direction, and later it was rather awful to find those empty heaps of clothes around the house. Mrs. Updike's clothes were close to the front hall switch—that's how I know she did it. It got them all. But so long as we don't move we're fairly safe. Remember we're dealing with a hideous world in which we are practically helpless. . . . *Keep still!*"

The combined shock of the revelation and of the abrupt command gave me a kind of paralysis, and in my terror my mind again opened to the impressions coming from what Tillinghast called *"beyond."* I was now in a vortex of sound and motion, with confused pictures before my eyes. I saw the blurred outlines of the room, but from some point in space there seemed to be pouring a seething column of unrecognizable shapes or clouds, penetrating the solid roof at a point ahead and to the right of me. Then I glimpsed the temple-like effect again, but this time the pillars reached up into the aerial ocean of light, which sent down one blinding beam along the path of the cloudy column I had seen before. After that the scene was almost wholly kaleidoscopic, and in the jumble of sights, sounds, and unidentified sense-impressions I felt that I was about to dissolve or in some way lose the solid form. One definite flash I shall always remember. I seemed for an instant to behold a patch of strange night sky filled with shining, revolving spheres, and as it receded I saw that the glowing suns formed a constellation or galaxy of settled shape; this shape being the distorted face of Crawford Tillinghast. At another time I felt the huge animate things brushing past me and occasionally *walking or drifting through my supposedly solid body,* and thought I saw Tillinghast look at them as though his better trained senses could catch them visually. I recalled what he had said of the pineal gland, and wondered what he saw with this preternatural eye.

Suddenly I myself became possessed of a kind of augmented sight. Over and above the luminous and shadowy chaos arose a picture which, though vague, held the elements of consistency and permanence. It was indeed somewhat familiar, for the unusual part was superimposed upon the usual terrestrial scene much as a cinema view may be thrown upon the painted curtain of a theater. I saw the attic picture laboratory, the electrical machine, and the unsightly form of Tillinghast opposite me; but of all the space unoccupied by familiar objects not one particle was vacant. Indescribable shapes both alive and otherwise were mixed in disgusting disarray, and close to every known thing were whole worlds of alien, unknown entities. It likewise seemed that all the known things entered into the composition of other unknown things, and vice versa. Foremost among the living objects were inky, jellyish monstrosities which flabbily quivered in harmony with the vibrations from the machine. They were present in loathsome profusion, and I saw to my horror that they *overlapped;* that they were semi-fluid and capable of passing through one another and through what we know as solids. These things were never still, but seemed ever floating about with some malignant purpose. Sometimes they appeared to devour one another, the attacker launching itself at its victim and instantaneously obliterating the latter from sight. Shudderingly I felt that I knew what had obliterated the unfortunate servants, and could not exclude the things from my mind as I strove to observe other properties of the newly visible world that lies unseen around us. But Tillinghast had been watching me, and was speaking.

"You see them? You see them? You see the things that float and flop about you and through you every moment of your life? You see the creatures that form what men call the pure air and the blue sky? Have I not succeeded in breaking down the barrier; have I not shown you worlds that no other living men have seen?" I heard his scream through the horrible chaos, and looked at the wild face thrust so offensively close to mine. His eyes were pits of flame, and they glared at me with what I now saw was overwhelming hatred. The machine droned detestably.

"You think those floundering things wiped out the servants? Fool, they are harmless! But the servants *are* gone, aren't they? You tried to stop me; you discouraged me when I needed every drop of encouragement I could get; you were afraid of the cosmic truth, you damned coward, but now I've got you! What swept up the servants? What made them scream so loud? . . . Don't know, eh! You'll know soon enough. Look at me—listen to what I say—do you suppose there are really any such things as time and magnitude? Do you fancy there are such things as form or matter? I tell you, I have struck depths that your little brain can't picture. I have been beyond the bounds of infinity and drawn down dæmons from the stars . . . I have harnessed the shadows that stride from world to world to sow death and madness. . . . Space belongs to me, do you hear? Things are hunting me now—the things that devour and dissolve—but I know how to elude them. It is you they will get, as they got the servants. . . . Stirring, dear sir? I told you it was dangerous to move, I have saved you so far by telling you to keep still—saved you to see more sights and to listen to me. If you had moved, they would have been at you long ago. Don't worry, they won't *hurt* you. They didn't hurt the servants—it was the *seeing* that made the poor devils scream so. My pets are not pretty, for they come out of places where aesthetic standards are —*very different.* Disintegration is quite painless, I assure you—*but I want you to see them.* I almost saw them, but I knew how to stop. You are curious? I always knew you were no scientist. Trembling, eh. Trembling with anxiety to see the ultimate things I have discovered. Why don't you move, then? Tired? Well, don't worry, my friend, *for they are coming.* . . . Look, look, curse you, look . . . it's just over your left shoulder. . . ."

What remains to be told is very brief, and may be familiar to you from the newspaper accounts. The police heard a shot in the old Tillinghast house and found us there—Tillinghast dead and me unconscious. They arrested me because the revolver was in my hand, but released me in three hours, after they found it was apoplexy which had finished Tillinghast and saw that my shot had been directed at the noxious machine which now lay hopelessly shattered on the laboratory floor. I did not tell very much of what I had seen, for I feared the coroner would be skeptical; but from the evasive outline I did give, the doctor told me that I had undoubtedly been hypnotised by the vindictive and homicidal madman.

I wish I could believe that doctor. It would help my shaky nerves if I could dismiss what I now have to think of the air and sky about and above me. I never feel alone or comfortable, and a hideous sense of pursuit sometimes comes chillingly on me when I am weary. What prevents me from believing the doctor is this one simple fact—that the police never found the bodies of those servants whom they say Crawford Tillinghast murdered.

Selected Bibliography

Addison, Agnes. *Romanticism and the Gothic Revival.* New York: Gordian Press, 1967.

Birkhead, Edith. *The Tale of Terror: A Study of the Gothic Romance.* New York: Russell and Russell, 1963.

Bleiler, Everett F., ed. *The Checklist of Fantastic Literature: A Bibliography of Fantasy, Weird, and Science Fiction Books Published in the English Language.* Chicago: Shasta, 1948.

Clark, Kenneth, *The Gothic Revival: an Essay in the History of Taste.* rev. ed. New York: Scribners, 1950.

Foster, James R. *History of the Pre-Romantic Novel in England.* New York: MLA, 1949. Reprinted New York: Kraus, 1966.

Frankl, Paul. *The Gothic: Literary Sources and Interpretations through Eight Centuries.* New Jersey: Princeton Univ. Press, 1960.

Lovecraft, H. P. "Supernatural Horror in Literature." *Dagon and Other Macabre Tales.* Wisconsin: Arkham House, 1965.

Penzoldt, Peter. *The Supernatural in Fiction.* London: Peter Nevill, 1952.

Praz, Mario. *The Romantic Agony,* 2nd ed. London: Oxford Univ. Press, 1954.

Railo, Eino. *The Haunted Castle: A Study of the Elements of English Romanticism.* New York: Humanities Press, 1964.

Redden, M. M., sister. *The Gothic Fiction in the American Magazines (1765–1800).* Washington, D.C.: The Catholic Univ. of America Press, 1939.

Scarborough, Dorothy. *The Supernatural in Modern English Fiction.* New York: Putnam, 1917.

Summers, Montague. *The Gothic Quest: A History of the Gothic Novel.* Reprinted New York: Russell and Russell, 1964.

Varma, Devendra P. *The Gothic Flame: Being a History of the Gothic Novel in England: Its Origins, Efflorescence, Disintegration, and Residuary Influences.* New York: Russell and Russell, 1966.

Tompkins, J. M. S. *The Popular Novel in England 1770–1800.* Reprinted Lincoln: Univ. of Nebraska Press, 1961.

About the Authors

ALGERNON BLACKWOOD (1869–1951), born in Kent, England, was educated in Britain and abroad and lived for a time in Canada and New York City. He was intensely interested in two fields, nature and the psychic world, and in "The Willows" he has joined these two interests to produce one of the most gripping horror short stories in literature.

EMILY JANE BRONTE (1818–1848) was one of three sisters noted for their literary accomplishments. Her only novel, *Wuthering Heights,* published a year before her death, reflects her fiercely reserved, taciturn, and introverted nature. In *Wuthering Heights* her vivid imagination acts on impressions of the bleak Yorkshire countryside in which she lived, producing some of the most haunting descriptions in Gothic literature.

CHARLES BROCKDEN BROWN (1771–1810), novelist and journalist born in Philadelphia of a Quaker family who came to Pennsylvania with William Penn, was a child prodigy who began writing at an early age. The characteristic tormented states of mind in his novels made him popular with a wide reading public, including Sir Walter Scott, William Godwin, and Percy Shelley. A master of abnormal psychology, of terror and suspense, Brown deals with the soaring passions and intellectual energies of his characters, but he is careful in his writings to leave nothing of the weird unexplained.

EDWARD BULWER-LYTTON (EDWARD GEORGE EARLE LYTTON) (1803–1873), First Baron Lytton, was born in London of an aristocratic family. Something of an infant prodigy, he was graduated from Cambridge and later served as a member of Parliament. A prolific writer, he produced one or two novels a year in addition to poems and plays, all of which were extremely popular. Much of his work deals with his strong interest in the supernatural and the occult.

RALPH ADAMS CRAM (1863–1942), son of a Unitarian minister, was born in Hampton Falls, New Hampshire, and spent most of his life as an architect. He taught at the Massachusetts Institute of Technology and planned, or helped to plan, many noted buildings and complexes in America. Greatly influenced by Gothic architecture, especially the cathedrals of Spain, he tried to adapt that design to modern culture. His deep feeling for the Gothic spirit undoubtedly stimulated him in the writing of fiction concerning matters beyond the rational, as in "The Dead Valley."

CHARLES DICKENS (1812–1870), born in Portsea, England, son of a navy clerk who went to prison for debt, reflected his impoverished childhood in all his books. Although he was a prolific writer whose fame rests on such novels of social criticism as *Pickwick Papers*, *David Copperfield*, and *Bleak House*, he was interested in a variety of subjects, including the supernatural.

CHARLOTTE PERKINS GILMAN (1860–1935), an American writer and lecturer in ethics, economics, and sociology, was associated with movements to improve the conditions of labor and to advance the cause of women. Her particular significance in Gothic literature is due mainly to her use of the theme of horror within—the abnormal mind terrorizing itself in the dim regions of insanity.

EDMOND HAMILTON (1904–   ), a novelist and science fiction writer born in Youngstown, Ohio, has written novels, television scripts, and over three hundred science fiction stories for magazines. Noted more for his science fiction than for Gothic tales, Hamilton nonetheless represents that broad area of speculative fiction in which the Gothic and science fiction blend—where science fiction is used less for admonitory purposes than for the creation of an atmosphere of terror.

NATHANIEL HAWTHORNE (1804–1864) was born in Salem, Massachusetts, of a long line of Puritan ancestry—a background reflected in all his writing. His novels and numerous short stories stress guilt and psychological horror rather than physical threat, and this preoccupation with the darker aspects of the American spirit gives his work a somber tone similar to that of Poe's.

HENRY JAMES, JR. (1843–1916), a novelist born in New York City, was a son of the philosopher-theologian Henry James, Sr., and the brother of the psychologist William James. He was educated in America and in the Europe he loved so well, and he knew from an early age that he wanted only to be a writer. He looked to Hawthorne, Balzac, George Eliot, and Turgenev for his models, and he stressed the psychological element in his novels and short stories. As a "psychological realist" he was often on the border of the Gothic or supernatural, the point where the material and spiritual fuse.

MONTAGUE RHODES JAMES (1862–1936), British scholar and author born in Kent, England, was provost successively of King's College, Cambridge, and of Eton College, and was a noted antiquarian who also served as director of the Fitzwilliam Museum and as vice-chancellor of Cambridge. His interest in antiquity, manuscripts, Biblical texts, and medieval literature provided a rich background for his numerous stories of ghosts and the supernatural, the most popular collection being *Ghost Stories of an Antiquary*, from which the selection in this volume is taken.

MATTHEW GREGORY ("MONK") LEWIS (1775–1818) was born in London of a wealthy family which provided him with an excellent education. At nineteen he was appointed attaché to the British embassy at the Hague, and before he was twenty he had written *Ambrosio: or, The Monk,* the publication of which made him both famous and infamous—praised by some but considered immoral by others. A follower of Radcliffe, Monk Lewis was also influenced by the German Gothic tradition which concentrated on explicit details of horror.

HOWARD PHILLIPS LOVECRAFT (1890–1937) was born in Providence, Rhode Island, and spent much of his life there. An antiquarian in taste and recluse by nature, he was scholarly and an authority on the history of New England—a fact which accounts for the detail that makes his New England studies of supernatural horror so convincing. He was published in periodicals including *Weird Tales* and *Astounding Stories,* and is considered by many as the successor to Poe and perhaps Poe's master in handling cumulative horror.

CHARLES ROBERT MATURIN (1780–1824), born in Dublin, studied for the clergy and eventually became curate of St. Peter's in Dublin, a position he held until his death. His natural Gothic bent was stimulated further by an early interest in Radcliffe, Lewis, and other Gothic writers. A fine example of Gothic terror, *Melmoth,* Maturin's greatest success, combines the power of his satanic-Faustian theme with an unusual technique of interwoven episodes.

GUY DE MAUPASSANT (1850–1893), French novelist and short story writer, was born in Normandy, neighbor of the famous writer Gustave Flaubert, who guided Maupassant's writing for a number of years. With the publication of the short story "Ball of

Fat" in 1880, Maupassant became a tremendous success. He was a prodigious worker, writing on many themes, one of his favorites being that of the mysterious or unexplainable.

HECTOR HUGH MUNRO (1870–1916), pen name "Saki," was born in Burma and followed a varied career—but always a career concerned with writing. For a time he wrote political satires for the *Westminster Gazette,* and later he was a correspondent in the Balkans, Russia, and Paris. His primary creative bent was in the short story, where he frequently joined the humorous with the macabre to produce such individualistic masterpieces as "Sredni Vashtar."

FITZ-JAMES O'BRIEN (1828?–1862) was born in County Limerick, Ireland, son of an attorney. A bohemian by nature, he lived a wandering, undisciplined life, often suffering hardships because of wild extravagances. He supported himself for a time in New York City as a journalist, then joined the New York National Guard at the outbreak of the Civil War and in subsequent action was fatally wounded. O'Brien's best stories of the weird and the uncanny are "The Diamond Lens," "Wondersmith," and "What Was It?".

EDGAR ALLAN POE (1809–1849), born in Boston and orphaned at an early age, was destined for a life of poverty, drugs, and alcoholism. His work reveals a brilliant but tortured mind, one continually fighting a descent into insanity. This concern is easily seen in both "The Pit and the Pendulum" and "The Fall of the House of Usher."

ANN (WARD) RADCLIFFE (1764–1823), daughter of a merchant, was born in London. She received little formal education. A highly successful novelist, one greatly admired by Sir Walter Scott, she received unusually high sums for her novels, the best of which are *The Romance of the Forest, The Mysteries of Udolpho,* and *The Italian.* Although most frequently praised for her descriptions of wild scenery, she is also an expert at handling suspense.

CLARA REEVE (1729–1807), born and died in Ipswich, England, was educated by her father, a clergyman. Her first novel, *The Champion of Virtue, a Gothic Story,* later called *The Old English Baron,* was patterned on Walpole's *The Castle of Otranto* but was intended to make the supernatural more credible. The book, a marked success, probably influenced the work of Mrs. Radcliffe and subsequent writers of the Gothic.

GEORGE WILLIAM MCARTHUR REYNOLDS (1814–1879), born in Sandwich, England, son of a naval captain, was educated privately in England and on the Continent. He served for a number of years as editor of various London publications including the *Journal* and *Reynolds's Miscellany*. Always in sympathy with the plight of the working class, he was a leader of the Chartists, a radical organization of the time. His revolutionary turn of mind is reflected in the sensationalism characteristic of his Gothic writing.

MARY WOLLSTONECRAFT GODWIN SHELLEY (1797–1851) was the daughter of famous parents, the radical philosopher William Godwin and the early feminist Mary Wollstonecraft. At sixteen she ran away with the married poet Percy Shelley and began a life of poverty and tragedy. Her Gothic masterpiece, *Frankenstein*, was written when she was twenty-one, and it remains almost unique in Gothic literature. It is a model on which much subsequent science fiction has been based.

ROBERT LOUIS STEVENSON (1850–1894), born in Edinburgh, was the son of a civil engineer. Despite ill health which plagued him all his life, his restless nature caused him to travel extensively and did not prevent him from studying for several professions, among them engineering and law. His main interest, however, was always literature. He was successful in several areas of writing, including juvenile, travel, and the macabre. Stevenson's most famous Gothic story, *Dr. Jekyll and Mr. Hyde*, was a tremendously popular success, selling forty thousand copies in six months.

BRAM (ABRAHAM) STOKER (1847–1912), born in Dublin, followed a varied career, first as a civil servant, then as a newspaper editor, drama critic, and finally as manager for almost thirty years to the successful actor Henry Irving. Publication of *Dracula* in 1897 brought Stoker success and notoriety, but it was his only work to achieve a lasting place in the world of literature.

HORACE WALPOLE (1717–1797), Fourth Earl of Oxford, was born in London, educated at Eton and Cambridge, and was a member of Parliament for twenty-nine years. An intellectual aristocrat, he published numerous books, the most famous of which was *The Castle of Otranto*, a pioneer Gothic novel and one of the first to introduce supernaturalism into romantic literature.

HERBERT GEORGE WELLS (1866–1946), born in Kent, England, studied under T. H. Huxley at the Royal College of Science in London and received his degree with honors. He began as a scientist, even writing a textbook on biology, but switched to journalism and then to literature. All his writing reflects his lifelong scientific interest. His science fantasies are notable for a quality of realism, a fact amply demonstrated in 1938 when Orson Welles adapted *The War of the Worlds* for radio and caused widespread panic.

JOHN WYNDHAM (JOHN BEYNON HARRIS) (1904–1969) was an English author noted primarily for his highly popular science fiction novels. Like his compatriot H.G. Wells, with whom Wyndham shares the honor of having done more than any other British writer to popularize science fiction, Wyndham used up-to-date technology in his stories. He is noted for plot inventiveness, clarity in writing, and a profound sympathy for mankind in the nuclear age; he was one of the very first writers to include mention of nuclear bombs and other terrifying modern devices in his novels. He is best known for *The Day of the Triffids* and *The Kraken Wakes,* the former made into a very successful film. Like the work of many science fiction writers, Wyndham's stories are essentially modernized Gothic.